The Shroud of Turin

Unraveling the Mystery

PROCEEDINGS OF THE 1998 DALLAS SYMPOSIUM

Compiled by
Michael Minor,
Conference Organizer

Edited by
Alan D. Adler, Ph.D.
Dame Isabel Piczek
Michael Minor

Alexander Books
Alexander, North Carolina

Publisher: Ralph Roberts

Editors: Pat Roberts, Vanessa Razzano
Cover Design: Ralph Roberts
Interior Design & Electronic Page Assembly: **WorldComm®**

10 9 8 7 6 5 4 3 2 1

ISBN: 1-57090-110-4 Trade Paper
ISBN: 1-57090-168-6 Hardback

Alexander Books™—a division of Creativity, Inc.—is a full-service publisher located at 65 Macedonia Road, Alexander NC 28701. Phone (828) 252–9515, Fax (828) 255–8719. For orders only: 1-800-472-0438. Visa and MasterCard accepted.

This book is also available on the internet in the **Publishers CyberMall.** Set your browser to http://abooks.com and enjoy the many fine values available there.

Dedication

Fondly dedicated to the memories of Father Adam J. Otterbein C.Ss.R., Father Peter Rinaldi, S.D.B., Donald J. Lynn, and Dr. Alan D. Adler, all of whom made significant contributions to the research on and knowledge of the Shroud of Turin, the most intensively studied object on Earth.

SPECIAL NOTE OF THANKS

We wish to give special thanks to Jo M. Pierce, whose able assistance and many hours of prayer helped make this conference a success, and to Dorothy Crispino, doyenne of sindonology, who was the original impetus for this conference. Although Dorothy was unable to attend the conference her sage counsel and wisdom guided us along the way.

In Memoriam

The American Shroud of Turin Assocciation for Research (AMSTAR), announces with deep regret the death of Dr. Alan D. Adler on June 11, 2000 and Donald J. Lynn on October 14, 2000. Both were founding board members of the American Shroud of Turin Assocciation for Research (AMSTAR), a scientific organization dedicated to conducting research in connection with the Shroud of Turin.

Dr. Adler was an internationally renowned chemist and an acclaimed expert on porphryns, a component of human blood. Dr. Adler's research proved that the blood-stained areas on the Shroud are human blood. Dr. Adler was involved in sindonological research for many years, particularly in the area of conservation of the Shroud. However, his encyclopedic knowledge extended to virtually every scientific discipline. His death leaves an inestimable void in sindonological research. Dr. Adler served on the Conservation Commissions of both Cardinal Saldarini and Archbishop Poletto. He was a member of ACS, APS, AAAS, NYAS, HSS, American Assn of Clin. Chem., American Soc. Photobiol. and Sigma Xi.

Donald J. Lynn worked for many years at the prestigious Jet Propulsion Laboratory (JPL) in Pasadena, California. He was a supervisor in the Image Processing Laboratory where his primary areas of concentration were digital image processing and image analysis. It was his expertise in these areas which proved that the Image on the Shroud of Turin has no directionality, thus proving the Image is not a painting.

CONTENTS

ARCHIVING

SECURITY

FINAL THOUGHTS

SECTION III
The 1997 Fire

INTRODUCTION

BY ALAN D. ADLER, PH.D.

The American Shroud of Turin Association for Research, Inc. (AMSTAR) was incorporated in 1996 to promote research on the Shroud of Turin; assist in archiving all Shroud-related data; conduct symposia concerning the Shroud; publish material on such Shroud research; and support the conservation program that has recently been authorized by the ecclesiastical authorities. We further wish to foster cooperative efforts not only amongst researchers in this country, but on the international scene as well. Published material should disseminate valid information and useful ideas not only to dedicated sindonologists, but also to the lay public in order to counter the welter of misinformation concerning the Shroud that has been propagated to the public at large since the radiocarbon testing.

To meet these objectives, a meeting of American sindonologists was convened at the Catholic Conference Information Center in Dallas, TX, on 6-8 November 1998. The meeting was fondly dedicated to the memories and contributions of Father Adam J. Otterbein, C.Ss.R. and Father Peter Rinaldi, S.D.B. who were Shroud research pioneers and role models. Rev. Dreisbach will tell you more about these great men in Section I of this book.

The Dallas sessions were uniformly informative and the exchanges of ideas amongst the participants were stimulating. Our suggestions for the future course of Shroud studies based on the review of the corpus of past solid knowledge and acknowledged standing problems is recorded in this monograph in order that we might share them with others concerned about the future of the Shroud of Turin.

Alan D. Adler
West Redding, CT
April 2000

I

THE 1998 DALLAS SYMPOSIUM
ON THE
Shroud of Turin

ISABEL PICZEK

Isabel Piczek is an internationally renowned monumental artist and long time Shroud researcher. Many of her articles appear on the Internet. Isabel gave an inspirational introduction to the 1998 Dallas Meeting of American Sindonology that described the hopes and aims of future Shroud research.

Introduction and General Remarks

The Dallas meeting, no doubt, was one of the most important gatherings of Shroud researchers ever held, one that is destined to become a landmark of our history.

We have just completed the first one-hundred years of serious Shroud research (1898-1998). Here and now, we are making the first pioneering steps into a new century of research, on a path not yet clearly seen. Better defining our path was a significant accomplishment of the Dallas meeting. The first century of Shroud research started with one of the most startling discoveries of all times, Pia's negative. The energy and excitement generated by it was the moving force that has carried interest in Shroud research for a hundred years.

What triggering force will animate and inspire our activities and give them life through the forthcoming years? The Church, and as a matter of fact, the world itself, will assume a new face, new initiatives, new programs, and new priorities due to the energetic activities of the Jubilee Year of 2000. At this historic moment, what can we hold on to? What will energize us? What will secure the survival of Shroud research in the years to come?

It seems to me the answers to these questions were presented at the Dallas Conference. They were anchored to the formidable force of sharing a common interest that unites us. In Dallas, there was no umbrella or leading organization nor was there a need for it. There was no dominant head. We have simply answered a strange, commanding urge to meet, heard each other's call and came. This phenomenon is not unique to us. People were meeting all over the world at approximately the same time. There is a new birthed global unity among Shroud researches who are following the same strange, commanding urge. This miracle happened without anyone creating or directing it. The miracle of unification is here and we are simply obeying it. The power of their unifying force seems to equal the power of Pia's great discovery. It is under these grand auspices that we start a new century of Shroud research.

The Dallas conference was organized with a structural arrangement in mind. The great results of the past one-hundred years were summarized. That is our great heritage, on which we can build.

Each major discipline was presented by an invited expert who not only addressed the great results of the past, but also promulgated and shared new ideas and plans for the future in many disciplines, including history, physics, chemistry, conservation, radiation studies, and so on. Modern communication methods were also discussed in the service of the Shroud. We were shown the need for archiving, both actual and electronic. The plans for education, both for the young and adults, through new methods were addressed. The major Shroud Centers gave presentations about their work. Finally, the need for ecumenism was presented and emphasized.

The Dallas conference was not a formal symposium. Rather, the talks were informal with one aim: the hope that a unified program would emerge with a new path into the future.

In Dallas all joined their energy, inspirations and dreams, together savoring the foretaste of the projected future. It is our hope that our work will continue. Emerson said, "A friend is one before whom I may think aloud." This was precisely what we did during the glorious two-and-a-half days in Dallas.

I wish to thank our dear friend and colleague, Mike Minor, for his most efficient and generous efforts in organizing this much-needed conference, which he did with so much love, care, and attention to detail. We all felt surrounded by a marvelous atmosphere of friendship, which was created by Mike. The Dallas Conference was the second time Mike has so generously created for us every good circumstance enabling us to meet, work, plan, and go forward with our research. I thank Mike Minor in the name of all those who were present and all those around the world who will benefit from the results of the Dallas meeting. I also thank Joe Pierce for her generous and selfless work in preparation for, as well as at, the Dallas Conference, without which the Conference could not have been held.

PAUL C. MALONEY

GEN. PROJ. DIR., ASSIST

Paul Maloney is an archaeologist and long time Shroud scholar. He is General Projects Director for the Association of Scientists and Scholars International for the Shroud of Turin (ASSIST). During the 1998 Dallas Meeting of American Sindonology, Mr. Maloney delivered a comprehensive presentation that summarized every important aspect of Shroud science of the last one hundred years. Everyone in attendance agreed that this excellent presentation is one of the best overviews of Shroud research ever done.

Researching the Shroud of Turin: 1898 to the Present

A Brief Survey of Findings and Views[1]

I. Introduction

Many years ago C.P. Snow presented us with his now-famous "two cultures" study (1956, 1961, 1964)—the difficulty or lack of communication between science and the intellectual tradition, in his term "literary intellectuals." His basic appeal was to attempt to break down the walls the various disciplines raise—with their jargon and exotic concepts—which make it difficult for specialists in one field to clearly understand what specialists in another field do.

Also, while it is not my purpose to enjoin sindonology to the so-called "science wars," I believe there are some observations about the findings on the Shroud that will make a simple "list" much more relevant to our interests as we stand on the threshold of the new millennium. My approach, therefore, in this paper will, at points, be to offer a gentle critique of Shroud research and some suggestions for further research as part of my plea for the need for communication between our many disciplines. I hope that such remarks can contribute in some small way toward honing new plans for the study of the Shroud in the next millennium.

The immediate inspiration for my approach, however, is not Snow but rather—in that same general vein—two more recent studies by Harry Collins and Trevor Pinch entitled *The Golem: What you need to know about Science* and *The Golem at Large: What you need to know about Technology*. The first book, published by Cambridge University Press in 1993, set out to explore further the notion that scientists on the one hand and the "rest of us" on the other, view and react to science differently. They also proposed that not all of science's findings were on as secure a ground as we are often led to believe. After all, science is conducted by individual human beings who wield their science through personal biases, convictions, and cultural filters—leaving the imprint of their own personalities stamped upon the results.

Collins and Pinch have drafted a figure from Jewish mythology to illustrate their point. Here's what they say about the Golem:

> *It is a humanoid made by man from clay and water, with incantations and spells. It is powerful. It grows a little more powerful every day. It will follow orders, do your work, and protect you from the ever-threatening enemy. But it is clumsy and dangerous. Without control, a golem may destroy its masters with its flailing vigor.*
>
> *...[I]t is also worth noting that in the mediaeval tradition the creature of clay was animated by having the Hebrew 'EMETH' meaning truth, inscribed on its forehead--it is truth that drives it on--but this does not mean that it understands truth--far from it.*
>
> *...We aim to show that it is not an evil creature but it is a little daft. Golem Science is not to be blamed for its mistakes; they are our mistakes. A golem cannot be blamed if it is doing its best. But we must not expect too much. A golem, powerful though it is, is the creature of our art and our craft.* (1998a, pp. 1-2)

In other words science serves us well so long as we are careful to apply it according to proper methodologies: proper design and construction of testable hypotheses, the use of controls, the application of the concept of repeatability, and other important scientific criteria. We must also be cognizant that science covers a much broader field than each of our own sub-disciplines. Fr. Dreisbach has often noted that—and I paraphrase here—an expert in one field is an abject novice in another. Communicative teamwork is therefore mandatory to get the bigger picture and the most appropriate interpretation.

The best way to point out the psychological problem in science is to quote Festinger, Riecken and Schachter: "A man with a conviction is a hard man to change. Tell him you disagree and he turns away. Show him facts or figures and he questions your sources. Appeal to logic and he fails to see your point." (Festinger, et al., 1956, p. 3). Although these authors have made their statement in the context of a study of a religious group the definition applies across the board to all studies. We have all encountered students and/or critics of the Shroud who have had convictions different from our own interpretation of the array of findings. And even in spite of the broad collection of facts we may find ourselves frustrated when we try to convince the "other side" of the view we believe to be correct. We will probably meet one or two of these before the end of this paper.

So, it is not my purpose to provide students of the Shroud with a "cut and dried" list of important events and scientific accomplishments over this century. You can find that information in most books dealing with the history of the study of the Shroud.[2] To illustrate my case I have selected ten disciplines that have been applied to the Shroud. In the process I also wish to show the dependence of the past, the present, and the future upon each other. In all of this, please understand that my remarks come as from a friend of the Shroud, from an enquiring mind seeking to advance our understanding of this object we continue to study.

In recent years the custodian of the Shroud has rightly emphasized conservation. The question is: "What are we conserving?" During one of my phone conversations with Al Adler—conversations I always savor— he said to me: "No one has ever tried to conserve a cloth with an image on it and blood exudate with the configuration of other biological and botanical materials." (Cf. Adler & Schwalbe, 1993; also Rome proceedings, 1995). In my view every base we touch has to do with conservation because it contributes toward the fund of knowledge we need to determine just how we will conserve it. The following list will try to reflect that implicitly throughout.

II. Ten Areas of Research
1. Photography

Secondo Pia liked to photograph and was very good at what he did. In 1886 he photographed the church of San Pietro di Avigliana and the Castello di Rivoli.[3] In 1887 he photographed the Sant'Antonio di Ranverso.[4] By 1898 he had honed his talents to the point where he was well suited for the special task of photographing the Shroud.[5] His photography launched the scientific era of investigation. In the wake of his work the case for or against authenticity was soon under way with men such as Yves Delage and Paul Vignon arguing in favor. But not a few suspected that the photograph itself was to be questioned. Photographs are the researcher's mainstay, his "primary source" on which a large portion of his observations depend.

In 1931 Giuseppe Enrie, using an 8x10 format and orthochromatic film, photographed the Shroud and presented the world with the first truly sharp photographs of the Shroud. (Enrie, 1933). His results thus confirmed Pia's work. Enrie's photographs are probably the best known and most used. But are we really looking at the Shroud when we study them? Can we trust these photographs to provide a solid foundation for all the conclusions we draw?

In 1969 G.B. Judica Cordiglia made another advancement in the photography of the Shroud with the first color photos. When we look at a color photo of it are we really seeing the original color? Is it accurately portrayed everywhere we look? Or can the printing/publishing process distort it somehow to "discolor" our conclusions? Adler has noted: "It actually does[. D]ependent on color temperature, the blood can appear reddish or almost indistinguishable from the image—this presents a lighting problem when displayed." (Personal communication, Feb. 22, 1999).

The first television exhibition occurred in 1973—the same time frame during which the second exam of the Pellegrino commission took place.

But it wasn't until the STURP exam of 1978 that the battery of scientific photography headed by Vernon Miller and the Brooks Institute team, the very extensive, prolific and important documentation accomplished by Barrie Schwortz, the x-radiography by Bill Mottern and his colleagues, and the infrared study by Accetta and Baumgart was applied to the Shroud. Some of this documentation remains unpublished.

Moreover, to my knowledge, with the exception of the actual photographs of the radiocarbon sampling and some of the actual samples themselves, most of the imaging done during the 1988 session has never been made available to the public. Certainly not the 14 hours of video tape taken of the sampling study (now kept at the Wuenschel Library) nor, with the exception of some snippets shared at the Evansville, Indiana, conference in 1994, have we had access to the full video sequences done separately by Riggi's son of Riggi's own vacuuming work performed at that same time.[6] At this juncture very little is known of the details of this work. Yet, not only are these tapes of archival importance, in them also lie clues to how we should plan for future testing.

The most recent ostension has been that which was held in June of 1998. The private exams of the Shroud leading up to that exhibition were primarily to focus attention upon how best to achieve an immediate method for conserving the Shroud. Mind you, it does not address all the long-term questions of conservation. But it is a basic step forward to know that the Shroud will be preserved in a flattened condition and no longer stressed by being folded or rolled. When all of us looked at the genuine Shroud did we see it in its full color spectrum and hence exactly as the Shroud would have looked after the Poor Clares finished their repairs?

2. Computer Analysis

All of the sophisticated digitized image analysis done to date takes as its base the original photographs of the Shroud done by G. Enrie in 1931 and by STURP in 1978. The stunning results provided by the VP-8 Image Analyzer were based upon the Enrie shots. The aesthetically appealing 3-dimensional results done by Tamburelli and his successor N. Balossino in Italy are also based upon one or both of these basic sources. I will come back to this subject again when I discuss chemical analysis.

Paul Vignon was the first to suggest that there was a relationship between the image on the Shroud and cloth-body distance. I quote: "To sum up: an impression has been formed on the Shroud. The figure produced is not to be called a photograph, because light has had no part in forming it. In the language of science it is the result of *action at a distance* (that is to say without contact); geometrically speaking it is a *projection*."[7] In other words, although he does not use these words to describe the Shroud, he was proposing that the cloth wrapped a three-dimensional corpse because he goes on to say that the goal of his study is "to see at the same time if they [the prints of the image] comply everywhere to the *law of distances*." It remained for Paul Gastineau and Gabriel Quidor to put this concept into visual form by creating the 3-D results in 1926. Dr. Adler also reminds me that Vignon made it clear "that unlike a painting the image edges were not sharp, but appeared to fade into the background (also implying a projection)." (personal communication, Feb. 22, 1999)[8]

The application of the VP-8 (developed by Pete Schumacher) by Jackson, Jumper and Mottern to an Enrie photograph of the Shroud brought 3-dimensionality into the Space Age. Here a computer generated image could vividly illustrate what Vignon had argued in 1902 and repeatedly illustrated by Kevin Moran in his presentations about the VP-8 and the Shroud.

The special studies of computer experts such as Don Janey at Los Alamos and Don Lynn and Jean Lorre at the Jet Propulsion Laboratory brought to bear the power of the computer in basic image studies. The work of Giovanni Tamburelli and Nello Balossino in Italy has mirrored in many respects the image results obtained here in the U.S.[9]

3. Chemistry

Regarding the image there currently exists two separately prominent views about its nature. The first is that proposed by Walter C. McCrone based primarily upon work using the light microscope. (McCrone 1980,

1981). From this study he has concluded that the image is an artist's rendition of the crucified Christ.

The second is that proposed by STURP, founded on the micro-chemical analysis done by Heller and Adler (1981) that the image is composed of dehydrated oxidized cellulose. The advantage of this proposal is that it is supported by the wide battery of other work done by STURP. (Jumper, et al., 1984).

However, both proposals suffer from a singular weakness--the 1978 sticky tapes. A private meeting to examine the Max Frei tapes was convened by ASSIST on July 23, 1988 and hosted at the Philadelphia Academy of Natural Science by the chairman of the Department of Botany, the lamented late Benjamin C. Stone. During that meeting Dr. Stuart Fleming, Director of MASCA—the Museum Applied Science Center for Archaeology of the University of Pennsylvania—asked a very astute and revealing question: When one looks at all the debris on these sticky tapes, by what criterion does one decide that one is actually looking at a fiber that truly represents the image from all those fibers that may have come from other sources? McCrone used a statistical approach on which to base his conclusions.[10] Adler confirms that this is valid; he and Heller used a similar method (personal communication, Dallas, 1998, and Feb. 1999; see Heller & Adler, 1981, p. 86). They note that they "arbitrarily set a minimum threshold of 15 specimens of a particular set of characteristics to constitute a class of fibrils and particles typical of a specific location on the cloth." Yet—reflecting Fleming's question—from the scientific standpoint, we know this issue of criteria remains a genuine problem because it allows for a measure of subjectivity in place of the precision scientists prefer.

Regarding the burns, STURP discovered that there is a fundamental difference between the burns known to have existed prior to 1516 and those of the fire of 1532. The latter are demonstrated to have occurred inside a closed space, the confines of the reliquary, and fluoresce an orange color whereas the pre-1516 burns apparently occurred exposed to open air—under UV they glow with a bluish fluorescence "on the outer edges." (Adler, personal communication, Dallas, 1998, and Feb. 22, 1999[11]). The pre-1516 burns are a source of some interest and I shall return to discuss them further below.

Conversations with Don Lynn suggest that it is possible to go beyond the aesthetic already achieved in modern computer analysis of the Shroud. He notes that if we can obtain actual chemical signatures from a wide selection of areas on the Shroud these could then be correlated with the digitized image to achieve maps of elemental distribution across the Shroud. Indeed, the paper presented at Dallas by Dr. Warren Grundfest shows that a spectroscopic scan, a non-destructive technique, could archive the chemical fingerprints on the Shroud in a major step in that direction.

4. Hematology

One of the earliest questions that investigators asked was "Is the reddish material blood?" Frache, Rizzatti and Mari came up with negative answers. (Frache 1976). But the reason for their result is clearly stated in their report:

> È da sottolineare anzi che il trattamento chimico con acido acetico, benzidina, acqua ossigenata non ha modificato minimamente il colore delle granulazaioni; non è stato osservato, inoltre, alcun fenomeno di *solubilizzazione* delle stesse... ...con l'osservazione microscopica si fosse rilevata la *mancata solubilizzazione* dei granuli... (Frache, et al., p. 52, 53, emphasis mine). ["It is to be emphasised also that the chemical treatment with acetic acid, benzidine, and oxygenated water did not in the least modify the colour of the granulations, neither was there observed any *solutionising* of these. (p. 53) ...under microscopic observation the unsuccessful *solutionising* of the granules was perceived..."] (–Jepps, et al., translation, p. 54, emphasis mine)
>
> To their credit they say in their conclusion: "...la risposta negativa delle indagini praticate *non* consente un giudizio *assoluto* di esclusione della natura ematica del materiale in esame" (Frache, et al. 1976, p. 54; emphasis, Frache, et al.) ["...the negative answer given by the investigations we carried out does not permit us to make an absolute judgment about the exclusion of haematic substance from the material under examination."] (Jepps, et al. unpublished translation, n. d., p. 55)

Old and dried blood is very difficult to work with. The lack of any success in getting the dried material into solution is the key here.[12] But experienced paleo-pathologists might have been able to get positive results for even at the turn of this century scientists were already discovering ways to identify blood residue in ancient Egyptian (Sandison, 1955) and Peruvian mummies (Williams, 1927). As it stands we have one group of scientists who could not find blood, one group of scientists who, using far more sophisticated methods did, and a microscopist who has identified the reddish material as iron oxide.

One of the hallmarks of science is the concept of repeatability. Work done independently by P.L. Baima Bollone does support the work of Heller and Adler. (Baima Bollone, 1990, chapter 12, pp. 189-198, and works cited in nn. 6, 8-10 on pp. 197f).

Beyond the general identification of the reddish material as blood, Heller and Adler (1981) have succeeded in showing evidence of blood breakdown products—namely, bilirubin, serum albumen, and other significant proteins. And although Baima Bollone and his colleagues have published their tests and conclusions that identify the blood not only as human but even type as AB, (1983) I have heard it through the grapevine that there may be questions about the certainty of those findings. However, their major conclusions are confirmed by the immunological work of Adler (Jumper, et al. 1984, p. 461f) and by the position of the near UV bilirubin peak (Jumper, et al., 1984, p. 461 and Adler, 1998b, p. 181 [the latter in Italian only]).

DNA has undoubtedly been found on the Shroud. It has been identified by both Marcello Canale (Wilson, 1996) and Carlo Goldoni (1995) in Italy and by Victor Tryon at the University of Texas Health Science Center (Personal communication, April 22, 1996). But the question is not "Is there DNA on the Shroud" but rather "Does the DNA found there come from the Man of the Shroud?" More importantly, where did these samples come from? The provenance is unknown and no scientifically verifiable resource has ever been published.

Aside from the above highly significant issue, science relies on the very important concept of controls and statistical sampling. Of the samples used by Tryon, one taken from the blood flow across the back is highly suggestive of a positive answer. Dr. Tryon informed me that on a reddish coated fiber he tested he got positive results but on a non-reddish coated fiber used as a control taken only millimeters away from the first fiber he got negative results. But the real resolution of this question, as Dr. Tryon emphasizes, would require testing of single reddish-coated fibers micro-manipulated from blood areas all across the Shroud and their non-reddish controls micro-manipulated from near these sample areas.

5. Physics

I hope Harry Gove will forgive me for the following remarks—but, in my judgment, the radiocarbon dating effort fails to qualify as good science at the most fundamental level. Although Gove cannot be blamed for the actual mechanics of the sampling procedure, he does bear some general responsibilities as I will soon show. My criticism is not of AMS technology nor of the laboratories involved—they did a good job testing their samples and, given the basic assumptions of their testing, achieved results with great precision. But are their results accurate?

When, on the evening of November 21, 1987, I had dinner with Prof. Luigi Gonella, it became patently clear that he wanted to go with one lab and one sample only. And he implied that that sample would come from one place: the Raes' corner! When we had parted my concern had turned to alarm.

In the wake of that meeting I called Dr. Marian Scott in Edinburgh, Scotland, who was the chief statistician for the International Inter-comparison Programme for radiocarbon laboratories. She told me that the bottom line statistically was a sampling from at least three *different* places on the Shroud. Thus, from a scientific standpoint, the basic failure occurred at the front line of research with the decision to limit the sampling to only one area. But Meacham, long ago, had already questioned this tactic noting (1986; 1987) that if one sampled only a single site how would we ever determine that there was not something anomalous about that site? Following recent studies by Adler (1996) it appears that the Raes' corner is indeed different in chemical composition from the rest of the Shroud. Gove, according to his book, (1996) had pushed hard to divest STURP's and others' proposals from the radiocarbon testing so that science could achieve the dating first.

Some years ago, in a private manuscript entitled "The Titanic Syndrome," I wrote a brief evaluation of the radiocarbon dating that illustrates the foibles of the human interface. In 1912 the Titanic was launched on her maiden voyage ending in a disaster that was recently brought poignantly to mind by the movie of the same name. When Robert Ballard and his team recovered pieces of metal from the ship in the mid-80s these were tested for their contents and tensile strength and it was discovered that ship building technology had apparently outstripped the metallurgical technology of the day. Had the ship builders understood their materials better the history of the Titanic might have been very different.

It seems obvious to me that a similar problem occurred with regard to the radiocarbon dating of the Shroud. On the one hand we had a group of specialists in the use of accelerator mass spectrometry avidly wishing to demonstrate the viability and success of their technology (Gove, 1996) and on the other hand a team representing a broader array of scientific disciplines that proposed to set the radiocarbon dating project within the wider context of the study of the nature of the material being tested. Gove won the day and no further study of the material was ever approved. In the aftermath of the test it seems clear that AMS radiocarbon dating technology had outstripped our understanding of the material to which it was being applied. Thus, Adler notes, we cannot speak of accuracy based upon a single sample. (Personal communication, Feb. 22, 1999).

6. Textile Studies

Heller and Adler (1981; Adler, 1996) have published their considerable study of the cellulose of the Shroud cloth as have Kouznetsov and his colleagues (1995; 1996). The latter have suggested that perhaps linen cloth may not be best dated by the AMS radiocarbon technique. They have suggested that further research may demonstrate that a method specifically tailored to cellulosic textiles could be developed. However, much further research would have to go into this idea in order to demonstrate its validity. To my knowledge, work on this approach has, as of the current time, come to a halt.

My conversations with Ray Rogers regarding thermal studies have shown that there is much work to do in this field and little, if any, has been published relevant to the study of the Shroud. But this lacuna is woefully in need of being filled. For example, can the interstices of the threads or the wrinkles in the cloth act as a conduit for heat? There is some image evidence on the Shroud that it can. But actual research needs to be conducted to demonstrate the mechanics of it. On the Shroud we have two different types of burns—those made in a closed environment and those made in an open one. Moreover, I suspect that those on the pre-1516 burns may have been made by a molten resin and/or flaming liquid.[13] But, here again, experiments need to be conducted to see if threads can carry, through capillary action, such a liquid in one direction. This question is significant in the light of a remark by G. Raes cited by Remi van Haelst:

> *It is impossible that traces, made by scorching, are visible in only one part of a thread and in only one direction of the weave. In the case of singe marks, both threads of the warp and the woof should have been singed with the same intensity, which is clearly not the case. The stains are caused by a liquid, probably blood, progressing in one direction.*
>
> —van Haelst, 1998, p. 191[14]

That this can happen does seem to be possible if gravity is playing a role. For example, during a study of the 1624 True Copy kept at the Monastery of Our Lady of the Rosary in Summit, N.J. I noted that the copy was painted while the cloth was hanging on a wall in the horizontal position because the *water seeped in the downward direction—i.e. with the vertical image lying on its side—and created unarguably clear and defined water stain margins. These margins were caused by an accumulation of iron oxide on the one side of the painting but not on the other side where the image tends to fade off into the cloth.* However, in the case of the pre-1516 burns the matter is far less clear because, obviously, the burn holes were made while the cloth was in a four-layer configuration lying flat on the surface of a table or altar. Therefore, questions remain about how, in that position, liquid could seemingly flow in one direction.

From published studies by A. Tonelli (1931; 1933), Gilbert Raes (1976), by M. Flury-Lemberg (1998), G. Vial (1991), F. Testore (1990), and other specialists in this field we now know a considerable amount of information about the cloth of the Shroud: It is a three-to-one herringbone weave containing numerous faults suggesting that it was manufactured on a primitive loom. It does not compare well with the only other cloth known from the same date range as that proposed by the radiocarbon date: a cloth kept in the Victoria and Albert Museum in England studied by Donald King. (1989). The late John Tyrer, at my request, also studied this cloth and confirmed King's findings.

The most recently published study of the side-strip problem has been done by Al Adler (1998). The question had been "When was the side-strip removed and reattached to the Shroud?" Adler's recent study, carefully examining the x-rays of the Shroud, had seemed to show that the so-called "side-strip" is not really a side-strip after all but rather continuous with the whole cloth and that the edge was folded under and stitched to the back making a hollow space from one end of the Shroud to the other. Despite the support of the x-rays Adler is now convinced that, in fact, the cloth was once cut away entirely from the main part of the Shroud and immediately rejoined (Personal communication, Feb. 22, 1999). Why this would have been done and when is a major puzzle yet to be solved.

In a study I did some years ago using the pre-1516 burn holes as alignment marks, burns which also appear in the picture preserved in the Hungarian Pray Codex dating to 1192-1195—a remarkably accurate rendering of them by the artist considering that it must have been done from memory—it is certain that the Shroud must have been as wide as it is today prior to that date. Hence, the creation of the side-strip must have occurred before the time of the painting in the Hungarian Pray Codex.

I have previously alluded to the fact that Adler has shown that there is something different in nature between the radiocarbon sample source, namely the Raes' corner, and the rest of the Shroud. Two different hypotheses have been proposed to explain this difference. Kouznetsov and his colleagues have tried to show that a carboxylation of the cellulose fibers took place, probably while it was confined in the reliquary during the Chambéry fire. Moroni has conducted simulations of this fire and has shown that there could have been at least a 1.47 percent increase in radiocarbon content (Personal communication, 1997). Jackson and Propp (1998) have further explored this and discern the probability that in the tests conducted by the Arizona lab to evaluate the Kouznetsov results, the increase would probably have occurred in the first several minutes of the test after which there was a fall off. Yet, even Kouznetsov, in his most generous view, could account for no more than 5 centuries of the missing 1300 years by this method. And the concept of bio-fractionation, as logical as it may appear on its face, may not resolve the remaining difference. A brief survey of some of my archaeological colleagues show they dismiss the possibility one hundred percent—they cite the fact that no previous radiocarbon dates on known-date cellulosic cloth has shown the slightest hint that bio-fractionation might play a role. If bio-fractionation does occur it remains to be scientifically demonstrated on known-date linen. Yet tests done on an Egyptian ibis wrapping have appeared to "show these effects, [a] difference between cellulose and feather proteins of the same date." (Adler, personal communication, Feb. 22, 1999).

Another hypothesis that has been presented is that by L.A. Garza-Valdes (1999) and his colleagues: the presence of a bio-plastic coating caused by microbial organisms. Wilson (1998) has wholeheartedly accepted this approach and, interestingly, even H.E. Gove subscribes to this possibility (1996, p. 308; Gove, et al., 1997). When I asked Dr. James A. Poupard, director of the Clinical Microbiology lab at SmithKline Beacham, he gave a thumbs-up view of the study. But he emphasized that much more research needed to go into this before it can explicate in detail any role it would have played in contaminating the radiocarbon samples from the Shroud. But the radiocarbon community has openly accepted this approach as the only possible one that can alter a date. Still, as Dr. Adler reminds me, Garza-Valdes' proposal has not been confirmed either by the chemistry (IR work) or by theoretical considerations (i.e., J.P. Jackson's presentation at the Turin Symposium, June, 1998). (Adler, personal communication, Feb. 22, 1999).

7. Forensics and Medicine

The anatomy of the image on the Shroud has been studied in this century by some very prominent forensic specialists and medical doctors. The list is too long for me to give here but I would suggest that although Paul Vignon was a trained biologist, the actual medical examination begins with the French surgeon, Dr. Pierre Barbet. And his conclusions have largely been reiterated and reinforced by other medical observers, Pietro Scotti, Giovanni Judica-Cordiglia, the Englishman Dr. David Willis, and more recently by the Italian forensic specialist Pier Luigi Baima Bollone, the French doctors Pierre Mérat and Olivier Pourrat, and in the United States by Robert Bucklin, Gilbert R. Lavoie, Joseph M. Gambescia, Frederick. T. Zugibe and many many others who also deserve recognition. The consensus of these greats—and let this statement be a special tribute to Dr. Robert Bucklin, who has led the way in his study of the Shroud for more than 50 years—is that the cloth did once wrap an actual corpse with all the attendant evidences of rigor mortis. I have long said, especially in the aftermath of the radiocarbon dating, that the medical view of the Shroud is by far the single most important opinion anyone could consult to build a case for authenticity.

Beginning with Dr. Barbet the blood flows are convincing evidence of a real corpse and of a genuine crucifixion. But what of their transfer from body to cloth and the kinds of patterns such flows would create? Dr. Gilbert R. Lavoie has made an extensive and detailed study of this problem and concludes that the configuration of the flows as we presently see on the arms--particularly off of the elbow--and on the head could only have come about with the body in the vertical position on the cross. (Lavoie, et al., 1983a; 1983b; 1986).

Although he is not a medical doctor, Gino Zaninotto's opinion must weigh in at this point. His detailed study in the archaeology of Roman crucifixion (n.d. [1985?]) shows that the evidence on the Shroud is consistent with that practiced by the masters of the Near East during the first half of the first century A.D. This archaeological evidence is underscored especially by the British doctor, David Willis (1969) and by the medical explorations of the Dutch physician, Dr. Frans J.M. Wijffels.[15]

There have been medically and forensically trained experts who have not always agreed with the majority of the medical community who have studied the Shroud. For example, the New York City based Dr. Michael Baden (Rhein, 1980) examined the photographs of the Shroud and stated that the precise markings of the blood flow did not accurately represent a corpse that had been beaten and then crucified. He had expected that the markings would be smeared and that the corpse would have exhibited much more blood than seen and therefore concluded that an artist must have painted it. To this Adler adds, "He ignored the possibility that these are images produced by clot exudates (as they are) and not by fresh whole blood." (Personal communication, Feb. 22, 1999). On the other hand, Dr. Frederick T. Zugibe, chief medical examiner of Rockland County, N.Y., himself a proponent of authenticity, thought that the best explanation was that the body had been washed (1989). This illustrates the problems and limitations of studying the Shroud from photographs alone. First of all, most such photos are already enhanced and do not show the subtle gradations of blood to cloth seen on the actual Shroud. Secondly, light reflection photographs do not show the possibility of small traces of blood that may be on the Shroud yet to be confirmed by closer examination.

I suggest this because my microscopic examination of Max Frei's 1978 tape sample labeled 2 Bd—a tape that is 8.7 cm in length which Frei removed from an ostensibly image only area (the shin of the left anatomical leg as determined from an examination of Barrie Schwortz' transparency collection)—shows tiny specks of some kind of coating on the fibers and these fibers may be found from one end of the tape to the other. Are these specks traces of blood? I brought this tape to the attention of Dr. Alan Adler who examined the specks, checking them microscopically for pleochroism and birefringence—both features indicative of iron oxide. The test failed on both counts (personal communication, 11/16/98). Therefore we can say what it is *not*, but we cannot say what it actually is. Only micro-chemical testing can tell us that. But it is suggestive of the possibility that there may be more blood on the Shroud than the reflection photographs have evidenced.[16]

But Adler has suggested that perhaps these coated fibers "could be mechanically displaced material." (Personal communication, Feb. 22, 1999). However, if we apply the statistical rule developed by Heller and Adler where if 15 or more of a given class of fiber is discovered, then the sample probably represents the area from which the material was taken (1981, p. 86). I therefore consulted the micro-notes of the work I did on this tape on Aug. 14, 1989 and Feb. 17, 1990. A note I made on 4/7/90 after re-examining the totality of my evidence states: "I have determined in a brief study that there are coated flax [fibers] on this tape all the way from one end (on front) to the other (on back [of the tape on the glass slide])." In fact, I photo-micrographed six of these fibers at random to preserve evidence of that coating; but there are many many more such fibers on this tape—I believe a careful count will discover numbers much higher than 15. In view of my findings, this concentration of coated fibers on 2 B/d probably does not constitute mechanically transposed material. But it remains for others to examine this tape again and either confirm or disprove my conclusion.

One further point—this about color photos. Earlier I wondered if when we looked at the Shroud were we actually seeing the color of all features accurately. Probably not. In 1990 Jackson (1990, p. 19) published some remarks about the off-elbow blood clot and observed that it was brownish whereas the rivulet down the arm connected to it was reddish. But if you look at published color photos of the Shroud the coloration is all the same. And even an examination of the Shroud during the ostension this past June led my eyes to believe that the coloration of the blood was the same everywhere. But we must keep in mind that unless a photograph or a real-life exhibition of the Shroud is made with the *full spectrum of light*, and Adler notes "at the appropriate color temperature," the features will not be seen in their original color.[17]

8. Botany and Palynology

Frei was permitted to take 12 tape samples from the frontal end of the Shroud in 1973 and it was from this resource that he constructed his study of the 58 plant types represented on the Shroud. (1982) In his view these were largely deposited on the Shroud via wind deposition.

In 1978 Frei and STURP both took sticky tape samples. Since ASSIST had access to the Frei samples from 1986 until 1993 and access to three of the STURP samples I was able to compare the two and suggested in my paper (presented in Paris in 1989; Maloney, 1990) that not only was there a distinct difference between the two methodologies of sampling, they represented two levels of material—STURP's samples preserving material from the crowns of the threads, Frei's samples included not only crown material but also material from deeper in the interstices of the weave of the cloth. To this we may add that Riggi's vacuum samples represent a third level of materials—apparently differing again both in their statistical nature and in the characteristics of the materials retrieved compared to the contents of the two sticky tape methods—from the backside of the Shroud.[18] But let me emphasize here that in all sampling methods the investigator will find some common denominators—red and blue silk, burned flax fibers, and pollen grains (Heller & Adler, 1981, p. 86)—indicative of the spectrum of debris found on the Shroud. And, despite Prof. Gonella's protests over Prof. Meacham's analogy that the investigation of the Shroud may be similar to an archaeological dig (personal communication, Nov. 21, 1987), the evidence of the three levels shows that the analogy may be apt after all.

But there is actually more than meets the eye when one examines the Frei tapes, or the STURP tapes, or the Riggi vacuum samples each on an individual basis. Conversations with Don Lynn (Dallas, 1998) turned up the fact that Frei and Riggi took their samples with the STURP table in the horizontal position. But STURP's samples were taken with the table in the vertical position. This means that Frei's samples were taken first followed by Riggi followed by STURP—in that sequence. I confirmed this observation with Barrie Schwortz (Personal communication, 11/29/98) whose remarkable color transparency collection is an excellent chronological record of the scientific work done in the 1978 examination. While Frei's tapes are rich in debris from the Shroud, STURP's are, by comparison, more lightly representative of Shroud material. Thus—as has been argued by scientists for years—not only can the *method* affect the nature of the observation, so also might the *sequence* in which the sampling was done. In this case Riggi may have vacuumed much of the material right through from the image side of the Shroud to the back and into his sampling vials so that when STURP proceeded to take their samples, there was much less dust matter to be taken! Although, as Adler has pointed out to me during a phone conversation, the weave of the Shroud is very tight, because it is a 3:1 herringbone pattern it is not the tightest weave possible; the plain or tabby weave is. But this sequence of events underscores the importance of developing a proper scientific protocol with all participating parties so that what one is doing first does not affect the results of someone else's work that occurs later.

Still more recently Dr. Marta Mariotti Lippi has shown that cloth can act as a pollen trap (1998). And Dr. Avinoam Danin, botanist at the Hebrew University of Jerusalem, with the assistance of Dr. Uri Baruch, palynologist with the Israel Antiquities Authority, have done a detailed study of several plants occurring on the Shroud and in Israel and, on the basis of the presence of *Zygophyllum dumosum*, concludes that the Shroud unquestionably was in the Holy Land as claimed by Max Frei. These findings were presented at the symposium held in Turin in June of this year.

In my judgment, as I remarked in my 1989 paper (Maloney, 1990), while wind may act as a depositor and, as Mariotti Lippi has determined that cloth may act as a trap to explain some of the deposition, the high numbers of pollen grains—most especially the 32 insect pollinated types noted in the Spring of 1986 by Dr. A. Orville Dahl of the University of Pennsylvania, can never be explained through this method. In Dahl's view these plants were physically laid upon the Shroud through some human activity. Dahl suggested a liturgical activity and I have suggested that first century Jewish funeral activity may also be a candidate. Dr. and Mrs. Alan D. Whanger have also experimented further with flowers and wilting times in conjunction with the coronal discharge experiments conducted by O. Scheuermann of Germany and together demonstrated an interesting sequence of events that persuade me and others, including the botanist, Dr. Danin, that many of the "floral images" on the Shroud may in fact be genuine imprints of flowers. (Whanger, 1998, pp. 71-85).[19]

Schafersman's recent criticism of the presence of pollen on the Shroud is that they could only have gotten there by someone fraudulently spiking the cloth with them. He argues that fresh plants don't shed their pollen grains so easily (1998, p. 36). Although he overstates the case he does raise a valuable point. My argument here is that *wilted flowers* do, in fact, shed pollen—and more than that. They will even shed their inflorescences, petals, their anthers and other associated botanical debris. Long ago Frei had already identified epithelial cells from *Aloe soccotrina* and a plant hair of *Platanus orientalis* on the Shroud; neither of these are wind transported. By Spring/Summer 1986 I had, with the help of Dr. Dahl, identified bracts from inflorescences, a filament, an anther (with the pollen still visible inside!) and other botanical cellular materials—all indicative of wilted plants or plants that had been "disassembled" for sprinkling on the Shroud in a liturgical setting.[20]

9. Art

If the Shroud is a mural painting then it ought to be evaluated as such. In this regard we could have no other better authority than Isabel Piczek who has clearly shown the problems connected with interpreting the Shroud as a painting. And she resolutely rejects any indication that an artist had any direct involvement in producing the image on the cloth we now know as the Shroud of Turin, thus controverting the claim made in 1389 by Bishop Pierre d'Arcis that it was a cunning work. (n.d.; 1995).

But Miss Piczek has done more than judge the Shroud in the light of mural paintings. She has also taken us back in time to the masters, to Cennino Cennini and to Theophilus, to show that even the formulas they recommended during the alleged period when the Shroud would have been created would not have fit the Shroud as we know it. (1994).

We have known from Pia's work about the negativity of the Shroud image. Negativity has most recently been explored in an excellent treatment of the topic by Isabel Piczek (1998) and briefly by Baima Bollone (1998, pp. 167-170).

In 1986, based upon a previous publication by Don Luigi Fossati who suggested that traces of some 52 different True Copies might have been left on the Shroud by contact transfer, (Fossati, 1984a; 1984b) Al Adler and I independently called for a serious exam of this question. At my request, Miss Piczek conducted a test with the aid of Dr. Arthur Koehler, a forensic pathologist who was kindly brought to her attention by Dr. Robert Bucklin. Her sampling showed that in fact such sloughing off of pigments—and not only pigments, but actual fibers with pigments on them—can occur.[21] Therefore, Dr. Fleming's question is right to the point of the matter. This can be resolved in the future by obtaining individual fibers from select areas on the Shroud through micro-manipulation—a technique suggested long ago by Dr. Adler. This, in turn, would make the use of the remainder of the material on all sticky tapes far more productive and persuasive from a strictly scientific point of view.

10. History

There is no longer any question but that the artist's rendition preserved in the Hungarian Pray Codex represents the cloth we now recognize as the Shroud of Turin. Moreover, by that rendition we know that this is the earliest firmly documented demonstrable viewpoint that the cloth we know as the Shroud of Turin was the actual burial cloth of Jesus Christ. In color photographs of the Codex even one set of the angular flows of blood down one of the arms is clearly visible—an observation I believe was first made by the Belgian scholar, Jef Leysen (personal communication, Spring, 1998). And here is shown—as already noted—a comparatively accurate portrayal of two different sets of holes that represent the pre-1516 burns at the two ends of the Shroud. Therefore, the pre-1516 burn marks are more accurately termed pre-1192 burn marks.

But, most importantly, their existence some 65 years prior to the first bracket of the 1260-1390 radiocarbon date creates a problem for the 95 percent confidence level claimed by the three labs because one must conservatively add at least 100 years onto the above date to allow for the development of a tradition that the cloth portrayed by the artist was in fact the burial cloth of Christ. On the other hand it would be commensurate with a 68 percent level of confidence which expands the window to a 500 year opening that would encompass that date. Still, the labs have insisted that the 95 percent confidence level is the level achieved by their tests.

A majority of Shroud scholars now accept Ian Wilson's hypothesis regarding the role of the Templars in taking the Shroud from Constantinople and bringing it to Lirey, France (Wilson, 1978; 1986). But scholarship is not unanimous in this as any reader of Malcolm Barber's work (1982; 1983) will discover. Yet, no pro-authenticity investigator has offered a viable alternative to Wilson's thesis.

Regarding years between 1204 and 1356, although numerous scholars have explored the de la Roche/Athens connection, the Besançon connection, and other possibilities, no one has yet suggested a comprehensively viable alternative that the majority of scholars can agree upon. I suspect that there may be more documents out there that have not yet been tapped that could help fill in the gap. Successful scholars like Dorothy Crispino, Daniel Raffard de Brienne and Daniel Scavone are to be complimented for their dogged pursuit of the history of the Shroud during these "missing years."

In the judgment of Ian Wilson perhaps one of the most interesting, even exciting explorations, has been that of Dr. Scavone's insight (Scavone, 1997; 1998) into the true meaning of the *Britio Edessenorum* wherein the so-called British King Lucius is actually the king of Edessa and the allusions to a grail are to the taking of the grail to Edessa. That does not rule out the presence of the Shroud/grail at Templecombe at a later time, but it does explain much that was puzzling about the Joseph of Arimathea legend.[22]

11. The Opposing Side

Although I have briefly touched upon ten selected areas of research it would not be a balanced presentation if I made no reference to opposing views. Following Secondo Pia's photography, Ulysse Chevalier (1902) quickly responded to popular views countering with his scholarly collection of documents attempting to show that the Shroud could not be authentic. The Jesuit, Fr. Herbert Thurston, writing in the journal *The Month* and in the *Catholic Encyclopedia* in 1903, 1912 respectively and later, especially singling out the Shroud, was a resolute voice against the cult of relic.[23]

In 1976 Pietro Caramello released the summary of the report representing the work of the secret commission brought together by Archbishop Michelle Cardinal Pelligrino to study the Shroud. It had been conducted in two phases: 1969 and 1973. A number of the contributors to that study either presented negative findings (Frache, et al., 1976) or gave a negative view of the image on the Shroud (Gabrielli, 1976). The report was immediately rebuted by members of the Centro Internazionale di Sindonologia di Torino (1976).

More recently Shroud science has been reviewed by Nickell in his book *Inquest on the Shroud* (1983), by Mueller, McCrone and Schafersman in the *Sceptical Inquirer* (1982) and an extensive critique by McCrone published in the hard-to-find papers of "The American Institute for the Conservation of Historic and Artistic Works for 1986." Most recently of all there has appeared on the Shroud scene the new Italian journal *Approfondimento Sindone* which, from an examination of its scientific committee, seems to be designed to present the opposing views of the Shroud. Numerous articles in this journal are done by scholars such as Antonio Lombatti, himself the editor of the journal, and by, for example, Pier Angelo Gramaglia (1998) and Niccolo Caldararo (1997). Many of the presentations appearing here are quite well done even if they do take a contrary view. Students of the Shroud need these opponents. They keep investigators on their toes. We should read them and be reminded that science is, after all, a golem.

I do not have serious problems with critique per se. However, I have long called for *responsible* review. I emphasize "responsible" because it is always possible for one's personal bias to be so heavy that it carries the reviewer away from the selected goal—the search for truth be it scientific or historical, pro or con.[24] The facts should always be objectively presented in an accurate, balanced, and fair-minded manner.

III. Closing

We do not necessarily have to agree with our critics but we must measure all such criticisms by a more rigorous appeal to science all the while understanding that humans conduct it. That is why we need to recognize that science itself is a Golem to be guided by us and used with respect and care—with diligent planning taking into account everything we know up until now, placing our findings into the overall context, and with the goal to repeat past experiments, to devise ways to test new hypotheses, to maintain controls, to address unresolved issues and, in the spirit of C.P. Snow, persistently attempting to cross the boundaries of our various disciplines to communicate. And I might add one additional factor: not allowing ourselves to be taken completely by a principle long used by science, Occam's razor.[25] I have a growing conviction that the Shroud is not the simple topic of study that many of us have thought it might be but in truth is far more complex. The study of the image is clearly such an example. Surely, this complexity is one of the revelations that will become clearer as we cross into the new millennium. And, I suspect, the Shroud holds many more secrets and surprises yet to be discovered.

Finally, in the field of communication I have one fond dream: to see the development and publication of a technically approved atlas of the Turin Shroud wherein all the experts come together and present their resources—x-radiographs, x-ray fluorescence studies, close-ups of infrared and ultraviolet photography as well as visible and transmitted light versions. Where we are supplied with color calibrated photographs published with Munson strips that have been checked properly against the original for accuracy. Moreover, such photographs need to be published with measuring devices set into them so that features on the Shroud can be correctly measured. Along with this a sequence of exam events can be recreated as a chronology of what happened, where samples were taken, and in what sequence. Only then will we have a proper archive tool for creating future protocols for the study and conservation of this very special cloth with its image and microscopic spectrum that represents the history through which it has already been.

References:

Adler, A. D. (1991, December). Conservation and Preservation of the Shroud of Turin. *Shroud Spectrum International,* 10(40), 2-6.

_____ (1996). Updating recent studies on the Shroud of Turin. In M. V. Orna (Ed.), "Archaeological chemistry: Organic, inorganic and biochemical analysis" (pp. 223-8). ACS Symposium Series, vol. 625. Washington, DC: American Chemical Society.

_____ (1998a). Concerning the side strip on the Shroud of Turin. In CIELT (Ed.), *ΑΧΕΙΠΟΟΙΗΤΟΣ ΑΞΗΕΙΡΟΠΟΙΕΤΟΣ*: "Non fait de main d'homme." *Actes du IIIème Symposium Scientifique International du CIELT*--Nice 1997 (pp. 103-6). Paris: Editions Du CIELT.

_____ (1998b). Aspetti fisico-chimici delle immagini sindoniche. In B. Barberis & G. M. Zaccone (Eds.), *Sindone: Cento anni di ricerca* (pp. 165-184). Torino: Istituto Poligrafico e Zecca dello Stato.

Adler, A. D., & Schwalbe, L. A. (1993, December). Conservation of the Shroud of Turin. *Shroud Spectrum International,* 12(42), 7-15. See also (1995), Conservation of the Shroud of Turin. In A.-A. Upinsky (Ed.), *L'Identification Scientifique de l'Homme du Linceul Jésus de Nazareth. Actes du Symposium Scientifique International*, Rome 1993 (pp. 135-8). Centre International d'Études sur le Linceul de Turin (CIELT). Paris: François-Xavier de Guibert.

Baima Bollone, P. L. (1990). *Sindone o no*. Torino, Italia: Società Editrice Internazionale.

_____ (1998). *Sindone: La prova*. Milano: Arnaldo Mondadori Editore S. P. A.

Baima Bollone, P. L., Jorio, M., & Massaro, A. L. (1983, March). Identification of the group of the traces of human blood on the Shroud. *Shroud Spectrum International*, 2(6), 2-6.

Barber, M. (1982, April). The Templars and the Turin Shroud. *The Catholic Historical Review*, 68(2), 206-5. Also published in *Shroud Spectrum International*, (1983, March) 2(6), 16-34.

Beecher, P. A. (1928). "The Holy Shroud. A reply to the Rev. Herbert Thurston," S.J. Dublin: M.H. Gill and Son, Ltd.

Borghesi, M., Ferraro, E., & Ricardi di Netro, T. (1998). Secondo Pia e l'arte fotografica. In G. M. Zaccone (Ed.), *L'immagine rivelata* (pp. 116-140). Torino: Centro Studi Piemontesi; Archivio di Stato di Torino.

Caldararo, N. (1997, Fall). The status of research into the authenticity of the Shroud. *Approfondimento Sindone: Rivista Scientifica internazionale di studi sindonici*, pp. 51-66.

Caramello, P., Mons. (1976). *La S. Sindone: Ricerche e studi della Commissione di Esperti nominata dall'Arcivescovo di Torino, Card. Michele Pellegrino, nel 1969*. Rivista Diocesana Torinese. Turin, Italy: Rivista Diocesana Torinese.

Caramello, P., Mons. (n. d. [1977]?). M. Jepps, O. F. M. (Ed.), Doyle, E., M. Green, Fr., & V. Ossola (Trans.). *Report of Turin Commission on the Holy Shroud*. Translation of: *La S. Sindone: Ricerche e studi della Commissione di Esperti nominata dall'Arcivescovo di Torino, Card. Michele Pellegrino, nel 1969*. (1976). Translated for research purposes to create "The Silent Witness" by David Rolfe. Translated in England.: Unpublished.

Centro Internazionale di Sindonologia (Eds & comp). (1976). *Osservazioni alle perizie ufficiali sulla Santa Sindone 1969-1976*. Centro Internazionale di Sindonologia. Turin, Italy: Centro Internazionale Di Sindonologia.

Chevalier, U. (1902). *Bibliothèque Liturgique*: Vol. 2. *St. Suaire de Lirey-Chambéry-Turin et les défenseurs de son authenticité*. vol. 5. Paris: Alphonse Picard et Fils, Libraires.

Collins, H., & Pinch, T. (1998a). *The Golem at large: What you should know about technology.* Cambridge, England: Cambridge University Press.

_____ (1998b). *The Golem: What you should know about science.* Cambridge, England: Cambridge University Press.

Enrie, G. (1933, 1938). *La Santa Sindone rivelata della fotografia.* Torino, Italia.

Festinger, L., Riecken, H. W., & Schachter, S. (1956). *When prophecy fails: A social and psychological study of a modern group that predicted the destruction of the world.* New York: Harper Torchbooks, the Academy Library.

Flury-Lemberg, M. (1998). Stato e problemi di conservazione della Sindone di Torino. In B. Barberis & G. M. Zaccone (Eds.), *Sindone: Cento anni di ricerca* (pp. 255-267). Torino: Istituto Poligrafico e Zecca Dello Stato.

Fossati, L., S.D.B. (1984a, September). Copies of the Holy Shroud. [Part I]. *Shroud Spectrum International,* 3(12), 7-23.

_____ (1984b, December). Copies of the Holy Shroud. [Parts II & III]. *Shroud Spectrum International,* 3(13), 23-39.

Frache, G., Rizzatti, E. M., & Mari, E. (1976). Relazione conclusiva sulla indagini d'ordine ematologico praticate su materiale prelevato dalla Sindone. In P. Caramello, Sac. (Ed.), *La S. Sindone: Ricerche e studi della Commissione di Experti nominata dall'Arcivescovo di Torino, Card. Michele Pellegrino, nel 1969.* (pp. 49-54). Rivista Diocesana Torinese. Turin, Italy: Rivista Diocesana Torinese.

Frei Sulzer, M. (1982, June). Nine years of palinological [sic] studies on the Shroud. *Shroud Spectrum International,* 1(3), 2-7.

Gabrielli, N. (1976). La Sindone nella storia dell'arte. In P. Caramello, Sac. (Ed.), *La S. Sindone: Ricerche e studi della Commissione di Experti nominata dall'Arcivescovo di Torino, Card. Michele Pellegrino, nel 1969.* (pp. 87-92). Rivista Diocesana Torinese. Turin, Italy: Rivista Diocesana Torinese.

Garza-Valdes, L. A. (1999). *The DNA of God?* New York: Doubleday.

Goldoni, C. (1995). Sang humain sur le Suaire d'Oviedo? In A. -A. Upinsky (Ed.), *L'Identification Scientifique de l'Homme du Linceul Jésus de Nazareth. Actes du Symposium Scientifique International, Rome 1993* (pp. 361-3). Centre International d'Études sur le Linceul de Turin (CIELT). Paris: François-Xavier de Guibert.

Gove, H. E. (1996). *Relic, icon or hoax? Carbon dating the Turin Shroud* (D.

A. Bromley, Foreword). Bristol & Philadelphia: Institute of Physics Publishing.

Gove, H. E., Mattingly, S. J., David, A. R., & Garza-Valdes, L. A. (1997). A problematic source of organic contamination of linen. *Nuclear Instruments and Methods in Physics Research*, B, 123, 504-7.

Gramaglia, P. A. (1998). Il problema della mentoniera. *Approfondimento Sindone: Rivista Scientifica internazionale di studi sindonici*, 1(2), 15-23.

Heller, J. H., & Adler, A. D. (1981). A chemical investigation of the Shroud of Turin. *Canadian Society for Forensic Science Journal*, 14(3), 81-103.

Jackson, J. P. (1990, March). Is the image on the Shroud due to a process heretofore unknown to modern science? *Shroud Spectrum International*, 9(34), 2-29.

Jackson, J. P., & Propp, K. (1998). On the evidence that the radiocarbon date of the Turin Shroud was significantly affected by the 1532 fire. In CIELT (Ed.), *ΑΧΕΙΠΟΟΙΗΤΟΣ ΑΞΗΕΙΡΟΠΟΙΕΤΟΣ:* "Non fait de main d'homme." *Actes du IIIème Symposium Scientifique International du CIELT--Nice 1997* (pp. 61-82). Paris: Editions Du CIELT.

Jepps translation: Please see under Caramello, P. or Frache, G.

Jumper, E. J., Adler, A. D., Jackson, J. P., Pellicori, S. F., Heller, J. H., & Druzik, J. R. (1984). A comprehensive examination of the various stains and images on the Shroud of Turin. In J. B. Lambert (Ed.), *Archaeological Chemistry--III* (pp. 447-476). Advances in Chemistry Series, 205. Washington, DC: American Chemical Society.

King, D. (1989). A parallel for the linen of the Turin Shroud. *Centre International d'Études des Textiles Anciens (CIETA), Bulletin*, 67, 25-26.

Kouznetsov, D. A., Ivanov, A. A., & Veletsky, P. R. (1996). Analysis of cellulose chemical modification: A potentially promising technique for characterizing archaeological textiles. In M. V. Orna (Ed.), *Archaeological chemistry: Organic, inorganic and biochemical analysis* (pp. 254-268). ACS Symposium Series, vol. 625. Washington, DC: American Chemical Society.

_____ (1995, December 1). Detection of alkylated cellulose derivatives in several archaeological linen textile samples by capillary electrophoresis/mass spectrometry. *Analytical Chemistry*, 66(23), 4359-65.

Lavoie, G. R., Lavoie, B. B., & Adler, A. D. (1986, September). Blood on the Shroud of Turin: Part III. *Shroud Spectrum International,* 5(20), 3-6.

Lavoie, G. R., Lavoie, B. B., Donovan, V. J., & Ballas, J. S. (1983, September). Blood on the Shroud of Turin: Part II. *Shroud Spectrum International,* 2(8), 2-10.

Lavoie, G. R., Lavoie, B. B., Donovan, V. J., & Ballas, J. S. (1983, June). Blood on the Shroud of Turin: Part I. *Shroud Spectrum International,* 2(7), 14-19.

Lippi, M. M. (1998). Fabrics as pollen traps: Some observations. In CIELT (Ed.), *ΑΧΕΙΠΟΟΙΗΤΟΣ ΑΞΗΕΙΡΟΠΟΙΕΤΟΣ*: "Non fait de main d'homme." *Actes du IIIème Symposium Scientifique International du CIELT--Nice 1997* (pp. 237-240). Paris: Editions Du CIELT.

McCrone, W. C. (1980, Third-Fourth quarter). Microscopical study of the Turin "Shroud" II. *The Microscope,* 28, 115-128.

_____ (1981). Microscopical study of the Turin "Shroud" III. *The Microscope,* 29(1), 19-38.

_____ (1982, Spring). Shroud image is the work of an artist. *The Skeptical Inquirer,* 6(3), 35-36.

_____ (1986). Microscopical study of the Turin "Shroud", IV. In *The American Institute for Conservation of Historic and Artistic Works: Preprints of papers presented at the fourteenth annual meeting, Chicago, Ill., 21-25 May 1986.* (pp. 77-96)

McCrone, W. C., & Skirius, C. (1980, Third-Fourth quarter). Microscopical study of the Turin "Shroud" I. *The Microscope,* 28, 105-3.

Maloney, P. C. (1990, June). The current status of pollen research and prospects for the future. *The ASSIST Newsletter,* 2(1), 1-7.

Meacham, W. (1986, June). On carbon dating the Turin Shroud. *Shroud Spectrum International,* 5(19), 15-25.

_____ (1987). Radiocarbon measurement and the age of the Turin Shroud: Possibilities and uncertainties. In W. Meacham (Ed.), *Turin Shroud--Image of Christ: Proceedings of a Symposium held in Hong Kong, March 1986.* (pp. 41-56). Turin Shroud Photographic Exhibition Organizing Committee: Hong Kong. Hong Kong: Cosmos Printing Press, Ltd.

Miller, V. D., & Pellicori, S. F. (1981, July). Ultraviolet fluorescence phototography [sic] of the Shroud of Turin. *Journal of Biological*

Photography, 49(3), 71-85.

Morgan, R. (Ed.). (1981, January). The Templecombe connection. *Shroud News,* 4, 2-3.

_____ (1987, August). Was the Holy Shroud in England? *Shroud News,* 42, 3-17.

_____ (1988, February). The Templecombe panel painting. *Shroud News,* 45, 3-8.

_____ (Ed.). (1988, April). Templecombe update. *Shroud News,* 46, 6-7.

_____ (1998). Did the French take the Shroud to England? More evidence from the Templecombe connection. In CIELT (Ed.), *ΑΧΕΙΠΟΠΟΙΗΤΟΣ ΑΞΗΕΙΡΟΠΟΙΕΤΟΣ*: "Non fait de main d'homme." *Actes du IIIème Symposium Scientifique International du CIELT--Nice 1997* (pp. 133-140). Paris: Editions Du CIELT.

Mueller, M. M. (1982, Spring). The Shroud of Turin: A critical appraisal. *The Skeptical Inquirer,* 6(3), 15-34. Also published in K. Frazier (ed.), *Science confronts the paranormal,* Buffalo, N. Y.: Prometheus Books.

Nickell, J. (1983). *Inquest on the Shroud of Turin. Buffalo,* New York: Prometheus Books.

Pickover, C. A. (1990). Image processing of the Shroud of Turin. In *Computers, pattern, chaos and beauty* (pp. 73-81). New York: St. Martin's Press.

Piczek, I. (1994, June). A response to the Craig-Bresee theory. *Shroud News,* 83, 15-18.

_____ (1995). Is the Shroud of Turin a painting? In A. -A. Upinsky (Ed.), *L'Identification Scientifique de l'Homme du Linceul Jésus de Nazareth. Actes du Symposium Scientifique International, Rome 1993* (pp. 265-271). Centre International d'Études sur le Linceul de Turin (CIELT). Paris: François-Xavier de Guibert.

_____ (1998). The concept of negativity through the ages. In CIELT (Ed.), *ΑΧΕΙΠΟΠΟΙΗΤΟΣ ΑΞΗΕΙΡΟΠΟΙΕΤΟΣ*: "Non fait de main d'homme." *Actes du IIIème Symposium Scientifique International du CIELT--Nice 1997* (pp. 31-38). Paris: Editions Du CIELT.

_____ (n.d. [1992]). Is the Turin Shroud a painting? In A. Berard, S.J. (Ed.), *History, science, theology and the Shroud.* (pp. 261-273). Symposium Proceedings: St. Louis, Missouri, June 22-23, 1991. St. Louis, Missouri: Privately Printed.

Raes, G. (1976). Appendix B--Rapport d'Analise: Pl. II-III. Conc.: Examen du 'Sindone'. In P. Caramello, Sac. (Ed.), *La S. Sindone: Ricerche e studi della Commissione di Experti nominata dall'Arcivescovo di Torino, Card. Michele Pellegrino, nel 1969.* (pp. 79-85). Rivista Diocesana Torinese. Turin, Italy: Rivista Diocesana Torinese.

Rhein, R. W. (1980, December 22). Shroud of Turin. *Medical World News*, pp. 40-50.

Sandison, A. T. (1955, November). The histological examination of mummified material. *Stain Technology*, 30(3), 277-283.

Scavone, D. C. (1997, February). British King Lucius and the Shroud (Part I of a series). *Shroud News*, 100, 30-39.

_____ (1998). The influence of the Edessa icon on the legend of the Holy Grail. In CIELT (Ed.), *ΑΑΧΕΙΠΟΠΟΙΗΤΟΣ ΑΞΗΕΙΡΟΠΟΙΕΤΟΣ:* "Non fait de main d'homme." *Actes du IIIème Symposium Scientifique International du CIELT--Nice 1997* (pp. 141-5). Paris: Editions Du CIELT.

Schafersman, S. D. (1998). Unraveling the Shroud of Turin. *Approfondimento Sindone: Rivista Scientifica internazionale di studi sindonici,* 2(2), 31-48.

_____ (1982, Spring). Science, the public, and the Shroud of Turin. *The Skeptical Inquirer,* 6(3), 37-56.

Snow, C. P. (1956, October 6). The Two Cultures. *New Statesman.*

_____ (1961). *The Two Cultures and the scientific revolution: The Rede Lecture—1959.* New York: Cambridge University Press.

_____ (1964). *The Two Cultures and a second look. An expanded version of the Two cultures and the scientific revolution.* New York: Cambridge University Press.

Tamburini, L. (1998). Le immagini di Secondo Pia. In G. M. Zaccone (Ed.), *L'immagine rivelata* (pp. 71-78). Torino: Centro Studi Piemontesi; Archivio Di Stato Di Torino.

Testore, F. (1990). Le Saint Suaire. Examen et prélèvement effectués le 21 avril 1988. In *Le Prélèvement du 21-4-1988 Études du Tissue: Actes du Symposium Scientifique International Paris 7-8 Septembre 1989.* (pp. 45-69). Centre International d'Études sur le Linceul de Turin. Paris: O.E.I.L.

Thurston, H., S.J. (1903). The Holy Shroud of Turin. *The Tablet,* 101, 284-5.

_____ (1912). Shroud, The Holy. In *The Catholic Encyclopedia.* (Vol. 13, pp. 762-3). New York: Robert Appleton Company.

Tonelli, A. (1931). *La Santa Sindone.* Torino.

_____ (1933, August). Verso l'ostensione della Sindone— Incendi...providenziali. *Rivista dei Giovanni,* pp. 472-480.

van Haelst, R. (1998). The red stains on the Lier Shroud copy. In CIELT (Ed.), *ΑΧΕΙΠΟΠΟΙΗΤΟΣ ΑΞΗΕΙΡΟΠΟΙΕΤΟΣ:* "Non fait de main d'homme." *Actes du IIIème Symposium Scientifique International du CIELT--Nice 1997* (pp. 183-192). Paris: Editions Du CIELT.

Vial, G. (1991, March-June). The Shroud of Turin: A technical study. *Shroud Spectrum International,* 9(38-39), 7-20.

Vignon, P. (n. d. [1902]). *The Shroud of Christ.* New York: E. P. Dutton & Co.

Walsh, J. E. (1963). *The Shroud.* New York, NY: Random House.

Whanger, M., & Whanger, A. (1998). *The Shroud of Turin: An adventure of Discovery.* Franklin, TN: Providence House Publishers.

Williams, H. U. (1927). Gross and microscopic anatomy of two Peruvian mummies. *Archives of Pathology,* 4, 26-33.

Willis, D. (1969). Did He die on the cross? *Ampleforth Journal,* 74(1).

Wilson, I., & Miller, V. (1986). *The Mysterious Shroud.* Garden City, NY: Doubleday & Company, Inc.

Wilson, I. (Ed.). (1996, June-July). News from around the world: Science Fiction to Science fact? Cloak and Dagger with Shroud DNA. *British Society for the Turin Shroud Newsletter,* 43, 4-8.

_____ (1998). *The blood and the Shroud. New Evidence that the world's most sacred relic is real.* New York: The Free Press.

Zaninotto, G. (n.d. [1985?]). La tecnica della crocifissione Romana. La Crocifissione. G. Ricci, Mons. (Ed.). *Emmaus,* 3, 37-53.

Zugibe, F. T. (1989, June). The Man of the Shroud was washed. *Sindon, Nuova Serie,* 1(1), 171-9.

Footnotes:

1 I am deeply indebted to Drs. Alan D. Adler and Robert Bucklin for their kind willingness to read an early version of this paper and offer corrections. I have incorporated most of them or have changed the text to reflect my further study of their critique. Where errors remain they are solely mine. My thanks to both for their generosity.

2 For example, one of the latest presentations is that found in P. L. Baima Bollone's book *Sindone: La Prova* (1998, pp. 139-185).

3 M. Borghesi, et al. in Zaccone, G. M. (ed). (1998). *L'immagine rivelata*, p. 132f.

4 L. Tamburini in Zaccone, G. M. (ed). (1998). *L'immagine rivelata*, p. 77.

5 For a more detailed survey of the history of Shroud science one can turn to P. L. Baima Bollone, (1998), *Sindone: La Prova*, pp. 139-185.

6 Riggi's archives contain a total of some thirty-three hours of video viewing related to Shroud research. (Riggi di Numana, personal communication, Feb. 12, 1994).

7 Vignon, P. [1902]. *The Shroud of Christ*, p. 137. Emphasis the author's.

8 That Vignon clearly recognized the gradual fading off of the image into the cloth see Vignon [1902], p. 130f : "Let us suppose that we are going to take the print of the front view of a corpse lying on the ground. We should firmly press the cloth along the central line of the body and more lightly on the sloping surfaces, graduating our passes so that the general contours take form by degrees. ...the operator, ... has stretched the linen with great care, fixing the edges; he will be content to let the cloth rest on the bridge of the nose, on the forehead, and on the chin; also on the cheek-bones. To make the modelling [sic] possible he will have made the cloth touch the sloping portions, such as the sides of the nose, lightly. He will have endeavoured to let it touch the lips with great delicacy." See also p. 145 where he states: "Here we see the upper cloth, x' y', resting gently on the body, sloping off gradually at the sides till it joins the under-cloth, x y." In this matter it is profitable for one to read John Walsh, *The Shroud*, New York: Random House, 1963, especially chapter 6, pp. 59-80.

9 See also C. Pickover (1990).

10 See Ian Wilson (1986), *The Mysterious Shroud*, p. 88, where he critiques McCrone on the matter of fiber determination. My thanks to Dr. Adler for bringing this reference to my attention.

11 This bluish fluorescence was first brought to Dr. Adler's attention by Samuel Pellicori when they were examining the large UV prints in the Brooks Exhibition in New London, Connecticut, 1980. In particular, Adler recalls that it was one of the holes on the frontal left

side view of the Shroud. (Personal phone communication, 8/28/99). That being the case, this would have been in quadrant four, the lower most layer of cloth in the four-layer configuration in which the Shroud would have been folded at the time of the creation of these pre-1516 burn holes.

12 Adler explained to me (personal communication, Dallas, 1998) that in order to get a readout from blood one must get it into a dissolved form for the tests they run. Adler noted that, "unlike fresh blood, old blood can only be dissolved with some difficulty and patience" (Personal communication, Feb. 22, 1999). My thanks to Dr. Adler for his detailed discussion on this matter and for bringing to my attention the solution to the negative results as presented in Frache, et al. (1976). (Additional personal communication, 8/28/99).

13 Adler explains that oil on the cloth would promote oxidation and thickness—hence the crust around the pre-1516 burns may have been caused by a flaming oil. (Personal communication, 8/28/99).

14 Dr. Adler observes (Personal communication, Feb. 22, 1999) that since the warp and weft threads come from different skeins therefore there would be different capillarity. However, has it been proven conclusively by direct examination that there is a progression of liquid in only one direction?

15 See his presentation in chapter 11 of my book *The Shroud of Turin: A case study in Document Authentication*, (Haworth Press, in preparation).

16 I explore this idea further in chapter 19 of my book *The Shroud of Turin: A Case Study in Document Authentication* (Haworth Press: in preparation).

17 The added comment about color temperature by Dr. Adler was through a personal communication on Feb. 22, 1999. Our problem with the interpretation of color is made difficult by the fact that color photographs are rarely, if ever, published with Munson strips to show the proper color. (Adler, personal communication, 8/28/99).

18 Discussed in greater detail in chapter 19 of my book to which I have alluded in footnote 13.

19 For a further explication of the botanical studies on the Turin Shroud one may consult my paper, "A Contribution toward a History

of Botanical Research on the Shroud of Turin," to be published in the forthcoming Proceedings of the Richmond, VA conference held in June of 1999.

20 Such practice is common in the Eastern Rite. A personal communication from a Copt living in Canada (Badawey, 1984) turned up a list of some 26 different floral materials used for their Easter service liturgy. And my wife and I personally witnessed the sprinkling of rose petals on an epitaphios in St. Nicholas Greek Orthodox Church, Allentown, PA during the Friday Easter service in 1985.

21 Ms. Piczek's full study may be found in chapter 8 of my book *The Shroud of Turin: A case study in Document Authentication*, (Haworth Press, in preparation).

22 See the studies of the Templecombe panel by Rex Morgan in the bibliography.

23 However, see P. A. Beecher's rebuttal in his 1928 publication: *The Holy Shroud. A reply to the Rev. Herbert Thurston*, S.J. My thanks to Dr. A. D. Adler for suggesting the inclusion of this reference.

24 The scene is punctuated by such commentators as Steven Schafersman who criticized STURP's work as "pseudo-science." (McCrone, 1996, pp. 298-308). In my judgment his writings about the Shroud are pseudo-review because they are filled with inaccuracies, invective and innuendo, incorrect chronology, invalid assumptions often based upon tertiary sources--themselves strongly biased, truncated statements about the facts that mis-portray the real situation, straw men he wishes to knock down, and strongly biased opinions (i.e. the Shroud can not possibly be the Shroud of Jesus therefore it is not!) which contribute little, if anything, to the scientific quest. My greatest objection is his insistence of fraud--in this case allegedly perpetrated by Max Frei--as one of the reasons why Shroud science cannot be valid. Otherwise, Schafersman admits that Frei's data would be excellent. His most recent critique may be found in *Approfondimento Sindone* 2:2, (1998), pp. 31-48.

A fairer and more balanced approach to the critique of Shroud study can be found in M. M. Mueller's (1982) and N. Caldararo's articles (1997). However, no review is without problems largely because those who execute them are not sindonologists. Reviewers often make statements about points of study they misunderstand because the items critiqued are taken out of context or because the reviewers lack knowledge about some important fact or feature from another discipline that negates their criticism.

25 Discussed in much greater detail in chapter 19 of my book referred to above in footnote 13 including the reasons why Occam's Razor may not always be a safe principle on which to base science.

REV. ALBERT "KIM" R. DREISBACH, JR.

FOUNDER OF THE ATLANTA INTERNATIONAL CENTER FOR THE CONTINUING STUDY OF THE SHROUD OF TURIN (AICCSST)

The Rev. Albert "Kim" R. Dreisbach, Jr., an Episcopal Priest, is the founder and Executive Director of the Atlanta International Center for the Continuing Study of the Shroud of Turin, Inc. (AICCSST). Selected for Marquis who's Who in Religion, Fr. Dreisbach is the author of numerous papers, a frequent lecturer—most recently at the III International Congress held in Turin in June of 1998. He has also lectured at St. Stephen's House, Oxford, Bologna, Mount St. Alphonus in Esopus, NY, at Emory's Senior University, Atlanta, and has often appeared on national radio and TV. He also served as a panelist with author Ian Wilson and Duke's Dr. Alan Whanger on Vatican Radio following the Bologna International Symposium in 1989. A commentator and technical advisor in a segment devoted to the Shroud on CBS's Mysteries of the Ancient World, he also has functioned in the same capacity for NBC's Unsolved Mysteries, CBN's Behold a Mystery, and for the newly released update on the Shroud for The Learning Channel titled "In Pursuit of the Shroud."

From the Empty Tomb in Jerusalem to its current resting place in Turin's Cathedral of St. John the Baptist, Fr. Dreisbach has traveled extensively in search of new insights regarding the Holy Shroud. Called by one newspaper "a man of the cloth who teaches about 'The' Man on the Cloth," Fr. Dreisbach sees the Holy Shroud as a superb vehicle for:

1. Low-level Evangelism to the 20th century skeptic who will not believe until he sees.
2. The best available "visual aid" (note that here the medium is the message) for Christian Education about our Lord's Passion, Death, and Resurrection.
3. As an Ecumentical bridge with meaning for all members of the Christian Church.

Like John Walsh, historian and author of Shroud, Fr. Dreisbach believes that:

> The Shroud of Turin is either the most awesome and instructive relic of Christ in existence...or...the most ingenious, unbelievably cleaver production of the human mind and hand on record. It is one or the other. There is no middle ground.

As the founder of the Atlanta International Center for the Continuing Study of the Shroud of Turin (AICCSST). Over the years, he acquired a large collection, including a full Shroud exhibit, which he made available to the public at the Omni, in Atlanta for several years. Unfortunately, the exhibit closed after he lost his lease. In his 1998 Dallas Meeting of American Sindonology presentation, Father Dreisbach discussed the Atlanta Center, which remains active in spite of the loss of its physical center. He also detailed the heartrending struggle and victory of the two founders of American sindonology—Fr. Adam Otterbein and Fr. Peter Rinaldi—and reviewed his ideas for archiving and safe storage of Shroud materials.

50

A Tribute to the Titans of American Sindonology

Those of you who have visited our home in Atlanta know that in my computer room are four pictures of America's foremost clerical sindonologists. They are in alphabetical order the Rev. Frs. Francis Filas, Adam J. Otterbein, Peter M. Rinaldi and Edward Wuenschel. Each morning as I begin my work, I am visually reminded of these men who have done so much in serving the apostolate of the Holy Shroud. I was blessed to have known three of them personally, and the fourth was made known to me through his indefatigable and brilliant scholarship.

We gather here in Dallas to honor two of these giants—Fr. Adam Otterbein and Fr. Peter Rinaldi. I have chosen to begin with Fr. Adam both because he was the first of the two whom I met, and because I always felt that he never got the proper credit for which he was so justly due. Each man had his own strengths and limitations. Together like the warp and weft threads of the Holy Shroud itself God used them to weave the strong fabric of America's sindonological knowledge and mutual support, which is responsible for our presence here today.

FR. ADAM J. OTTERBEIN, C.SS.R.
(Founder and President of the HOLY SHROUD GUILD)

When I first learned of Fr. Adam's death, I immediately sent the following message to Fr. Fred Brinkmann:

> *On behalf of the Officers and Board of Directors of the Atlanta International Center for the Continuing Study of the Shroud of Turin, Inc. I wish to extend our condolences to you, the Holy Shroud Guild and all those in the Redemptorist*

community who knew and were taught and inspired by him. He was the "glue" who kept the HSG together and whose organizational skills, fidelity to empiricism and multi-competence in many areas—from photography to teaching equestrian skills to seminarians at Mount Esopus—played a major role in promoting and investigating the Shroud. If his co-worker Fr. Peter Rinaldi, S.D.B. "opened the doors" for the 1978 investigation by STURP, it was Fr. Adam who made certain that the necessary support and organizational skills made entry through those doors a reality. His stepping in with the necessary financing to complete "The Silent Witness" by David Rolfe has provided countless persons to become acquainted with the Holy Shroud in an objective and moving way. He was especially kind to me personally and a strong supporter of AICCSST from its foundation in 1979. Both he and Fr. Rinaldi came to Atlanta on more than one occasion, and I will always treasure our times together whether at Mount Esopus, the various international symposia or sharing his favorite breakfast buffet at Shoney's when we were roommates on a visit to Durham. Fr. Adam was a Pennsylvanian and he nobly filled his role as a "keystone" for American sindonology. May his soul rest in peace and may he now "see face to face" the Savior he has so long served in the apostolate of the Holy Shroud.

Though I had corresponded with him since 1977 when my initial interest in the Shroud first began, I had never met him personally until June of 1981 when I drove from Atlanta to Ephrata, Pennsylvania where he was then assigned. He graciously spent the better part of a day with me and encouraged me regarding the newly formed Atlanta Center for the Continuing Study of the Shroud of Turin.

A few months later he saw to it that I had tickets for the STURP Symposium held in Groton/New London, Connecticut. To be in the same room with those scientists who had actually touched and studied the actual Holy Shroud for five days in 1978 was an experience that still sends chills down my spine. When Adam took me aside and gave me a full set of Vern Miller slides plus a silver poster with a life-size reproduction of the Face of the Man of the Shroud, no child on Christmas morning could have been happier than I was to have received such precious gifts.

By 1982 John Sturm of Contempo Design opened his fabulous TURIN SHROUD EXHIBIT at the New Trier High School in Northbrook, Illinois. It featured the actual table used by STURP in their 1978 examination and attached to it was the cloth replica of the Shroud created by for "The Silent Witness." On All Saints Day of that same year it opened at the Peachtree Center in Atlanta, Georgia. It was purchased by the Atlanta International Center for the Continuing Study of the Shroud of Turin and remained in that city until Easter of 1987 when it was forced to leave the Omni after Ted Turner had purchased that facility and renamed it the CNN Center. Both Fr. Adam and Fr. Peter visited the EXHIBIT on more than one occasion.

Fr. Adam made one such trip in 1985 to represent the HSG and act as an advisor for a meeting sponsored by the AICCSST to consider the creation of a centralized computer data bank devoted to sindonology. Present were represntatives of IBM, Georgia Tech, Emory University as well as some of us here today—Don Lynn representing STURP, Paul Maloney representing ASSIST and yours truly representing the host organization. My notes for that day reveal that Don Lynn and the representative from IBM were particularly interested in the creation of a system of artificial intelligence to relate the various sindonological sub-fields. Don was also hopeful that someday we might be able to store images permanently on laser discs for use by future researchers. Thanks to contacts made with officials of Delta Airlines, Fr. Adam was able to ship a full-size transparency of the Holy Shroud to Cardinal Anastasio Balestrero. It was flown it directly from Atlanta to Frankfurt and then delivered by truck to Turin.

I have particularly fond memories of a meeting at the home of Alan and Mary Whanger in Durham, NC in the spring of 1986. Adam and I were roommates at a local motel and he couldn't wait to begin the day with a full plate from the "Breakfast Bar" at Shoney's. It was one of the few times when he was willing to bend the rules regarding his diet and a marked departure from the toast with peanut butter which I had shared with him at the refectory at Mount Saint Alphonsus.

By 1988 the Atlanta Exhibit was stored in a warehouse gathering dust, but Fr. Adam drove from Esopus to Washington, D.C. to help set up the first showing of a mobile Shroud Exhibit in the crypt of the Shrine of the Immaculate Conception. David Walz Associates of Norcross, Georgia was the designer and builder of this traveling exhibit that was underwritten by the Koch Foundation thanks to a gift by Erica John, formerly of THE CENTER FOR THE STUDY OF THE PASSION OF

CHRIST & THE HOLY SHROUD. Kevin Moran, Dick & Gerry DeGraff and Erica joined us for the occasion.

Through the years Fr. Adam could be found wherever significant events connected with the Shroud took place. I can remember a trip to Rochester, NY in 1985 with Kevin Moran and Paul Maloney. We had gone to learn about the then new Kodak Photo CD's and witness a demonstration of Kodak's Premier digitization of the 1978 Vern Miller transparencies of the full-size Shroud. Not only was the machine able to achieve color consistency and eliminate the lines between the three sections of the original negatives, but the hope was that some day such digitalization could even recreate what the Shroud looked like prior to the fire of 1532 at Chambéry with its telltale burns, scorches and watermarks.

Fr. Adam attended the 1989 CIELT Symposium in Paris, the 1991 in St. Louis, and the 1993 CIELT Symposium in Rome. Earlier in April of that year members of the HSG's Archiving Committee meeting in Colorado Springs had been concerned about Fr. Adam's apparent "confusion". By June in Rome we were all saddened to witness the debilitating effects of this Alzheimer's disease and grateful beyond measure to his designated successor Fr. Fred Brinkmann, C.Ss.R. for the loving care and companionship provided him. It was Fr. Fred who arranged for the final long overdue tribute given to him at Esopus in 1996, and it was Fr. Fred who offered the following...at his funeral Mass in June of 1998:

> Father Adam Otterbein, C.Ss.R. had a long distinguished ministry in the Congregation of the Most Holy Redeemer. After his seminary training at Mount Saint Alphonsus in Esopus, NY, he received a Doctorate in Dogmatic Theology at Catholic University of America. He taught dogmatic theology at Mount St. Alphonsus for many years. He was a fine pastoral minister at OLPH in Opalaca, FL, St. Clement's Church in Ephrata, PA. and St. Peter's in Philadelphia. His interest in the Holy Shroud led him to be a protege of Fr. Edward Wuenschel. He collected the books of Fr. Wuenschel in 1964 and inaugurated the Wuenschel Collection at Esopus, NY. He founded the Holy Shroud Guild in 1951 with the support of the Redemptorist Community behind him. He sponsored many enterprises through the Holy Shroud Guild, including the famous documentary, "Silent Witness," which he produced with David Rolfe, and he patronized many of the experiments done by STURP during the late 1960's and through the 1970's. Working with Father Peter

Rinaldi at this time, they were both known as "Mr. Shroud." Father Otterbein lived in the image of Christ, and the Holy Shroud of Turin is a good parable for the life of Father Adam himself. He was a holy and sensitive man who took his ministry very seriously. His motto could very well have been, "A picture is worth a thousand words." The image of Christ in the Holy Shroud, which he honored as the true image of Our Lord, really is not half the image of Jesus Christ which was imprinted on the soul of my confrère and brother, Fr. Adam.

FR. PETER M. RINALDI, S.D.B.
(Pastor of Corpus Christi for 28 years: 1949-1977)

No one who ever met and spent any time with Fr. Peter Rinaldi will ever forget him. He truly was "A Man for all Seasons"—parish priest, pastor, scholar, linguist, international diplomat and indefatigable correspondent and promoter of the Holy Shroud. If Fr. Adam was the behind-the-scenes stage manager and organizer who was so quietly effective, Fr. Peter was the matinee idol who charmed all who were privileged to know him.

One might say that American sindonology was born in June of 1934 when Fr. Peter wrote a four-page article entitled "The Holy Shroud" in a magazine aptly titled *The Sign*. That article was read by Fr. Wuenschel who in turn "evangelized" his successor Fr. Otterbein and the rest is history. In 1951 the Holy Shroud Guild was founded by Fr. Adam and he and Fr. Peter served as president and vice president respectively.

It was in June of 1981 that I was blessed with my first meeting with Fr. Rinaldi. On my way to a college class reunion, I came off the expressway at Port Chester and turned left up the hill to Corpus Christi. Here Fr. Peter greeted me as if we had known one another for years and led me to the interior of the sanctuary where I first saw the life-size marble crucifix modeled on the Image of the Man of the Shroud. Next he guided me to the Chapel of the Holy Shroud which, in the words of one national magazine "has made Port Chester known all over the United States...A place visited by the humble and the great, the devout and the curious." As if his time and presence were not precious gifts enough, as he walked me to the parking lot he gave me my first lenticular/lenticil (*i.e.* Vari-Vue) of the Holy Face and Aggemian's portrait—a treasure which hangs in our home to this day. My wife and I visited Turin for the first time in 1984. We were returning from a trip to the Holy Land and it seemed quite appropriate—like the Shroud itself—to journey from the Tomb to Turin. There to greet us was Fr. Peter and his nephew Paolo as our chauffeur. Dropping us off at the Hotel Gran Sitea to drop off our bags and clean up, a few minutes later he was knocking at the door—his hands full of two of the largest ice cream cones we had ever seen. Off we went to the cathedral, and though we could not see the Shroud we were blessed to be in its presence and to admire the Guarini Chapel prior to the tragic fire of 1998. While in the sacristy, Fr. Peter lovingly told the story of how, as a young altar boy, he ran around the chapel until "shushed" by a priest who told him about the "linen of the Lord." Everywhere we went, the people knew and loved Fr. Peter—from the Due Lampioni to a restaurant overlooking the city where the proprietress rushed to retrieve an umbrella which he had left there some two years before.

Fr. Peter was a believer and practitioner of ecumenicity. He welcomed the late Anglican Bishop and New Testament scholar John A.T. Robinson into the fold, wrote an article in Turin's *La Stampa* extolling an ecumenical Office of the Holy Shroud held on August 16th, the Greek Orthodox Feast of the Holy Mandylion, to dedicate the exhibit in Atlanta and opened sindonological "doors" to "all sorts and conditions" of those of us who were not Roman Catholics.

I will never forget January of 1985 when Fr. Peter participated in the wedding of our daughter Dede. In 1984, each morning would find him at 5:30 A.M. sitting at our dining room table with only our faithful doberman, "Dirk," as his companion at that hour to share dawn's first light, saying the daily office and catching up on his voluminous correspondence. Not only did he participate in the nuptials, but the next day he preached and served with the cup at our Mass. As I drove him to the airport, he remarked: "There is no need to tell the local archbishop that I was here! I knew him in New York. Let us just say that not all Roman Catholics are so ecumenically inclined."

* * *

As the years went by, I frequently would make the trip to Port Chester—always treasuring those special moments—breakfast with Marcia Mascia and her sisters, meetings in Rye with ASSIST and, most joyful of all, the celebration of his Jubilee ordination to the priesthood. His beloved parishioners, friends from all over the world and a large number of American "shroudies" attended this well-deserved tribute—an honor he never wanted and attempted to cancel, mercifully without success. There were tributes from the Holy Father, President Reagan, John Cardinal O'Connor and scores of others. Maybe this honor was best expressed in a tribute to him by friend and fellow Salesian Raul Cardinal Silva Henriques of Chile:

> *May our Lord bless Father Rinaldi for his kindness, gener-*
> *osity, and priestly service to all. I think he is a great Salesian.*
> *He is affable, genial, and always ready to be of assistance,*
> *unstintedly giving of himself to others. I believe that ....[he],*
> *in his simple and ordinary ways hides a beautiful holiness,*
> *distinguished by his service to all mankind. Thank you, Fr.*
> *Peter, for your goodness and the fine example you give us.*

That "goodness and fine example" were his to the end. On Ash Wednesday, the 24th of February, 1993, Fr. Peter—though in poor health—had flown from the United States to be present at the transfer of the Holy Shroud from the Royal Chapel to a specially designed plate glass display case behind the cathedral's High Altar. Unfortunately he collapsed and was rushed to a Turin hospital where, four days later on February the 28th, he passed on to his heavenly reward.

We who are heirs to the apostolate of the Holy Shroud—in gratitude to the inspiration and support given so many of us gathered here by Frs. Otterbein and Rinaldi while they lived—are now charged with the sacred charge of nourishing and passing on that sacred mission to the next generation of sindonologists. Fr. Peter constantly reminded us to "Get beyond the linen to the Lord."

We would all to well to heed the caveat of one of his "disciples," the late Bishop John A.T. Robinson who, including the title of one of Fr. Peter's books, observed:

> If in the recognition of the face and hands and feet and
> all the other wounds (on the Holy Shroud),we, like those
> who knew Him best, are led to say, "It is the Lord!", then
> perhaps we may have to learn to count ourselves also
> among those who have "seen and believed." But that, as
> St. John makes clear, brings with it *no special blessing*
> (20:29)—rather *special responsibility* (17:18-21).[1]

Footnote:

1. The Rt. Rev. John A.T. Robinson. "The Shroud of Turin and the Grave Cloths of the Gospels." *Proceedings of the 1977 United States Conference of Research on the Shroud of Turin.* Bronx, NY: Holy Shroud Guild. 1977, p. 30. [*Italics* added.]

DR. DANIEL C. SCAVONE

PROFESSOR OF HISTORY
UNIVERSITY OF SOUTHERN INDIANA

Dr. Dan Scavone is one of the foremost Shroud historians, with many papers and articles to his credit (including several available on the internet). At the 1998 Dallas Meeting of American Sindonology, Dr. Scavone summarized all of the major theories about the missing years in Shroud history and made suggestions as to the direction of future studies.

58

A Hundred Years of Historical Studies on the Turin Shroud

In 1977, upon learning of the imminent display of the Shroud in Torino in the following year, I began to read what was easily available in English on the subject. I had no idea about the tremendous volume of material that was "out there." I did, however, notice how sketchy, tentative, and unsatisfying was its early history. Fr. Herbert Thurston's entry in the *Catholic Encyclopedia* was immediately discouraging to me, as it cited the powerful turn-of-the-century work of Canon Ulysse Chevalier, a seeming unassailable scholar who first raised the specter of the d'Arcis Memorandum. D'Arcis is still introduced into every anti-Shroud argument as if it stood alone in the 14th c. in defining the non-authenticity of the Shroud. It is to the credit of Fr. Luigi Fossati (*La Santa Sindone: Nuova Luce su Antichi Documenti* (Torino: Borla, 1961) and Fr. Paul de Gail (*Histoire religieuse du linceul du Christ* (Paris: Editions France-Empire, 1973) that we can today show that Chevalier's documents tell an entirely different story if they are taken *in toto*. Yet, my first recommendation is that this proper interpretation of the Memorandum be promoted more actively so as to lay it to rest once and for all. The minds of Thurston and of the scholars of Paris, who in 1901 denounced Vignon and even Delage out of hand, were swayed by Chevalier's profound researches much as the radiocarbon date today has unfortunately captured the mind of scholars and news people.

On August 30, 1978, on the very last day of a summer spent in our American Academy nine-room apartment in Rome, my family and I went to Turin and saw the Shroud on the first, drizzly day of its exposition. There I met Fr. Francis Filas, already an idol of mine since I had viewed his TV presentation on the Shroud in Chicago every Good

Friday of my mind's life; and I met Dorothy Crispino, whose Indiana accents I immediately recognized, to my delight. She would become my mentor for several years to come, and as a nearby history academician, I was among those she consulted in planning for the publication of *Shroud Spectrum International.* But it was my meeting with Fr. Peter Rinaldi that made the major impact—indeed he shaped my life, even until this very moment, by hearing my request to be permitted to attend the Congress of October 1978 and, after telling me straight out how impossible it was to add people, sending me his personal and official invitation a month later.

My intention at that moment—I had been teaching college Latin, Greek, and history already fifteen years—was to write a solid history of the Shroud. That October I met Ian Wilson, whose 1978 book had recently been published. And after that, all that was left for me was to follow his leads and try to provide details where his book's agenda did not permit him to do so. And that is what I have tried to do for the last twenty-one years.

Back home, Dorothy Crispino's personal library provided for me the moment of my rude awakening to the massive amount of Shroud literature in French and Italian. This included Andre Perret's "Essay sur l'histoire du Saint Suaire du XIVe au XVIe siècle," (*Mémoires de l'Academie des Sciences, Belles-lettres et Arts de Savoie*, sixième série, Tome IV, 1960, 49-121). This long article still provides the most reliable account of the Shroud's career as it fell into the hands of Marguerite, daughter of Geoffroy II de Charny, and was passed to the Savoy family in 1453. I have not felt a need to look elsewhere for this later and better-known Shroud history. As my fields were classical, ancient, and early medieval history, I saw the need to fill the space of the Shroud's early and more elusive history.

Coming towards the end of the promised one hundred years of my title was Ian Wilson's great insight—insights such as this drive and revolutionize historical researches. His identification of the Edessa facial icon as the *actual face* of Jesus, the man of the Shroud, was no less than stupendous in its day. This face-on-cloth had previously been considered merely the earliest true *copy* of the Shroud face. Could its historical record, Wilson asked, provide a much-needed documentation for the centuries during which no burial shroud *per se* was mentioned in antiquity? Scholarship that has followed Wilson's lead has tended to corroborate more and more precisely the correctness of his assumption.

With the same insight, Wilson discovered the thin documentary thread that suggested how this Edessa *mandylion* really held more than just a face: it was large enough to couch the image of a full-sized man. In short, the Edessa icon—unfolded—was always the Turin Shroud. The Shroud, virtually absent from the historical record—*anywhere*—found its own historical pedigree in the documents of Edessa. To put it more moderately, if Wilson's insight is found wanting, Shroud historians have no better scenario, at this moment, to fill the centuries between the Crucifixion and the twelfth century. Virtually everything about Shroud history makes sense only in terms of its Edessa sojourn.

Wilson owes a large debt and vocally pays homage to his mentor, Fr. Maurus Green of his native England. To read Fr. Maurus' research in the famous *Ampleforth Journal* article is to read the seeds of many of Ian's contributions to Shroud historical studies ("Enshrouded in Silence. In Search of the First Millennium of the Holy Shroud," *Ampleforth Journal*, Vol. 74, III, 1969, 321-345). Indeed, Green was the first to recognize the merit of Wilson's immense Edessa insight.

Robert Drews, professor of classical antiquity at Vanderbilt University, was the first American academician to produce a book on the Shroud's history (*In Search of the Shroud of Turin*. Totowa, NJ: Rowman and Allanheld, 1984). His research did much to supply more substance for the notion of the *mandylion* as a transfer of some sort from the actual body of Jesus. Carpocratian gnostics in Edessa had the icon—actually the Shroud, Drews thought—and it was they who developed some technique, now lost, of capturing the Shroud's subtle image by direct contact with Jesus' body. In spite of Drews' excellent researches which began from and supported Wilson's views, his book was received grudgingly, at best, by sindonologists convinced that the image was never produced by men but was either a purely natural or supernatural phenomenon. Scholars of Shroud history will do well to reread Drews for the *richesse* of solid history that his studies have turned up.

In 1985 appeared yet another major historical book, like Drews', based upon the author's familiarity with primary sources in their original languages. Fr. A.M. Dubarle (*Histoire ancienne du linceul de Turin jusqu'au XIIIe siècle*, Paris: O.E.I.L., Vol. I, 1985—and now Vol. II, 1998) has provided a solid commentary on the most important early texts bearing upon the Shroud. He also reviewed the most recent major concepts relating to the pros and cons of Wilson's Edessa thesis and came out in favor of Wilson: the actual Shroud *was* in Constantinople in 1200 and in Edessa before 944. Dubarle also summarized for us the best efforts of the current opposition-historians so that we might be alerted to new directions for research.

As if in preparation for the current generation of Shroud historians, at least three exceptional works were produced between 1957 and 1973. Msgr. Pietro Savio gathered numerous previously inaccessible documents into his anthology, *Ricerche storiche sulla Santa Sindone* (Torino: Società Editrice Internazionale, 1957). This hard-to-find volume is a treasure for anyone working from the original Latin and Greek texts.

Soon after this, in 1961, Fr. Luigi Fossati produced his *chef d'oeuvre*, thorough refutation of the sindonoclastic arguments based on Chevalier's publication of the d'Arcis Memorandum (*La Santa Sindone: Nuova Luce su Antichi Documenti*. Torino: Borla, 1961). A summary version of Fossati's researches in this important area appeared in *Shroud Spectrum* (SSI) 1983 as "The Lirey Controversy," Vol. 2. 8, 24-34, (tr. by Dorothy Crispino and Daniel Scavone.) His argument is buttressed by dated primary sources. On the motives of Bishop d'Arcis, see also Scavone, "The Turin Shroud from 1200 to 1400," in W.J. Cherf, ed., *Alpha to Omega: Studies in Honor of George John Szemler* (Chicago: Ares Publishers, 1993) 187-225.

More recently, Fr. Fossati has made another important contribution by collecting photographs of over fifty copies of the Shroud made over the centuries. The inability of artists to replicate the subtleties of the Shroud's image makes manifest that the Shroud was not a work of art, whether medieval or earlier. See his articles "Copies of the Holy Shroud." Pt. I: *SSI*, 12, Sept. 1984, 7-23; Pt. II: *SSI*, 13, Dec. 1984, 23-39. They are a natural complement to Isabel Piczek's several articles that clarify why the Shroud's image is not a painting.

Next came a phenomenal work by Fr. Paul de Gail, S.J. (copy given to me by Crispino at the start of my own researches, and devoured in its entire 385 pages) *Histoire religieuse du linceul du Christ* (Paris: Editions France-Empire 1973). De Gail traces the texts of Constantinople and elsewhere in the Near East and Europe through the 16th c., providing much information about the French literature on the Shroud. Having refuted the Besançon hypothesis (more later on this), de Gail proffers in its stead the notion that Geoffroy I de Charny somehow acquired the Shroud while briefly on the Smyrna Crusade of 1345-47, led by the dauphin Humbert II de Viennois. His acquisition of the Shroud is, of course, not documented in the least. By the way, Edessa and Abgar are not to be found in de Gail's vocabulary.

The Father of American sindonology is Fr. Edward Wuenschel, who in the 1930s accumulated—and read—the entire collection named for him and housed in the Redemptorist Seminary at Esopus, New York. The collection includes books (all marginally annotated by Wuenschel), photostatic copies of the actual Shroud-related documents found in libraries and archives of Europe, and Wuenschel's personal note-cards and papers. Wuenschel has made available for scholars of the Shroud many of the most significant early works and conjectures about its history. His own work on Jewish burial customs is one of the best researched articles showing that Shroud burial was used in the first century ("The Shroud of Turin and the Burial of Christ," *Catholic Biblical Quarterly*, Pt. I, Vol. 7, 1945, 405-437; Pt. II, Vol. 8, 1946, 135-178). Equally important, Wuenschel's work effectively countered the arguments of Thurston, who in his 1901 entry in the *Catholic Encyclopedia* based his opposition to the Shroud's authenticity upon the writings of Canon Usysse Chevalier.

Shortly before and since the radiocarbon situation, the person who arguably has done the most towards refurbishing the Shroud's credibility is Prof. Gino Zaninotto of Rome. In one of a series of spectacular papers developed from his researches in the Vatican Archives, Zaninotto reported on an ancient document of Roman crucifixion methods, practically a "how to" handbook. The document showed that 1st c. Roman crucifixions were, in fact, performed with a tau-shaped cross. It was only later (2nd-3rd c.) that major variations were introduced, such as the X-shaped cross or the stipes-only crucifixion ("The Penalty of the Cross," *SSI* 25, Dec. 1987, 3-12). Zaninotto also "discovered" the MS of the Gregory Referendarius Sermon, dated August 16, 944, the day after the arrival of the Edessa icon in Constantinople. It is an autograph text in 10th c. Greek written, it seems, by Gregory himself. He had been one of the clerics involved in the reception of the icon in the capital, the ceremonies celebrating it, and the honors rendered it. Gregory again recited the Abgar story, stating that the image showed bloodstains from thorns on the head and suggesting that blood and water (clear serum, as we know today) could be seen emanating from Jesus' side ("Il Codice Vat. Gr. 511, ff. 143-150v: Una conferma dell'identità tra l'immagine Edessena e la Sindone di Torino?" *Collegamento*, March/April 1988, 14-25). Wilson's circumstantial evidence that the Edessa cloth held a full-body image was now very possibly eyewitness-proved. Significant studies, however, have raised questions over the conclusions to be drawn from this important text, in process of translation into French by Dubarle.

Sadly, *I* might have discovered the Gregory Sermon! But I did not. In his 1899 masterpiece *Christusbilder* (*Christ Images*), Ernst von Dobschütz has an apology tucked into a footnote in one of his 1000-plus pages that he knew of, but had not had the opportunity to look closely at, Cod. Vat.

Lat. 511. I own a copy of von Dobschütz, and I might have checked it out. The rest is "history according to Gino Zaninotto."

I cannot name here all the men and women who have contributed to our understanding of the Shroud's history. I must be concerned with only those individuals whose expertise or chief effort is in Shroud history. Certainly Emanuela Marinelli, and especially Fr. Werner Bulst and Bro. Bruno Bonnet-Eymard (major papers in *The Catholic Counter-Reformation of the 20th c.*), must be mentioned for creatively presenting Shroud history in Italian, German, and French based on their own ventures in the primary documents. Crispino has traced the affairs of the Charny family in her journal, *Shroud Spectrum*, 1982-1993. Also to be mentioned in this context is the archaeological foray of Rex and Christopher Morgan and Isabel Piczek in the Domitilla Catacomb in Rome in 1996. The important result of their research is the redating of a profile painting of Jesus in the Orpheus Cubiculum as 1st c.; it was previously assigned a 3rd c. date. This profile seems to be another view of the frontal Shroud face, the two faces tending to corroborate each other. (Report privately published by the Morgans in 1996; see also Rex Morgan, "New Evidence for the Earliest Portrait of Jesus," *SSI*, no. 42, Dec. 1993, 28-30.)

If it is accepted that the questions raised by the d'Arcis Memorandum have been answered (if not laid to rest), today the historian's chief preoccupation is to fill the "lost years" (1204-1355) between Constantinople and Lirey. The problem has two horns: the first is to show that the Lirey-Chambery-Turin Shroud is the same as that shroud documented in Constantinople 944-1204. Sindonoclasts worldwide have leapt upon this point, and until recently there was no cogent proof that the two objects were one and the same. The second horn is to discover where the Shroud might have been during its missing years.

The level of evidence for the identification of the Lirey-Chambery-Turin Shroud with the Constantinople Shroud has risen sharply since Zaninotto's publication of the Sermon of Gregory Referendarius, suggesting that, based upon the sermon's allusions to the blood and water (possibly seen by Gregory) emanating from the side of the shroud-man, the Edessa face-only icon of the legends may always have been a full-body image. Another recent discovery is an illustration in the Hungarian Codex-Pray, for the moment more important than the Gregory Sermon because it is clear and specific in its resonance with the Shroud. In the upper frame, we see Jesus lying in state, with hands folded in a Shroud-like manner and with thumbs remarkably absent as on the Shroud. In the lower register, the artist presents the empty tomb and the shroud-wrappings. In the latter can be seen two red zigzag lines strongly recalling the blood-flow down the Shroud-man's arms. (If this interpretation is incorrect, then that zigzag line is entirely whimsical.) More significantly, the artist has painted two of the four sets of burn-holes still seen on the Turin Shroud at the frontal and dorsal hips. The major expert in the research of this codex, Ilona Berkovits, who knows nothing of Shroud controversies, places a date of 1192-95 or earlier on this codex and on its illustrations (*Illuminated Manuscripts in Hungary, XI-XVI Centuries*, Z. Horn, tr., NY: Frederick A. Praeger, 1969). Since we may be reasonably certain that the Turin Shroud inspired these details, and since the Shroud would have been in Constantinople when this illustration was made, one must assert that both the Turin Shroud and the Constantinople Shroud bore the same burn marks. In this connection, a 1516 artist's copy of the Turin Shroud, today in Lierre, Belgium, also shows the identical four sets of burn holes (but not the marks of destruction from the later fire of 1532 while the Shroud was in Chambery). Thus we have two dated documents, the Codex-Pray and the Lierre copy, pointing backward and placing the Shroud in Constantinople with virtual certainty. These documents harmonize with other eyewitness documents, such as the *Narratio* of 944, which calls the face image a moist secretion without the painter's art, and the 1203 testimony of Robert de Clary, who saw the *sydoines* (singular) with the Lord's image on it. We may consider this aspect of the problem of the "lost years" essentially closed—but this fact *must* be broadcast so as to preclude and defuse future claims in opposition to it.

Regarding the second part of the 150-year gap (1204-1355) in the Shroud's history there is much more to be said. In his book *The Turin Shroud* (London: Gollancz, 1978), Wilson proposed an excellent and cogent scenario for the Shroud's whereabouts during these years. Evidence, even depositions taken from members of the Knights Templar during their trial in 1307-14, suggests the Templars had the Shroud in their possession towards the end of the "lost years." It was given out as a pagan or Moslem idol which several Templars confessed to being ordered to worship. Some descriptions of the idol seem Shroudlike. The Templars had impregnable castles that would have been secure, and even secret, housing for the Shroud—as of other treasures and precious objects. Rex Morgan's Templecombe research, to which Wilson originally pointed the way, has furthered this theory. At this one-time Templar headquarters a wooden box with hinged lid has been found, the lid bearing a frontal face quite similar to that on the Shroud. Was this a copy of the Templar idol? The box is of a size that would accommodate something with the dimensions of the Shroud when folded. One strength of Wilson's Templar period lies in the fact that no direct reference to the Shroud exists from these 150 lost years. This in turn suggests that the Shroud lay somewhere in secure and secretive keeping during much of that time, the alternative being that it was kept in some family and passed from father to son—incredibly without a single leak for six generations. This alternative was offered by Noel Currer-Briggs with unfortunate and improbable results (*The Shroud and the Grail,* NY: St. Martin's, 1987).

Fr. Dubarle has offered a not-so-viable second scenario ("La première captivité de Geoffroy de Charny et l'acquisition du Linceul," *Montre-nous ton Visage,* no. 8, 1992, 6-18). He offers documentation to show that after the Fourth Crusade the Shroud remained in the possession of the Latin Byzantine emperors until the 1230s and 1240s, when Baldwin II, needing funds to defend his realm, was forced to mortgage the relic collection of the Byzantine emperors to Venetian and other bankers, perhaps including the Templars. So much is undisputed. Then, Dubarle argues, the *toella* that Robert de Clari saw hanging by a chain in a chest in the Pharos Chapel was, in fact, still the original Edessa cloth, that is, the folded Shroud. Taking a cue from an article of the late Hilda Leynen ("A propos du Mandilion," separately printed Extract from *Soudarion,* [Flemish journal] 1991, 1-23), he presumes that this chest still held the Edessa Shroud. Riant was my source for the information and the actual letters documenting French King (St.) Louis IX's redemption of the relics from various bankers. He later built the fabulous Sainte Chapelle in Paris to house the Crown of Thorns, deemed by him to be the prize of the relic collection, and other relics. Since this Pharos chest appears in the periodic inventories of the Sainte Chapelle, Dubarle urges that inside was the Shroud, though it was not considered to be as important as the *Spinea Corona.* The weakness of this position starts from Leynen's interpretation that Robert de Clari was confused about what he saw in the Chapel of Our Lady of Blachernes: that, in fact, he saw no burial shroud with the figure of the Lord but something else. Unfortunately for Leynen's interpretation, the words and the context of Clari are clear. He knew a painting when he saw one, and he knew the *sydoines* in Blachernes was something other than a painting. Moreover, Clari never said he saw the contents of the chest hanging in the Pharos in 1203-04. It may well have been empty or just a copy by that time, as surmised by Wilson in 1978, since its former contents, the Shroud of Edessa, seems surely to have been in Blachernes in 1203-04. Dubarle continues that a subsequent king of France, Philip VI (1328-1350) or John II the Good

(1350-1364), gave the object in the chest, but not the chest itself, to Geoffroy I, *porte-oriflamme* for the king of France. (Fr. Dubarle, a magnificent scholar whose two-volume Shroud history is indispensible, is currently making a translation with commentary of the Gregory Sermon of 944.)

About ten years ago I reintroduced the often-voiced and as often resisted theory of the Shroud's sojourn in Besançon, a city straddling medieval France and the German Holy Roman Empire. It is important to state that Ian Wilson does not live or die by his Templar theory, and I do not insist that Besançon possessed the Shroud. But the facts available today, some I personally uncovered, are much stronger than what was commonly known two generations ago when Vignon persuaded Wuenschel away from the same theory (Daniel Scavone, "The Turin Shroud from 1200 to 1400," in W.J. Cherf, ed., *Alpha to Omega: Studies in Honor of George John Szemler*, Chicago: Ares Publishers, 1993, 187-226).

Documents that are stronger than most that deal with the Shroud point to Othon de La Roche, high-ranking knight of the Fourth Crusade, as receiving the fiefdom of Athens as his reward for service—and also the Constantinople Shroud. He was a native knight of Franche-Comté, capital city, Besançon. This city alone has claimed the Shroud during the 150 "lost" years, but its presence there is much debated. Let me summarize here the positive elements of this Besançon theory. In 1349 the St. Etienne (St. Stephen) Church burned down. The shroud lodged there was lost. In 1353-1354 Jeanne de Vergy, of a prominent Besançon family, wed Geoffroy I de Charny. One of the Vergys customarily held the post of seneschal of Besançon. We know only from the 1389 memorandum of Bishop d'Arcis that this Geoffroy I possessed the Shroud in Lirey by 1355. Geoffroy went to his death in 1356 never having announced this himself. Sometime later, Jeanne's family crest of arms appeared next to Geoffroy's on the Seine Medallion. She was his second wife, and her family's arms there is significant, suggesting a share in the Shroud's ownership.

In 1376, when Jeanne's cousin Guillaume de Vergy was Bishop in Besançon, the city's lost shroud mysteriously reappeared there. Its authenticity was "proved" by raising a corpse back to life. This new shroud was a copy (the original is well-attested for twenty years already in Lirey) and was depicted as the original in Jean Jacques Chifflet's 1624 book on the Shroud of Christ (*De linteis supulchralibus Christi Servatoris crisis historica*. Antwerp: 1624). It had only the frontal image and was clearly only a painting.

In 1389 d'Arcis had said an artist of "about thirty-four years" prior had admitted making the Lirey image. It makes sense that it was Jeanne who carried the original Besançon Shroud—the present Turin Shroud—out of her city and that it was she who did commission an artist to paint (*depictus*) a copy in Lirey, possibly specifically to be sent to Besançon, and it was this painting that an unnamed and insignificant artist may have admitted producing. Therefore, it would have been this painting that "reappeared" in Besançon in 1376 with the complicity of Jeanne's cousin Guillaume de Vergy, the then bishop. It was this copy that quieted a new generation of Bisontines, who had never seen the original, and precluded their ever complaining and filing suit because the canons of the Lirey church possessed a priceless relic that rightly belonged in their city. Hilary de Crémiers ("The Holy Shroud Refound—From Constantinople to Lirey [1204-1354]," *CRC* No. 238, pp. 42-47) recently reintroduced the idea of Jeanne's "cover-up" copy, first suggested by E. Faure in 1918. Faure, however, did not name Jeanne, but only "a member of the Vergy family" as the person who carried the original Shroud to Philip VI (E. Faure, *Le portrait authentique du Christ révélé par la photographie de Saint-Suaire de Turin*, Paris: 1918. Cited in Dubarle's article, "La première captivité. . .").

As a final note, in Besançon, on the frontier between France and Germany, the Vergys were in the party that wished the city to be a part of France. It would follow from the reconstruction thus far that Jeanne took the Shroud after the fire (1349-50) to King Philip VI, thus saving it for France, and he made it his wedding gift to his *porte-oriflamme* Geoffroy I and his new bride. A text of 1525 that begins "To Know the Truth" (*pour scavoir la Verité*) and found at Lirey stated that "Philip had the Shroud," and Dubarle has also accepted its implications: the Shroud as a royal gift to Geoffroy I.

This hypothesis must yet pass sindonic peer-review. We know that the documents pertaining to a shroud in Besançon do not clearly go back to Othon, Franche-comptois knight who surely received the one in Constantinople in 1204; we also know that the archives of Besançon were destroyed once in the 14th c. fire and again during the French Revolution, when the second shroud was declared (rightly) to be an artwork and was torn into strips for bandages. Today the Besançon archives begin only in 1412, meaning that all or nearly all documents before that no longer exist. We are asked to accept here the smoking gun-evidence.

* * *

Recently, an article appeared that both altered and actually tended to buttress the Templar-possession theory of Wilson. Robert Babinet ("La Profession de Foi en Jésus-Christ des Derrniers Templiers," in *La Pensée*

Catholique, vol. 281, Mar.-Apr. 1996, 49-74) has argued that the Templars really did secure the Shroud in one of their impregnable castles, where towards 1300 some of them began practicing a kind of gnostic docetism, believing that Jesus, Son of God, could never be fully human, and they therefore spat upon the Cross and performed other not entirely comprehensible offensive acts. Bishop d'Arcis was, then, sincere in condemning the Shroud of Lirey sight unseen, since he considered it a vile object as connected with such a vile sect. The whole composite argument does seem to me to hang together, though again, it remains a theory with inconclusive evidence. One must wonder why Bishop Henri de Poitiers, predecessor of d'Arcis, gave such lavish blessings on the Lirey church. Also, by 1389, the misdeeds of the Templars must have been widely broadcast and well known among the clergy; the "scandal" to which d'Arcis refers does not seem to warrant the secrecy implied in his expressed need for a personal conference with the pope. Babinet finally names a member of the Templars bearing the name of Milo de Charny, but not Geoffroy de Charnay, the Norman Preceptor of Wilson's scenario, as potential carrier of the Templar's Shroud to the Charny family. The mystery of the "lost" years is not solved.

In 1997 I presented evidence that the literature of the Edessa icon and a number of Greek New Testament apocrypha were used in the 13th c. creation of the most salient details of the legend of the Holy Grail. The thesis involved accepting the fact that the king of Edessa who espoused Christianity was not Abgar V Uchama (13-50 A.D.) (or if he did, it did not take hold), but Abgar VIII the Great (177-212). The question arises whether the Shroud really did come to that city soon after the Crucifixion, as the Edessa legend says, or in the reign of Abgar the Great. I am in agreement with Wilson that it is entirely possible that there were two conversions of two Edessan kings, but one must expect a serious difference of viewpoints among scholars in the future.

Already Jack Markwardt has urged the view that *if* the Shroud was not in Edessa from about 30 A.D., it may have been in Antioch for some 200 years, along with the Holy Grail and the Holy Lance. As historians know, there are no references to the Shroud in Antioch. We know only of an image of Christ by the Gate of the Cherubim in Antioch in the late 6th c. But Markwardt has noted rightly that certain apocrypha assign an early possession of Jesus' shroud to St. Peter, who was also Antioch's first bishop. However, there do not seem to be any early sources for the Grail or Lance in Antioch. He has also been working assiduously at constructing evidence to support his hypothesis that the Shroud was in possession of the heretical Cathar sect in southern France during the 150 "lost" years, again with no explicit historical reference to a shroud in Montsegur. But Markwardt has inserted his theories into the known history of these places in an effective manner. Right or wrong, he has struck forth in fresh new historical directions and given the "old guard" ideas to think about. See his papers on **www.shroud.com** and in the Proceedings of the 1997 Nice, 1998 Turin, and 1999 Richmond meetings.

Another "budding" Shroud historian has been Fr. Kim Dreisbach. He will deny that he is a fine historian, but we must deny him his modesty. His incessant reading has turned up more possibly Shroud-related information (his patented "spy-clues"), especially from the first seven centuries, than anyone except, perhaps, Maurus Green. Most recently in his researches he noticed several Byzantine *epitaphioi* from Eastern Europe dating between 1200 and 1500, cloths that mimicked the Constantinople Shroud—and cloths that show Jesus in death lying upon a shroud *with herringbone weave*. This discovery may fortify the Codex-Pray and help prove that the Shroud of Lirey was the same as that of Constantinople, which had been that of the Edessa documents from the 4th c., all which seriously challenge the C14 date. This discovery led to an informal collaboration and concluded with a paper on "Greek Epitaphioi and Other Evidence for the Shroud in Constantinople up to 1204," to be presented at the Richmond, VA, Shroud Symposium and published in its Proceedings, forthcoming.

Looming increasingly important, too, as we enter the third millennium are the studies of the Oviedo Sudarium being performed by Mark Guscin. In time this research will surely shed light on Shroud history. Professor of history Karlheinz Dietz (University of Würzburg) has become much more vocal and is always quite solid in his research into the Shroud's history. His important survey appeared (in German) in *MUT, Forum fur kultur Politik und Geschichte*, No. 332, April 1995, 72-87.

* * *

My recommendation for the immediate future of historical study of the Shroud is to identify and devise definitive responses to those oft-repeated points of opposition:
- The d'Arcis memorandum
- The "confession" of the artist of 1355
- The identification of the Constantinople Shroud with the Lirey Shroud
- The notion that C14 testing is flawless

Additionally, work should continue to seek evidence for the venue(s) of the Shroud during the "lost" years.

My final point in closing is to alert those who read this of the attack on Shroud history being launched by the journal *Approfondimento di Sindone*. This journal devoted to the Shroud has a board consisting of nearly every living sindonoclast. If many of them are insignificant or have been often refuted, Antonio Lombatti and Prof. Piero Gramaglia are keen scholars who have themselves done a good deal of research and will require Shroud historians to beef up their level of solid primary source research. It will no longer be sufficient to conjecture about where the Shroud might ever have been in the course of its twenty centuries or to develop scenarios without documentary support of the firmest kind. These are luxuries that Shroud enthusiasts have been able to publish and share in friendly conversation. Henceforth such efforts will not only be critiqued in a kindly manner by fellow sindonologists but will also be cruelly laughed out of contention by angry sindonoclasts—opponents of the Shroud well-trained in their specific fields, breathless to pounce upon every argument that is not thoroughly researched in all possible sources. But as Shroud research was actually enhanced by the challenge of the medieval radiocarbon dating, so now that Shroud history has entered a new arena of concerted opposition to the Shroud, the search for the truth—wherever it may lie—will be pursued the more vigorously and always to the advancement of our knowledge of the Shroud's true history.

DR. GILBERT R. LAVOIE, M.D.

Dr. Gilbert Lavoie is a long term Shroud researcher and author of the recent book *Unlocking the Secrets of the Shroud*. In his interesting presentation, Dr. Lavoie reviewed his theories on image formation and the transfer of blood from the man to the cloth.

BLOOD TRANSFER THEORY

For many years the positive image of the shroud face (Figure 1) hung on any office wall. Almost every day I looked across my desk at that face, sometimes partially closing my eyes as I gazed at the image, wondering if the face held some secret. I'll admit that I was looking for something almost magical. During those years, I would always delight in showing any interested observer the blood marks of the face and hair, the contusion under the left eye, and the way the face would seem to follow me as I walked from one side of the room to the other.

Figure 1 - Shroud face, positive image

In 1986, I discovered something new. It came subtly, gradually, and without magic. Over time, as I would observe the blood of the forehead and hair, I wondered if the blood came out a little too far on either side of the face. I wondered if it were not the same phenomenon as is seen at the off-image blood mark at the left elbow. Eventually I took the life-size picture of the shroud face from the wall and brought it home. I asked my daughters, Catherine and Marguerite, to outline on tracing paper the blood marks of the forehead and hair. I also asked them to trace the position of the eyes and nose. I then had Catherine make a cutout of the tracing, remove the paper within the outlined blood marks, and make holes at the eyes that would be large enough to see through. When she finished, I took her work and went to a mirror and placed the tracing paper with its cutout over my face, aligning the eyes and nose of the figure with my own. As I looked through the eye slits at the reflection of the paper that covered my face, I was stunned by what I saw. Wanting confirmation from an objective observer regarding the reflection in the mirror, I sent the cutout to Alan Adler with the following instructions: "Go to a mirror, then align and wrap the cutout on your face, and let me know what you think you are looking at."

He called back. "When I first saw your cutout, I thought that you had finally lost your mind and had started playing with paper dolls. But I decided that I'd humor you and play along. I went to the mirror to look, and I couldn't believe what I saw. The blood is not on the hair. It's on the sides of the face!" Alan came to the same conclusion as I had. It was as simple as cutting out paper dolls, but the information helps us to better understand, the shroud.

Visually reproducing this was fairly simple. All I needed was a bearded man. Reverend Dan Twomey of my own parish volunteered. It was while I was taking the first picture of Father Dan as he was sitting at my dining-room table that I suddenly realized that I had made a mistake. I was not working with a vertical image, on the shroud, but with a horizontal image, so I asked him if he would lie down (Figure 2) so that I could retake his picture in the correct position. Using my full-size photograph of the shroud face, we had already prepared another cutout of the blood marks of the face and hair, but this time we used cloth (Figure 3). I draped the cloth with the cutout of the blood marks over Father Dan's face (Figure 4), aligning his eyes and nose with that of the tracing. While the cloth was over his face, I applied paint to his skin through each blood-mark cutout. I then removed the cloth from his face. The painted blood marks graphically demon-

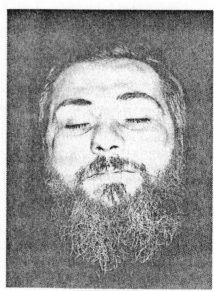

Figure 2 - Man's face in a lying position

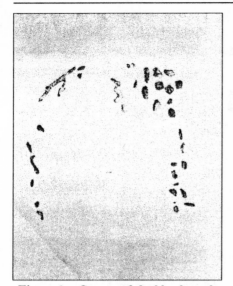 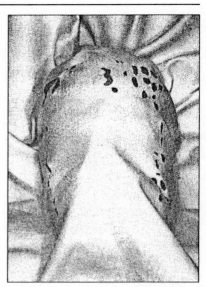

Figure 3 – Cutout of the blood marks
of the face and hair of the shroud

Figure 4 – Cutout of the blood
marks draped over a man's face

strated that all the blood marks seen on the hair of the shroud image had been originally on the face. Yes, they had been on the temples and checks of the man who had been under the shroud (Figure 5). The blood marks are consistent with a cloth having been draped over a man's face covered with moist clots.

These same blood marks of the face also told me something about the facial image: the shroud cloth had been in intimate contact not only with the front of the face but also with the sides of the face (Figure 5). Yet despite the intimate contact that the shroud cloth had with the temples and cheeks, no images of the sides of the face are seen (Figure 1). In contrast, if images had been produced where the shroud cloth came in contact with the sides of the face, the resulting facial image would have been markedly distorted. The cheeks and temples would have extended out to the blood marks seen in the hair. It would have looked like Vignon's experiment, that of the flattened face that Bonnie and I saw in Turin in 1978.

Only now do I finally realize that Vignon's experiment with aloes and ammonia[1] was simply a straightforward contact process. That is why the nose and cheeks of the experiment were broad and distorted. The cloth had touched the sides of the nose and draped over the roundness of the cheeks and temples. That resulted in the accentuated broad flat face. But the nose and checks of the shroud are not

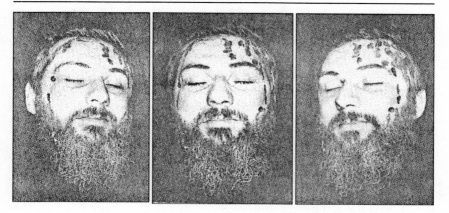

Figure 5 - Blood marks painted on the man's face through the cutout

broadened, and the face of the shroud image is not grotesque. Rather, what you see is the frontal view of a normal face, the same frontal view that you would see of yourself in a mirror or photograph. What does the absence of the images of the sides of the Shroud face mean? It means that the shroud image could not possibly have been formed by a cloth-to-body contact process. Then what had caused the image? I did not know, but as time passed, I began to realize that the blood on the face and hair had more to reveal about the image.

As I contemplated the facial image and the graphics of the blood marks, the chasm between the two grew deeper and wider until I could no longer look upon the shroud image in the same way. The key to the puzzle— a puzzle that I previously had not even known existed—was the spatial relationship of the cloth to the face that it covered. I now understood that to produce the blood marks that are seen on the face and hair of the shroud, the shroud cloth had to be draped over a three-dimensional face that was covered by moist blood clots. Because of this understanding, I began to look at the shroud's facial image from a different point of view. I started to recognize the obvious: the temples and the checks of the image do not exhibit the blood marks that had been on the face of the man who had been covered by the shroud. Those blood marks are now out in the hair. Furthermore, if the blood marks were on the face of the shroud image, the final facial image would be more like Figure 5 instead of Figure 1.

The relationship of the blood marks to the facial image (Figure 6) demanded an answer to the following question: What does this lack of congruence say with regard to image formation? It says that image formation did not take place at the time that the cloth was draped over the face. Why? Because the draped cloth that was touching the temples and the cheeks carries the mirror image of the moist blood clots that were originally on the draped man's temples and cheeks. These blood marks are now in the hair that falls along the sides of the face (Figure 1).

Furthermore, and most important, the direct frontal view of the cheeks and temples of the facial image lies in between the blood marks that were originally on the temples of the man draped by the shroud (Figure 6). It seems that the facial image was created not at the time of the draping, but at a time when the cloth was stretched out and a negative photograph of the face appeared on the flattened cloth between the blood marks. The visual information at hand tells its own story. The production of the blood marks and the formation of the body image are much more than two different phenomena each caused by a different process. They really tell us something much more profound: the formation of the blood marks and the creation of the image had to have been two separate events, separate in space and separate in time!

Which came first, the blood or the image? Alan Adler discovered that the fibers of cloth that were covered by blood were all white. There were no yellowed image fibers under the blood. Given this, Adler concluded that the blood must have protected the fibers from whatever process caused image formation.[2] Therefore, on a micro level, Adler found that the formation of the blood marks and the creation of the image had a separate time sequence; they were two separate events, and the blood came first.

In the final analysis, the blood oh the face and hair illustrates three important points: (1) The blood demonstrates a pattern that is consistent with that of a cloth having been draped over a supine body. (2) The direction of the blood flows illustrates that the body had previously been in the vertical position. (3) These blood marks are consistent in demonstrating that one process formed the blood marks and that another completely different process created the image. More specifically, most of the blood marks on the cloth are a contact process formed by cloth coming in direct contact with moist blood clots. The image, however, is not a contact mechanism. Finally the blood on the face and the hair uniquely illustrates that the formation of the blood marks and the creation of the image are two separate events, separate in space and separate in time.[3]

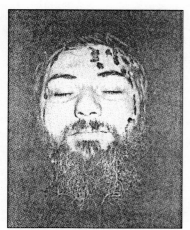

Positive

Negative

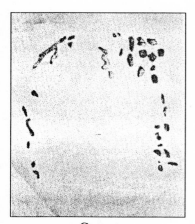

Cutout

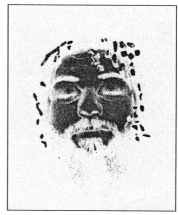

Coutout superimposed over negative

Figure 6

Footnotes:

1. Pierre Barbet, A Doctor at Calvary (New York: Doubleday and Co., Inc., 1953): 32.

2. Eric Jumper, Alan Adler, John Jackson, Samuel Pellicori, John Heller, and James Druzik, "A Comprehensive Examination of the Various Stains and Images on the Shroud of Turin," *Archaelogical Chemistry* III, ACS Advances in Chemistry, edited by J. Lambert, no 205 (1984): 470 and 474.

3. Gilbert Lavoie, Bonnie Lavoie and Alan Adler, "Blood on the Shroud of Turin: Part III, The Blood on the Face," *Shroud Spectrum International* (September 1986) 3-6.

DR. WARREN S. GRUNDFEST, M.D.

**DIRECTOR, LASER RESEARCH & TECHNOLOGY DEVELOPMENT LABORATYORY
CEDARSSINAI MEDICAL CENTER**

Dr. Warren Grundfest is widely recognized as an expert in lasers and scientific/medical imaging and lectures regularly on the subject worldwide. He is relatively new to Shroud research, but has been an active supporter of the Shroud of Turin Website since its inception and serves as the Executive Producer of the Shroud of Turin CD-ROM. Dr. Grundfest's presentation at the 1998 Dallas Meeting of American Sindonology was one of the highlights of the conference, detailing a new, non-destructive imaging technology that could provide complete spectral data and chemical analysis for every point on the Shroud and make a significant contribution to the conservation of the cloth.

IMAGING SPECTROSCOPY, A NEW NONDESTRUCTIVE METHOD FOR MATERIALS ANALYSIS

PHOTOGRAPHY & DIGITAL IMAGING ©BARRIE M. SCHWORTS
TEXT ©DR. WARREN S. GRUNDFEST, ALL RIGHTS RESERVED
VERBATIM TRANSCRIPT (FROM AUDIO TAPE) OF PRESENTATION MADE BY
DR. WARREN GRUNDFEST ON SEPTEMBER 6, 1998 AT THE SHROUD
MEETING IN DALLAS, TEXAS.

(Note that Dr. Grundfest projected a number of slides to illustrate his presentation. Wherever possible, these have been included in the text of this transcript.)

Introduction by Barrie Schwortz:

For those of you who have known me for a long time, I think you've all heard me, over the years, talk about my friend and mentor, Dr. Warren Grundfest. Dr. Grundfest is the Director of the Laser Research and Technology Development Laboratory at Cedars-Sinai Medical Center, and there are many other credits that I could give him, but the biggest credit I want to give him is that he has supported me in my work, both on the Internet (Shroud of Turin Website at **http://www.shroud.com**) and the Shroud of Turin CD-ROM for the last three years. So I am very proud and pleased to present Dr. Warren Grundfest.

Dr. Warren Grundfest:

Thank you Barrie. It's been my pleasure to work with Barrie and, through him, I've got a much greater and better understanding of the Shroud of Turin and its implications. I think what you may not know is that I've known Barrie since 1987 and since that time, from the very first time I walked into his studio, he began showing me some of the images he had taken back in 1978. So that's where this comes from. Over the years we've talked about can we better preserve the Shroud of Turin.

Recently, in our laboratory we've helped design some very exciting and interesting technology for optical imaging. And so what I'm going to talk you about today is something called imaging spectroscopy. This is a new, non-destructive method for materials analysis.

I will show you some of the medical applications which will hopefully give you an idea of how we can apply this to the Shroud of Turin, which may yield some very fascinating and, I believe, important information.

This is actually a joint effort between Barrie and myself. Barrie is an imaging expert in his own right and has had a lot to do with some of the concepts I'm going to present today. Just for everybody in the room, for the non-scientists, everybody knows if you see light coming out of a flashlight, it's white. But in fact that white light is composed of the entire spectrum, from red to orange to yellow to green to blue to purple and into the infrared or up into the ultra-violet, depending upon which direction you're going. But your eye doesn't perceive it as such. We perceive it as one color at one point in space, red or green or blue or white or yellow or gold.

Optical spectroscopy is a non-destructive, quantifiable analysis of the optical signals from an object by light wavelengths or light colors. So that we can determine how much of a particular color is at each point in an image. Now optical imaging, I think you're all familiar with, is the use of light to record the structural characteristics of an object. What is its shape, what is its form? And we do this on everything from microscope slides to standard camera images.

What really has become available only very recently and only through a lot of work by NASA, are the types of devices they put up in spacecraft that really aren't adaptable to something we use in a room. We've developed something that allows us to obtain wavelength intensity information. That means how much color from each type of light at each point in space from every point in an optical image.

Now in the past you could do this point by point by point, and you'd be there for a week trying to get one image. However, we can now do this all at once. I think you are all familiar with the so-called CCD or "chip" cameras that we all use in our camcorders and other things. Well, however many pixels there are, however many little squares there are (on the chip) in that camera, we can get that many number of pixels to give us a complete image. So for every point in that image, we can now get an optical spectrum at that point. This is a tremendous amount of information; it is 90 megabytes of data per image. So part of the problem is how do you analyze all that data and what does it mean?

* * *

The human eye perceives light reflected into it from objects in the environment. This optical signal is composed of the various wavelengths of light: red, green, blue, yellow. The eye and the brain process this information into a perceived color. They unify it. They take it all together and give you one color, which is a sum of all the wavelengths for a given point in the image.

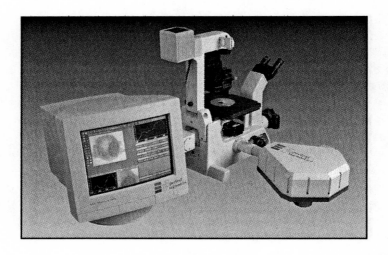

With our device, we do the reverse. Spectral imaging separates out all the colors at each point in the image. The various substances that absorb and reflect light at a specific wavelength can be determined, allowing precise, non-destructive analysis of the tissue. So if we have a protein such as hemoglobin or albumen, or if we have materials like cellulose, we can in fact understand those spectral patterns.

In direct reference to the Shroud, what we see in medical imaging will not be the same, because these materials have been exposed to oxygen and to heat. So it's not quite so simple as taking something out of a textbook. But in fact, we believe very strongly that this technique can be used with any optical image, specifically looking at the Shroud of Turin. And by comparing known spectral patterns that we create in the laboratory, we can then obtain information from the imaging spectrometer and develop a map of chemical species. So we can see things that you can't see with the naked eye. That are impossible to see with the naked eye. So we can see if the blood spatters drip in a particular direction. We can see how the albumen is leached out. We can see patterns in the cellulose or the fibers that are not visible, even to polarized light microscopy, although we can use these techniques and they are additive. They may give us different results and then we have to reconcile them, but they can be all put together to give us much more information.

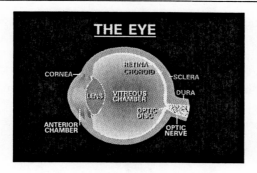

I just want to show you a few of the medical applications to illustrate this. I think you are all familiar with the eye. The human eye is a marvelous device. The light comes in through the lens, the cornea and it's focused on the retina. How does the retina exist? It has no blood vessels of its own. It has a layer behind it called the choroid. And that's where a lot of diseases take place. But imaging that choroid, imaging behind the retina is a problem, because you've got to see through the retina to get there. And remember, the purpose of the retina is to absorb light, so seeing through something that absorbs light is not necessarily easy.

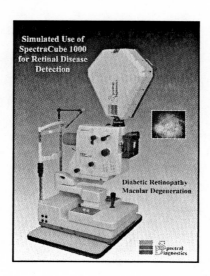

We came up with this technology which is a box like this (see illustration above). This is the device we use to take standard images of the eye called a retinal camera. We use it for diagnosing various diseases that occur with diabetes or with macular degeneration, which is a leading cause of blindness in the elderly. What we get is an image that is quite spectacular. Quite different than any image obtained so far.

To give you an idea of how this works, this is your standard image (see illustrations below). This is what the retina looks like when we look through that camera at high resolution. You can see the arteries and veins.

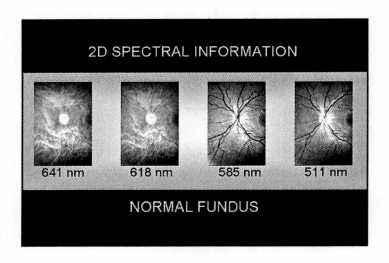

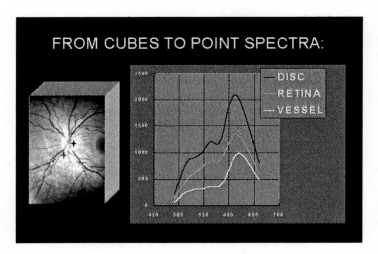

But at every point in that image we can get a spectra, whether it is similar to hemoglobin or similar to the proteins, I won't go into the details. But we can, with very high resolution now, map in the retina the spectral components.

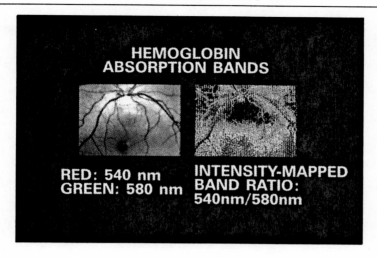

HEMOGLOBIN
ABSORPTION BANDS

RED: 540 nm
GREEN: 580 nm

INTENSITY-MAPPED
BAND RATIO:
540nm/580nm

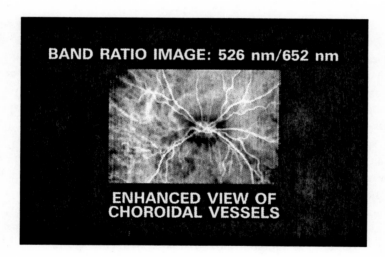

BAND RATIO IMAGE: 526 nm/652 nm

ENHANCED VIEW OF
CHOROIDAL VESSELS

And what does that allow us to do? We can, in fact, record the veins, (the arteries here have disappeared) and the choroidal vessels, this white hazy material from all the veins in the back. Normally, we would need to give you an injection of dye and flash some bright xenon lights in your eye. The dye may make you get nauseous and throw up in the process, so this new technique is a little more pleasant for the patient.

But perhaps more spectacularly, after we process the image by doing some mathematics and ratioing the entire image between two different

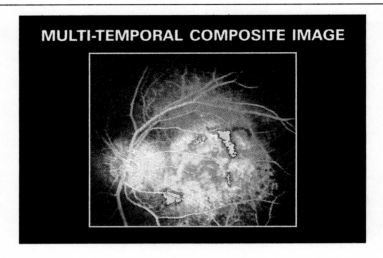

MULTI-TEMPORAL COMPOSITE IMAGE

wavelengths or two different colors, these vessels stand out. When we first showed this to our ophthalmologists they couldn't believe it. They said, "It shouldn't work. There should be lots of reasons it doesn't work." But it does.

I won't go into the mathematics of why. But the fact is we can now see things that you cannot see with the naked eye. Similarly, we can map hemoglobin. I just want to show you one example. This is intensity mapped ratios of oxygenated and deoxygenated hemoglobin in the eye. You can see very spectacular, very specific patterns in this patient who we know had certain areas, namely this area here (in reference to projected 35mm slide illustration), that had laser treatment. So there wasn't any hemoglobin. We can be very precise. We know where he was treated. Using the same techniques, we can obtain unique spectral patterns for various proteins, such as blood and saliva in the laboratory. Once we create a library of spectra, we can use them as a reference to what is on the actual cloth.

Comment from the audience interjected here by Dr. Alan Adler:

Also, the spectral state. Hemoglobin exists in lots of states and it's a real problem on the Shroud to know what some of those states are.

Dr. Grundfest:

This would allow us to do that in fact. He's talking about how much oxygen is in the hemoglobin, what the electronic state is and that determines its color and its absorption. So in fact, it would allow us to do that, not only for the hemoglobins, but also for the albumens and some of the other compounds, because this works in the infrared.

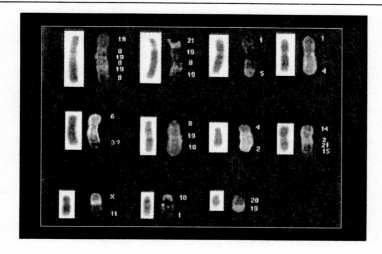

Now to give you an idea of how this works with dyes. You can say fine, that works for hemoglobin but what about for other things? This is a very nice application of this technology (see above illustration). After we developed it we went to Thomas Reid of the NIH (National Institute of Health) who is head of their genetics laboratory. People are always trying to look at genes. They are always trying to understand birth defects. What he was able to do by using five specific dyes and hooking this device up to a microscope was, for the first time in history, get spectral banding patterns in human chromosomes.

That means we can sort every chromosome by it spectral color or composition. So here's the swatch that you get when you take these out of the body and you grow some cells (it takes about 24 hours). We can go all the way from one through twenty-two and x and y and they all have their own unique characteristics. In fact, this was part of a publication in *Science* showing some translocations or genetic abnormalities. This is very important in diagnosing and treating children.

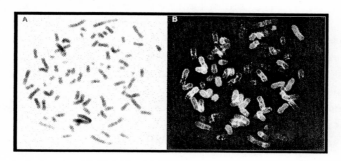

By looking at the color analysis if you will, this same mapping (was done). We were able to see little tiny bits of things at very high resolution. This is the old way of doing it (A, above left), the so-called black and white karyotype staining. And that's the new way (B, above right). I think that just from looking with your own eyes you can get the impression there's a lot more information here (above right) than there is there (above left).

That's not to say this doesn't work. It's to say that we've gone (to) the next step. Now, this actually got published in *Science* in July of 1996, and so we think this technique is quite valid. We've gone on at the start to apply this to studying cancers. And cancers themselves have their own particular spectra. Now there's no dye here. This is the dye that is endogenous to the tumors. This is the image under red light illumination (A, left below). This is the image mapped (B, below center). And this is a false color image (C, below right) and at each point there is a different spectra. We can actually find germinal centers of the tumor, the areas where the most active proliferation is. This also can help us find the borders so when we take out the tumor, we know we've got it all.

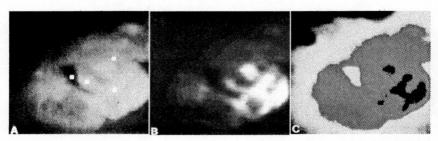

We can in fact, do anatomic mapping using this technology. Well how would we apply this to Shroud of Turin? How would we tell what's different? Whether its blood or other stains, we can take the area that we know and say we want to find all the areas that are spectrally identical and map it that way. We don't need apriori knowledge, because this machine has the ability to say well, I see this bump, let me find all the bumps that are similar in the whole image. And you can do that in either high resolution or looking just at a small area, or across the entire cloth. That is in fact what we would propose to do is take both high resolution and low resolution images (low meaning larger images, not necessarily a lower number of pixels).

By using carefully calibrated light sources, a pattern of reflected light can be used to map specific compounds on the Shroud as well. So we can use this in two ways. We can use it to say, let's find the areas that are similar and also let's see if we can identify some of these chemical species.

Now this allows us to image the Shroud and simultaneously map the various substances present. And we should be able to sort out those that are overlapping, which I think to date has been very difficult to do.

This includes the images areas, the bloodstains, the water marks, the scorches, the burns and the cloth itself. As we get more knowledge, we might be able to do this in real time. We can in fact begin to see where the overlaps are and which came first.

The technology, when combined with high resolution imaging and appropriate light sources, will allow us to characterize the properties of the image on the Shroud, versus the background. I think that perhaps may be the greatest value of this technology. From this data we can determine the rate of image degradation. I think the science is nice, the hypotheses are nice, but one of the things we want to do is really preserve this magnificent and quite special cloth. Over time, this technique should allow us to quantify the rate and causes of image degradation. The data can then guide future conservation and preservation efforts and hopefully, measure their effectiveness.

I don't want to stand here and say "we know" we can do all this all at once. This will take some time, and it may be that we can examine the Shroud once, and then have the opportunity to do that (again) at some later date. But we can gain an awful lot of information just from one image. From several images we can gain tremendous amounts. Remember, 90 megabytes of spectral data from one image.

This work can be supported by my laboratory at Cedars-Sinai Medical Center. And since we have the spectrometer, we have the light sources and we have Barrie's expertise, we look forward to hopefully examining the Shroud with this technology. Thank you.

* * *

(Note: A series of questions was then asked by members of the audience which led to further discussion of the technology. Unfortunately, there was no microphone set up to record the audience, so some of the questions were impossible to transcribe completely. In some cases the questions were summarized or paraphrased and are not completely verbatim. In all cases they are accurate as to general content. They are included here with that understanding.)

Question from Dr. Alan Adler:

Warren, as Gus said, my job is to rain on everybody's parade. I think it's no secret here that I'm on the Conservation Committee (referring to the committee of scientists and scholars appointed by the Archbishop of Turin to guide the future preservation and conservation efforts on the Shroud). And I've been suggesting to the Cardinal that we do some of these things for a number of years. *(continues for approximately one minute but unintelligible)*... I have to ask you, how far into the infrared can you go?

Dr. Grundfest:

The instrument we have only goes down to about 1.1 microns. We have access to an instrument, but we don't own it, that works all the way down to 10 microns.

Question from Dr. Alan Adler:

What is the resolution?

Dr. Grundfest:

In the blue, its about three nanometers. When you get down to the IR at about one micron its about fifteen nanometers, so it's pretty good. But by the time you're at ten (microns), it will probably be 100 nanometers, maybe 200.

Question from Kevin Moran:

What type of interferometer is used in your spectrometer?

Dr. Grundfest:

It's a Fourier Transform Signac Interferometer.

Question from Kevin Moran:

And what was the resolution time for example, in the retinal study where you were looking in the eye?

Dr. Grundfest:

The spatial resolution of the spectrometer depends upon the attached optics. When attached to a standard retinal imaging camera (fundus camera), the resolution is approximately 20 microns. Those images were acquired in eleven seconds, but newer versions of the instrument have reduced the time to a few seconds.

Question from Dr. Alan Adler:

...There's another problem on the Shroud. It may be a little naïve to say we're going to identify compounds. We can do that with the blood but I'm afraid that... with the images, you are really looking at a mixed structure to begin with...

Dr. Grundfest:
We've actually given a fair amount of thought to this.

Question from Dr. Alan Adler:
You could look at a peak in the UV and compare it with a peak in the near IR, that would tell us everywhere what the ratio of the final form was… even though you couldn't say how you got there.

Dr. Grundfest:
Exactly. In fact you would examine this using UV, visible and IR portions of the spectrum. This would need a lot of thought and a lot of planning. It's not, we show up and take pictures. One of the things that this would involve using the facilities not only in my laboratory but others, to postulate what the compounds are ahead of time and get a reference library of spectra. What that means is we take albumen, hemoglobin, sweat and a whole lot of other things on linen itself and age them and then expose them and then get reference spectra. And that doesn't mean we will be successful. I'm not going to stand here and tell you we can do this. I'm going to tell you we can get the information.

Question from Dr. Alan Adler:
…Recognizing the fact once you've got it into the computer, you can do all kinds of things that we never normally do…you don't have to understand everything.

Dr. Grundfest:
That's correct.

REV. WALTER M. ABBOTT, S.J.

Rev. Walter M. Abbott is a famous Jesuit theologian and author. In his presentation, he provided a spiritual outlook on the Shroud of Turin and reflected on its significance to the world. At the close of the meeting, Father Abbott celebrated a beautiful mass for the attendees.

REFLECTIONS ON THE BLOCKAGES
IN SHROUD STUDIES

At the risk of simplifying history, I'm going to say that in the past hundred years there have been three major hurdles, stumbling blocks, or blockages in the path of studies on the shroud of Turin. I'm going to comment on the first two, since I'm qualified to do so and have done something about them. The third and most recent blockage, the carbon-14 test of 1988, I'm going to leave to the science and art experts at this conference who are dealing with it in their papers.

The first blockage appeared at the beginning of the 20th century when a French scholar, Canon Ulysse Chevalier, published his research revealing a letter was sent by a bishop of the 14th century in southern France to the Pope telling him that in the bishop's archives there was a document from his predecessor certifying that an artist testified he had painted the images on a cloth venerated in a chapel of the bishop's diocese as the shroud of Christ. Canon Chevalier concluded that the testimony of history had spoken: since that cloth of the 14th century was the one that was moved to Turin in the 16th century, it was not the burial cloth of Christ.[1]

That was a major blockage indeed, and it was reverberating right up to the time, fifty years later, when I got into shroud studies.

In 1945, my Jesuit superior sent me to Oxford University to study Greek and Roman history and literature. In the summer of 1950, I had permission to take a summer course in Roman archaeology at the American Academy in Rome. I lived at the Pontifical Biblical Institute, staffed by fellow Jesuits who trained the future professors of Scripture at seminaries around the world. The professors and students were back in their home countries for the summer except six old professors who preferred not to travel., One was a bent-over German priest named Bea, a professor of Old Testament, who had been rector of the Institute but was now retired. Another was Fr. Alberto Vaccari, Italian, also a professor of Old Testament studies. I had supper with them every night. During our conversations, I learned about the shroud of Turin.

Father Vaccari told me about the controversy at the beginning of the century and also about what I'm going to call the second major blockage of the past century: the traditional idea transmitted by professors of Scripture to their students around the world that in accordance with Jewish custom, the body of Jesus would have been washed before being put into the burial cloth. If that were so, there would not be on the cloth what can be seen on the shroud of Turin. I learned that Fr. Vaccari was almost alone in holding that the evidence of the Gospel indicated Jesus had a hasty, provisional burial without the washing of the body. Yes, John's Gospel says Jesus was buried according to Jewish custom, but that statement is justified simply by the use of linen and spices, as recorded by John.[2] Fr. Vaccari believed the shroud of Turin was the burial cloth of Jesus.

During my subsequent theological and biblical studied, I read more and more about the shroud. I became more and more convinced that Canon Chevalier and his colleagues in historical studies were too much wedded to the idea that a document in the archives must be true. I challenged it in an article published in the *American Ecclesiastical Review* in 1955.[3] I made the case that the witness of the 14th century was lying. I had a good case because by that time there was already so much scientific evidence that what is on the shroud of Turin could not possibly be a painting. In the same article, I made a strong case for Fr. Vaccari's interpretation of the burial of Jesus. I attacked both major blockages in the path of shroud studies, though I had not used that term "blockage." Of course, I hoped I had helped to demolish them as well.

There was immediate supportive response and fascinating correspondence with E. A. Wuenschel, Scripture professor at the Redemptorist college in Rome, and Alfred O'Rahilly, professor of physics in Ireland who had become a priest in his old age. Most useful and providential, a letter from the editor of *The Catholic Encyclopedia* invited me to contribute an article on the shroud for the supplementary volume he was preparing to be published in 1957. It was an opportunity to refute the negative article on the shroud that had been published in the 15-volume encyclopedia in 1913. In writing my article, I felt I was doing something rather daring because I was refuting Dr. Herbert Thurston of England, a prominent Jesuit historian, who totally believed the document in the 14th-century archives, but I also felt I surely wasn't alone in holding what I thought.

I alerted Fr. Adam Otterbein, director of the Holy Shroud Guild, that I was going to do the encyclopedia article, and he came to Boston to visit me. He asked if he could be of help. I realized, of course, that he could and accepted his offer. When the article was published, with a full page of photographs provided by Fr. Otterbein's guild, I felt the full power of this important encyclopedia was behind a blow to both major blockages in the path of shroud studies, though at the time I was not using the term "blockage."

When I finished my theological and biblical studies qualified to be a professor in a seminary, to my great surprise, I was asked to be religion editor of *America* magazine in New York because it had a higher priority than teaching in the Jesuit order. I had so much to do in that job, covering national and international developments, that I could not continue to talk on the shroud. I had developed a slide lecture (cutting up film strips from Turin and Paris and mounting the photographs in glass) that I had given at the Jesuit seminary and the archdiocesan seminaries in Boston as well as in parishes. During those eight years in New York, I could only read about the shroud from time to time.

Something very important was coming for me and for the shroud of Turin, but it would be another twelve years before I would see it. In the middle of the Second Vatican Council, I was called to the council by one of the four moderators and became editor of the English edition of the council documents. During those last two years of the Council, I had the opportunity to lobby in favor of the idea of a common Bible—Catholics and non-Catholics agreeing on the Hebrew and Greek texts and on translations. I had written on the idea in *America* just before the Council began. The Council approved the idea near the end of the final year, and Pope Paul VI appointed me to see that the idea was implemented. I was to work under the supervision of an old friend from the summer of 1950, Fr. Augustin Bea, who was no Cardinal President of the secretariat for Promoting Christian Unity. when Pope John XXIII made Fr. Bea a cardinal just before the Council began, the old man straightened up, had a new look in his eye, and had a whole new life. The technical term for the making of a cardinal is "create," and Pope John certainly created something new out of the old German professor who became a power in the Second Vatican Council. In twelve years, the common Bible project was finished—new interconfessionally approved translations in 150 languages—and I returned to Boston to teach Scripture in adult-education programs including Pope John National Seminary for late vocations. At last I was doing what I had been trained to do.

Finally, a focus on the shroud came back into my life as well. One day, I had a phone call from Dr. Gilbert Lavoie who asked if he could come to visit me. He had heard about me from one of my seminary students and thought perhaps I could help him at the point he had reached in his shroud studies. He had published studies about the blood on the shroud, Jewish burial customs, and the passage in the Mishnah stating that in the case of a violent death, a body was not washed and the blood was to be left as it was on this body—meaning John's Gospel account very much in conformity with Jewish custom, and the shroud of Turin showed it.[4] Dr. Lavoie had discovered that the image on the cloth showed an upright man, not a horizontal corpse. He had discerned possible connections between the upright man and passages in the Old Testament as well as the New. He wanted to know if I thought he was on the right track. I certainly did think so. I said, "You've got to get this into a book as soon as you can."

When Dr. Lavoie had his book done in a form that could be sent to publishers, I persuaded him to start with the biggest—Time-Warner, Doubleday, Harper Collins, Oxford. My thought was that such a sensational book should have a first printing of one million copies. Each publisher responded in a remarkable way by sending Dr. Lavoie a letter. During my eight years as an editor of *America* in New York, I had a share in the role of publisher of the magazine and of our book division, so I got to know how things were done in that business. I knew it was unusual to send a letter instead of a rejection slip. Dr. Lavoie got letters saying in substance: this is a very good book, well written, somebody should publish it, but we cannot because it doesn't fit into our marketing plans. Each time that happened, Dr. Lavoie would say to me, "We're running into the carbon-14 blockage."

It had been front-page news when the 1988 carbon-14 test resulted in a finding that the shroud was 14th century cloth. The difficulties and objections of other scientists had not yet begun to mount up. The announcement of that 1988 test was still a formidable blockage, but there was something about the publishers' letters that reminded me of what happened to St. Paul when he went up on the Areopagus Hill in Athens and talked about the resurrection. Remember what his hearers said to him? "We will hear more about this from you some other time, thank you."[5] There's reluctance on the part of the modern world, publishers, and the media, just as in the time of St. Paul, to accept the idea of the resurrection of Jesus. Dr. Lavoie's book brings the reader to the point where the man of the shroud, upright in the air, is about to open his eyes, raise his arms, and move. Something so phenomenal, so supernatural is too much for some people, perhaps many, who are preoccupied making money. Fortunately, we found a man who was, I knew, a Christian believer. He took the book for his smaller publishing house.[6]

I tell you all this because I think what I've just been describing is the most significant element and the most difficult one to deal with in the blockage that confronted Dr. Lavoie. I think, too, you will have to agree when you reflect on it that you too have experienced this same element. You have talked to many audiences about the shroud of Turin. Isn't it true that most people are polite and stay for the whole lecture but don't come up afterward to talk with you? Some, a minority, are profoundly moved by what you give them. I suggest that the same thing that happened to St. Paul at Athens has been happening to you. I suggest, too, it has run all through the past century and is even stronger today.

I offer these reflections in the hope that before we part from this conference, maybe we'll have some insights, even some signs, about the way to go in handling this persistent blockage.

Footnotes:

1. U. Chevalier, *Etude critique sur l'origine du Saint suarie de Lirey-Chambery-Turin* (Paris, 1900) and *Autour des Origines du suaire de Lirey* (Paris, 1903)

2. John 19:40. A. Vaccari's exegietical studies of this sentence include "Sondone, Bende e Sudario nella sepultura di Cristo" in *Secoli sul Mondo* (Alla Scoperta della Bibblia, Turin, 1953); "Sindone" in *Enciclopedia Cattolica*, XI (1954); *Miscellanea Biblica B. Ubach* (Montserrat, 1954), pp. 375-386.

3. W. M. Abbott, "The Holy Shroud and the Holy Face," *AER* CXXXII (1955), pp. 239-263.

4. "The Body of Jesus was not Washed According to Jewish Burial Custom," *Sindon* (Turin, December 1981), 19-29; "Jesus, the Turin Shroud and Jewish Burial Customs," *Biblical Archeologist* (Winter, 1981), 5-6; "In Accordance with Jewish Burial Custom, the Body of Jesus Was Not Washed," *Shroud Spectrum International*, Vol. I, No. 3 (June, 1982), 8-17; "Blood on the Shroud of Turing: Part I," *Shroud Spectrum International*, No. 7 (June, 1983), 15-20; "Blood on the Shtroud of Turin: Part II," *Shroud Spectrum International*, No. 8 (Sept., 1983), 2-10; "Blood on the Shroud of Turing: Part III The Blood on the Face," *Shroud Spectrum International*, No. 8 (Sept., 1986), 3-6.

5. Acts 17:32 (literally, "Now when they heard of the resurrection of the dead, some mocked, but others said, 'We will hear you agiain about this'."—Revised Standard Version).

6. Gilbert R. Lavoie, M.D., *Unlocking the Secrets of the Shroud*, Thomas More, An RCL Company (Allen, Texas, 1998).

Dr. Robert Bucklin, M.D., J.D.

Dr. Robert Bucklin has been a Shroud researcher for over fifty years. He has written countless articles dealing with the medical and forensic information on the Shroud and is one of the most respected sindonologists in the world. In his presentation at the Symposium, Dr. Bucklin provided an excellent summary of Shroud medical research from his expert perspective.

Is the Past Prologue?

I have been asked to review the medical investigations which have been done on the Shroud of Turin for the past century and to present suggestions as to what should be done to further the medical studies.

One of the most important dates was 1898, at which time the Shroud was displayed to the public at an exposition of sacred art held in Turin, Italy. It was at that time that Secondo Pia was permitted to take photographs of the Shroud. All of us have seen those photos and many of us have examined the camera which Pia used. Those photos opened the door to the investigation of the Shroud that still continues. One of the first investigators was Paul Joseph Vignon. In addition to his other accomplishments, Vignon was a painter. He became acquainted with Yves Delage who was of France's foremost biologists as well as a Director of the Museum of Natural History and a member of the French Academy of Sciences. Vignon actually became Delage's personal assistant and was an instructor in biology at the Sorbonne. Vignon was a Catholic and Delage was an agnostic. Their interest in the Shroud study was enhanced by the comments of Canon Chevalier who was convinced that the Shroud was not authentic.

Delage and Vgnon, as well as other scientists, began to investigate the Shroud, and Vignon reported his findings in a book, *The Shroud of Christ*, published in 1902.

At one point in his experiments, Vignon put on a false beard, covered himself with fine red chalk, and covered his body with a strip of linen upon which there had been placed albumin to pick up the chalk impressions from the body. The results of this experiment never produced a satisfactory image with any of the anatomic detail that exists on the Shroud. Vignon concluded that since he was unsuccessful in producing a negative image on the cloth that is was not conceivable that a painter in the 14th century could have created a negative image.

It was Vignon who developed the concept that, based on the fact that the Shroud had been anointed with myrrh and aloes during the burial rituals, there might have been a chemical reaction that produced a compound called aloetine, which was brown under the influence of alkaline type vapors. Vignon suggested that, during a crisis of pain, the body emits sweat that has a content of urea, and that during fermentation, the urea produces ammonium carbonate.

On April 21, 1902, Delage read a paper that Vignon had prepared at the French Academy of Science. It was during the presentation of that paper that Delage, the agnostic, made the statement that the man of the Shroud was Christ. Following that event, Vignon and Delage were highly criticized, and Delage returned to other scientific endeavors. His vaporographic theory has of course been determined to be unlikely, but it was nevertheless his idea that started into motion the extensive research on the Shroud that followed. The Shroud was not made available for further studies for the next 32 years. It remained locked in a silver casket above the altar of the Royal Chapel of Turin. The only items available for study were Pia photos.

In 1931, the King's son, Crown Prince Humbert, was to be married, and the House of Savoy planned to celebrate the occasion with a public display of their prized possession, the Shroud of Turin. It was during that display time that Giuseppe Enrie, who was regarded as one of Italy's best photographers, was permitted to take photos of the Shroud. The photos were taken in the presence of witnesses and were determined at that time to be faithful in detail to their subject. The Enrie photos are the source of medical facts that many of us have developed by examination of the Shroud pictures.

One of the first and undoubtedly the most influential of the investigators was Dr. Pierre Barbet. At that time, his medical and anatomic experiments had provided the most comprehensive evidence of the medical details of the man on the Shroud. Barbet was Surgeon General at St. Joseph's Hospital in Paris and was admired for his surgical skills. The most important part of his work was done between 1932 and 1935. Barbet was allowed to see the cloth during the 1933 Holy Year Display arranged by Pope Pius XI. Barbet's first publication, *The Corporal Passion of Jesus Christ*, was published in 1940. His earlier works were considered to be too much in detail for the comprehension of an average layman. The English translation of Barbet's book was published in 1953.

Barbet was the first to make note of the pronounced differences between the appearance of the body images and those of the blood stains. He noted that the image diffused into the cloth to the point that there were no lines of demarcation but merely subtle changes in the light and shade of the brownish color of the image. In distinctions, the blood stains are much darker and richer in color and have more precise outlines. Barbet even commented on the presence of what he called "*halos*" around the stains and he opined that these were caused by serum separating from the blood mass. It was obvious to Barbet that the bloodstains were positive images while the body outlined was a negative image. He felt that the blood flowing from the wounds had coagulated on the skin and was transferred to the cloth by direct contact.

The details of Barbet's findings include vivid descriptions of the injuries to the head as well as to the trunk, back, and extremities. All of us who have carefully examined the wounds have generally supported the findings of Pierre Barbet as far as their anatomic aspects are concerned. During the years following Barbet, there have of course been additional conclusions and refinements, particularly as related to the wound in the side, the details of the puncture wounds in the scalp, and investigation of the injuries to the feet.

It was Barbet who first nullified the concept that the hands had been nailed through the palms rather than through the wrists as is currently believed. Barbet's conclusion as to the cause of death of the man on the cross was asphyxia and exhaustion.

In the matter of the blood and water issuing from the body after the wound in the side, it was Barbet's opinion that the "water" was pericardial fluid. This particular concept has not been widely accepted and has been disputed by both Sava and Bucklin. Sava felt that there might have been a hydro-hemothorax caused by chest trauma. With gravity causing a separation of the blood and the watery fluid, he felt the outflow of these two substances comprised the blood and water. Bucklin feels that there was more likely a pleural effusion related to congestive heart failure, and that the water represented pleural fluid and the blood represented material from the right side of the heart. It is at this point that Bucklin gave consideration to the early Greek translation of the New Testament that indicates that the sequence of flow was water and blood rather than blood and water.

Hynek concurred generally with Barbet in the description of the injuries and their causation, and he also approved of the concept that asphyxia was the death event. Moedder of Cologne was a radiologist who experimented on students to determine the physical effect of crucifixion and Judica-Cordiglia of Milan also reconstructed how the body and bloodstains might have been transferred from the body onto the cloth.

Willis of England was active in his investigations and published in 1969. He was foremost in refuting the claim of Berna that Christ did not die on the cross. Others who have contributed significantly to the medical investigation of the Shroud include British Pathologist Cameron, Australian Professor Blunt, and Italian Professor Baima Bollone. Each of these individuals has expressed his thoughts in the scientific literature relative to the Shroud of Turin.

Gambescia of Philadelphia has added some significant work to the injuries to the foot and it is his opinion that two nails may well have been used in impaling the feet.

Medical comments on the Shroud images and bloodstains have not been limited to Pathologists and much valuable data has been accumulated by Lavoie, Jackson, Adler, Heller, Whanger, and numerous others. Work of these individuals has served to expand our knowledge of certain specific injuries and to explain blood flows on the cloth that are "off image." Rodante of Italy has presented a detailed study of the injuries to the head and has indicated the precise vascular origin of many of the wounds caused by the crown of thorns. With the advent of STURP in 1977, there has been a flurry of reports including many without a medical impact. Since this summary is limited to medical developments, I will not explore or attempt to analyze the non-medical matters.

My work started about 1950, and my first publication was in 1958. During my more than 45 years of interest and research activity relative to the medical aspects of the crucifixion, there have been a number of publications and there will probably be more to come.

If we take a quick overlook at the events of the last century, it is very clear that a tremendous amount of work has been done. We have gone from point zero relative to medical knowledge of the Shroud to a point where it would seem that there is very little more that can be learned. I believe that the groundwork and the basic concepts of the wounds suffered by the man on the cross as well as his actual cause of death have been so well documented that there may not be major alterations in what has already been said. However, without question, there remains the need for more interpretation of individual wounds in order to extract as much detail as is possible. It is here that physicist and chemist working with the pathologist can do a great deal to enhance our basic concepts and knowledge. There is certainly much that can be done in relation to the image and to a study of the cloth itself. DNA studies will be extremely valuable as well as biochemical and bacteriological explorations of the stains and the blood itself that is on the Shroud.

If I may be permitted a personal comment or two, I would like to talk for a few moments about what I personally would like to do in relation to a further study of the Shroud. I feel very strongly that the Shroud is authentic and that the image is that of Jesus Christ. As a physician and a pathologist, I can clearly see and interpret the multitude of injuries that involve nearly all aspects of the body. It is not a long step to take to interpret the effects on the crucified individual of the injuries that are so clearly documented on the Shroud. It is not hard to project how much pain could have been sustained by each of these injuries as well as how much physical damage was done to the integrity to the body itself. If this is put into the Christian concept that Jesus allowed himself to be traumatized, crucified, and killed in order to satisfy the sins of mankind, then it would seem appropriate for this matter to be enunciated and broadcast to the world. I believe that an attempt must be made to explain the true meaning of the sufferings and death of Jesus Christ.

We human beings, for the most part, react to objective presentations. It is well and good to say, "Jesus Christ suffered and died for the sins of mankind," but to be able to analyze the significance of the injuries that produced that suffering and the mechanism by which death occurred would be a very powerful tool. As a practical matter, as of this moment, I am not entirely sure how this can be accomplished, but if it can, I want to do it!

In conclusion, if we can truly say that the past is prologue, we must gratefully accept the fact that the work done by so many dedicated persons, which has been documented in the world's literature regarding the medical studies on the Shroud of Turin, and all done in one century, then it boggles the imagination to attempt to predict what can and might be done in the future.

Rev. Frederick C. Brinkmann, C.Ss.R.

Holy Shoud Guild President and Weunschel Collection Curator

Father Fred Brinkmann is president of the Holy Shroud Guild, taking over the task of leading America's oldest Shroud organization after the recent passing of its founder, Gather Adam Otterbein. Father Brinkmann is now curator of the Weunschel Collection in Esopus, NY, where the Guild is headquartered. It is one of the largest Shroud collections in the world and Fr. Brinkmann's 1998 Dallas Meeting of American Sindonology presentation provided an update on the status of the archiving and other current activities of the Holy Shroud Guild.

HISTORY OF THE HOLY SHROUD GUILD

I am privileged to address this gathering of Sindonologists in Dallas, TX. Since our last gathering of any size, Father Adam Otterbein, C.Ss.R., has left us, and I personally miss him very much. It would be appropriate here to summarize the history and the ministry of the Holy Shroud Guild as a tribute to Father Adam and to remind us all of his significant contribution to the ministry of devotion to the Holy Shroud of Turin. The following is a short history of the Holy Shroud Guild as I have received it from Father Adam Otterbein, C.Ss.R.

Father William Barry, C.Ss.R., studied and earned a degree in Sacred Scripture in Rome. Suring his studies, he became friendly with an English priest who told him about the Shroud of Turin and suggested a visit to Turin when Father Barry was en route back to the States. Father Barry visited Turin, said mass at the Shroud altar in the cathedral, and met Comm. Enrie who photographed the Shroud in 1931. Enrie gave Father Barry a set of 3x4 glass slides of the Shroud pictures. He returned to Esopus and began to teach Sacred Scripture.

Some time later, Father Edward Wuenschel, C.Ss.R., read an article on the Shroud and became interested. When Father Barry quietly mentioned that he had met Enrie and had slides, Father Wuenschel borrowed the slides and his interest in the Shroud lead to the publication by Father Wuenschel of a lengthy article in 1935 in the *American Ecclesiastical Review*. During the next ten years, Father Wuenschel did extensive research on the subject. He corresponded with Enrie and Paul Vignon, who had begun the scientific investigation of the Shroud after Pia Segunda's photograph in 1898.

In 1946, Father Wuenschel published two articles in *Biblical Studies*. These articles were the result of extensive research into the Biblical aspect of the Passion according to all four of the Evangelists, burial customs, and the Shroud of Turin. He was assisted in these studies by Father Louis Hartman, C.Ss.R., and Father William Barry, C.Ss.R. The articles were important because they pointed out that there is no necessary contradiction between the Gospel accounts and the Shroud nor between true historical Jewish burial customs of Christ's time.

In 1950, Father Wuenschel was appointed Director of the Schola Alfonsiana in Rome. Before going to Rome, he asked Father Adam J. Otterbein, C.Ss.R., to continue his work of making the Shroud known in America. Father Otterbein first became interested in the Shroud when as a student in 1938 Father Wuenschel asked Frater Otterbein to make some photographic copies of the Shroud photographs. Father Wuenschel directed Father Otterbein's doctoral dissertation, and when Father Otterbein joined the faculty at Esopus, his interest in the shroud increased by the research of Father Wuenshcel, Barry, and Hartman. Father Wuenschel shared with Father Otterbein his correspondence with Enrie and Vignon. Hence, it was natural that when Father Wuenschel went to Rome, he asked Father Otterbein to continue his work.

With the aid of Father James Galvin, Father Otterbein published a pamphlet which he had asked Father Wuenschel to write. Later, he requested Father Wuenschel to expand the pamphlet and they published *Self Portrait of Christ*. Interest in America increased, and Father Otterbein asked Very Rev. John Sephton, C.Ss.R., for permission to become affiliated with the International Center in Turin. The first step was approval by the local Ordinary. Hence, Father Sephton requested Francis Cardinal Spellman to canonically erect the Holy Shroud Guild at Esopus, New York. The Guild was then affiliated with the Center in Turin in 1951.

Two years later, Father Otterbein was relieved of his teaching duties in order that he might devote full time to research and propagation of correct information about the Shroud with special emphasis on an aspect which was truly Redemptoristic—the Passion of Christ.

For several years, Father Otterbein spread information by newspaper articles, lectures, television programs, and a thirty-minute film, which was distributed by a commercial company. He also endeavored to promote research by contacting scholars and scientists (Eastman Kodak Company, New York City Police Crime Lab, Federal Bureau of Investigation in Washington, DC, etc.). Meanwhile, he kept contact with Father Wuenschel, who visited the United States occasionally.

In 1962, Father Otterbein was assigned to Philadelphia to promote devotion to Our Mother of Perpetual Help by preaching novenas. Several years later, he was assigned to help Father Francis Litz, C.Ss.R., Vice-Postulator for the cause of Bishop John Nupomucene Neumann. During all these years however, he maintained his interest and contacts he had made for Shroud matters, since he was re-appointed by the Archbishop of New York as President of the Holy Shroud Guild. In 1970, Father Otterbein was appointed Secretary of the Baltimore Province. It was shortly thereafter that Captain John Jackson contacted him about the Shroud of Turin. Jackson had read a book on the Shroud by John Walsh, and since Jackson was engaged in the study and interpretation of pictures sent back by satellite of the moon and Mars, he was curious about what the result would be were he to study pictures of the Shroud with the same equipment. We agreed to send Jackson one of the Enrie glass slides. That was the beginning of the American scientific investigation of the Shroud. Jackson interested his friend, Captain Eric Jumper, and they consulted other scientists. Then they made their famous discovery of a 3-D characteristic of the Shroud photo. Just as the variation in densities in pictures from the moon indicated the height of mountains and the depth of craters, so the variation of densities in the photographs of the Shroud indicated the variation in distance between the Shroud cloth and the object (body) that produced the image on the Shroud. Vignon suspected this in 1902. Jackson and Jumper proved it with the aid of space-age equipment.

Many more scientists became interested and finally Jackson and Jumper asked the Holy Shroud Guild to sponsor a Scientific Conference in Albuquerque, New Mexico in March, 1977. The Conference increased interest and resulted in a suggested program of scientific tests. In September 1977, the Holy Shroud Guild took a group of scientists to Turin where they presented their proposed program of tests with the hope that permission would be given for the tests during 1978, the 40th anniversary of the arrival of the Shroud in Turin. Approval was given in April 1978, and the American scientists quickly organized a non-profit corporation, worked out details for the tests, and borrowed and brought about $100,000 worth of equipment.

The Shroud was on public exposition in Turin from August 26 to September 8. On September 29, the group of about 32 American scientists arrived in Turin with 70 crates of sophisticated equipment. They were allowed to examine and photograph the Shroud from 12 A.M.

on Sunday until 10 P.M. on Friday—more than 96 hours. They returned to the U.S. with so much data that they are still working to reduce the data and to test it by experiments. They have published some articles but only in recognized scientific journals. They are now preparing to publish a report on their work.

The Holy Shroud Guild was greatly impressed and appreciative of the willingness of Archbishop Ballestrero to permit the tests in 1978 in spite of some opposition. The scientists were most impressed by his insistence that the results of the tests need not be submitted to him for approval but could be published without any Nihil Obstat from him. As a result, the officers of the Holy Shroud Guild felt it would be most fitting that the scientists should, out of courtesy and as a token of appreciation, report to the Archbishop, at least in general non-technical language, the results of their work during the past two years. Hence an offer was made by the Guild to STURP (Shroud of Turin Research Corporation) to bring a representative of STURP to Turin to inform the Cardinal. The offer was accepted and two representatives, Dr. Larry Schwalbe and Dr. John Jackson, were chosen. Father Otterbein, the President of the Holy Shroud Guild and Father Peter Rinaldi, the Vice President of the Guild, accompanied them. They were joined by two Italian members of STURP, Dr. L. Gonella and Dr. G. Riggi.

The Archbishop, Cardinal Ballestrero, graciously granted the group an hour and a half to make a presentation and to discuss the results. The scientists were greatly encouraged by the Archbishop's interest and, as a result of the discussion, obtained a better understanding and insight into his attitude toward tests both past and future. They also feel that the Archbishop now has a better understanding of the quality of the research which has been done in America and of the reasons why the Americans have not published results in the popular press, preferring to publish in recognized scientific journals in order to establish credibility in the scientific world.

From Rome, we went to Casicais, Portugal, where we met with the Former King of Italy, Umberto II, who still legally owns the Shroud of Turin. He was very interested in the briefing about the scientific research done by the American scientists. King Umberto recalled his meeting with Father Otterbein, author John Walsh, and publisher Bennet Cerf in New York around 1963. We expressed out appreciation to the King for his permission and cooperation in making the tests possible in 1978, and we assured him that all information would be published and made available to all, especially to scientists throughout the world.

When I returned to the U.S., I learned that interest was still running high in the Photographic Exhibit at Brooks Institute in Santa Barbara, CA. The dates were extended from June 15 to September 6. When I visited the exhibit again on August 14-20, I learned that they had more than 45,000 visitors.

Father Adam Otterbein, C.Ss.R.

THE HOLY SHROUD GUILD: 1990-2000

Father Adam Otterbein, C.Ss.R., passed from us on June 9, 1998. Since then, the Holy Shroud Guild has endeavored to find its place in a new world of Sindonology. Father Fred Brinkmann, C.Ss.R., has attempted to continue the work of Father Adam, Father Peter Rinaldi, and many of the others who have been associated with the Guild. Father Wuenschel's library, Father Otterbein's correspondence, and Father Brinkmann's Holy Shroud bookstore continue to be the backbone of the Guild. Father John Kennington, C.Ss.R., has been the librarian for the Wuenschel collection, and we have endeavored to keep the collection in order and up-to-date.

C. RICHARD ORAREO

BOSTON COLLECTION OWNER AND CURATOR

Richard Orareo is the owner and curator of the Boston Collection, arguably the largest collection of Shroud books, materials and artifacts in the world. Richard has dedicated twenty-five years to building this unique collection and work is now underway to digitally archive the materials. At the 1998 Dallas Meeting of American Sindonology, Richard presented an overview of the need to physically archive the materials in the future. He also presented some great insights into ways of building a collection and where to find Shroud materials.

The Boston Collection

It is my pleasure to introduce to you the holy shroud library of Boston. The Boston Collection represents nearly thirty years of searching out and procuring books, periodicals, works of art, and photographic images of the Shroud of Turin. As this accumulated treasure of mine has grown and developed, so too has my appreciation grown for those who have done the research and written the books and the papers. It has been my pleasure to have met many shroud researchers over these years. Some, now deceased, whose names are immediately recognizable as icons of shroud research and others who are now nearly forgotten. All merit mention and recognition. Dr. David Willis, Vera Barclay, and Group Captain Cheshire, all of England; Freida Frasier of Australia; Paul de Gail of France; Kurt Berna of Germany; Giovanni Judica Cordiglia, Don Coero Borga, Mons. Giulio Ricci, Count Lovera de Maria, all of Italy; and Herman Doepner and Sister Mary Bernard, brother and sister research team of Minnesota. These and so many others have produced books and pamphlets, papers in peer-reviewed journals, and unpublished manuscripts. They have kindly presented their works to me to be included in the Boston Collection.

My awareness of the Shroud began with a television show during the Lenten season. The television set was on with no one watching it. It was just background noise in a very busy household. It was the voice of Fr. Francis Filas, S.J., that caught my attention. He was talking about something I had never heard of, the Holy Shroud of Turin. My curiosity was aroused. I sat down and listened intently, feeling, "how could this exist and my not know about it?" Then, my skepticism surfaced—it was just too good to be true. The influence of God in my life had always been subtle. This seemed too blatant, too visual, too "in your face" to be real.

The program ended with an invitation to send a self-addressed, stamped envelope to receive a free picture of the shroud. By return mail, I received the Holy Cards produced by The Holy Shroud Guild (the Holy face and the frontal image) with a pamphlet explaining the image. Included with the Holy Cards was a list of books that were available at the time: the book by Bulst, the two works by Wuenschel, and the John Walsh. They satisfied my curiosity and relieved my skepticism somewhat. The Walsh book brought me to Corpus Christi Church, Port Chester, New York, and a life-long friendship with Father Peter Rinaldi. He gave me a copy of his first book, *I Saw the Holy Shroud*, dated 1940. Along with a film strip and a recording with the directive, "You will lecture to the people of Boston and New England." Well, decades later I am still lecturing about the Shroud. My first lecture was to a Lutheran prayer group in a Unitarian church. There were 12 people there. My largest lecture attracted 1500 people in a downtown Boston chapel.

These first few books have now grown to over 1000 titles. They range from a copy of the first book ever published on the shroud, Filiberto Pingonio's *Sindon Evangelica*, 1581, to the most recent work by Ian Wilson, *The Blood and the Shroud*. The newly released works of Gil Lavoie, John Iannone, Mark Guscin, and Mary and Al Whanger have been added to the collection. Eagerly anticipated are the works of Paul Maloney, Garza-Valdez, Mark Antonacci, and John Beldon Scott. These books present formal historical and scientific research, personal experiences, and spiritual journeys. Some are factual, others are fanciful. Some are scholarly works, others are novels.

The range of languages includes English, Italian, French, German, Spanish, Japanese, Flemish, Latin, Hindu, and yes, even a picture book in Braille. The scope runs from the 16th century through to the present.

Also included is the periodical collection. From the early 1900s to the present are popular magazines and newspapers, scientific and theological journals. There are original copies of *Scientific American*, *Readers Digest*, *Catholic Digest*, early French, Italian, German, and Irish theological journals; *National Geographic*, *Omni*, *The Rolling Stone*, *Esquire*, *Time*, *Life*, *Look*, *People*, *The Saturday Evening Post*, even *The National Enquirer*. The range is national and international, popular and obscure, pro-authenticity and anti-authenticity; all are in The Boston Collection.

In addition to the books and periodicals, there is also a collection of devotional art. There is a copy of the earliest known engraving of the Shroud, depicting a portrait likeness of Saint Charles Borromeo holding the Shroud to be seen by the people of Turin at its transfer from

Chambery to Turin. This engraving is dated 1578. Another important engraving is the Tasnieri, which depicts the shroud being shown over the balcony of the Guarini Chapel prior to the construction of the bronze and glass barrier as we knew it before the recent fire that destroyed the chapel.

In addition, there are other engravings, embroideries, serographs, lithographs, icons, photographs, fragments of the silk wrappings, bas reliefs in metal and glass—over 100 works of art. This collection is equal in interest and importance to that of the museum of the Centro in Turin and that of the House of Savoy in Switzerland.

But, this collection remains incomplete and without an adequate plan for its future. I view this collection as a treasure that needs a permanent home. It is my recommendation to the American shroud community that a logical plan would be to meld The Wuenschel Collection and The Boston Collection into one comprehensive unit.

Combined, these two great collections would be the basis of a shroud center unequalled anywhere in the world. With its repository in a research center or a university, it could become the clearinghouse for education, research, and investigation. This kind of center could be the focal point for Foundation Grants and international meetings. Either secular or religious, this center could promote the spiritual aspects of the Shroud.

I firmly believe that the efforts of Shroud scholars from around the world could be integrated in such a center. The extent of the present holdings would grow exponentially. This kind of comprehensive center could become the physical repository of all past present and future shroud research.

We are now well into the age of electronic storage and dissemination of information, the emphasis of which is the decentralization of data and the globalization of communication. The intimate harmonizing of efforts and the cooperation of individuals and groups from divergent cultures, beliefs, perspectives, and structures will become ever more apparent as the camera and the microscope bring the Shroud into the modern scientific age. The computer and the advancement of technology will reveal to the world what is already known, what is planned, and in my belief, that the best of the Shroud is yet to be known.

To paraphrase Emily Dickinson, "The truth of the Shroud must dazzle gradually, else every eye be blinded by it." Regardless of the scholarly, the scientific, and the pedantic, the basic truth about the shroud is its spiritual message. I believe the words of blessed Sebastian Valfre, the revered bishop of Turin, said it best: "The cross received the body of Jesus alive and returned it dead; the Shroud received the body of Jesus dead and returned it alive." To the Christian believer, the Shroud of Turin is the actual holy sepulcher.

REV. ALBERT "KIM" R. DREISBACH, JR.

FOUNDER OF THE ATLANTA INTERNATIONAL CENTER FOR THE CONTINUING STUDY OF THE SHROUD OF TURIN (AICCSST)

The Rev. Albert "Kim" R. Dreisbach, Jr., an Episcopal Priest, is the founder and Executive Director of the Atlanta International Center for the Continuing Study of the Shroud of Turin, Inc. (AICCSST). Selected for Marquis who's Who in Religion, Fr. Dreisbach is the author of numerous papers, a frequent lecturer—most recently at the III International Congress held in Turin in June of 1998. He has also lectured at St. Stephen's House, Oxford, Bologna, Mount St. Alphonus in Esopus, NY, at Emory's Senior University, Atlanta, and has often appeared on national radio and TV. He also served as a panelist with author Ian Wilson and Duke's Dr. Alan Whanger on Vatican Radio following the Bologna International Symposium in 1989. A commentator and technical advisor in a segment devoted to the Shroud on CBS's Mysteries of the Ancient World, he also has functioned in the same capacity for NBC's Unsolved Mysteries, CBN's Behold a Mystery, and for the newly released update on the Shroud for The Learning Channel titled "In Pursuit of the Shroud."

THE ECUMENICAL IMPERATIVE: PRESERVATION AND PROCLAMATION

In preparing for this Dallas Conference, I went to my files and dug out a memo that I had sent some of you ten years ago in June of 1988. As I re-read it, I was amazed how many of its conclusions and recommendations might still be applicable to the present. With minor revision and editing, I offer for your consideration what I believe should be the direction and emphases taken by those groups like the Holy Shroud Guild, The Atlanta International Center for the Continuing Study of the Shroud of Turin and any and all other groups gathered here in Dallas for this specially called Meeting of American Sindonology whose primary concern with the Holy Shroud revolves around its religious significance and purpose.

With the emergence of Barrie Schwortz's premier web site **www.shroud.com**, sindonophiles around the world now have access right in their own homes to a wealth of Shroud graphics and articles never before available.

Lest we become too enamored with our own technological success, let us also be quick to acknowledge that some of the very basic texts (e.g. Paul Vignon's *The Shroud of Christ*, Pierre Barbet's *A Doctor at Calvary*, John Walsh's *The Shroud*, Werner Bulst's *The Shroud of Turin*, John Heller's *Report on the Shroud of Turin* and Ian Wilson's *The Shroud of Turin, The Mysterious Shroud, Holy Faces, Secret Places*) are now out of print, not readily available at the local library and sometimes difficult to obtain even via inter-library loan. Alas, many potential new "shroudies" inspired by both Barrie's site and Russ Breault's Shroud of Turin Education Project (STEP) **www.shroud2000.com** site are stymied in their research projects when the very texts they need are unavailable.

SHROUD LIBRARIES, RESEARCH PAPERS, ETC.

The demise of America's greatest contributor's to the promulgation of the Shroud's message (e.g. Frs, Rinaldi and Otterbein) warns us of the necessity not only to insure adequate plans for the preservation of their collections, but also of providing access to them for future generations of Shroud scholars. Had it not been for prompt action at the time of Fr. Filas' untimely death, his collection might well have been tragically lost or neglected by his fellow faculty members at Loyola, many of whom like his superior Fr. Robert Wilde not only failed to share his enthusiasm; but in, the latter's case, firmly believed the Shroud to be a fake. The whereabouts of much of Fr. Peter Weyland's work remains a cause for concern and needs to be located and catalogued.

There still remain scientific papers in the hands of individual STURP members that have been neither peer-reviewed nor published, possibly containing myriad clues for continuing research. These documents also need to be collected and catalogued in a central repository.

And while we struggle with the vast amount of material already known to exist, what definite plans have been made by the groups assembled here in Dallas to insure the preservation and effective utilization of their own collections? What is to become of the enormous collection of the Colorado Shroud Center when the Jacksons are no longer able to carry on their work? The same can be asked of the Whangers with regard to the Council for the Study of the Shroud of Turin. Add to these the unpublished research of individuals like Paul Maloney, Dan Scavone, Gus Accetta, Warren Grundfest, Kim Dreisbach and a host of others whose computer and paper files need to be passed on to future researchers?

For example in the AICCSST archives alone can be found the original 1961 manuscript of B.G. Sandhurst's (i.e. a pseudonym used by the father of Fr. Maurus Green) "The Silent Witness" complete with the original B&W photographs. We also have a xerox copy of the unpublished 1936 manuscript by Theodora Bates in which this amazing laywoman had already concluded that the Image of Edessa/"Shroud"(i.e. Mandylion) of Constantinople/ Shroud of Turin were one and the same. We have xeroxes of the original blueprints by Gabriel Quidor filed with the French patent office from which he produced in 1910 the first bas relief made directly from the densities on the Holy Cloth— 64 years before that process was achieved by his fellow countryman Paul Gastineau and 67 years before the now-famous 3-D "sculpture" created by Jackson and Jumper.

Sometime in the very near future we need to explore the expensive and time consuming process of digitizing these basic texts and creating a central source like the Vatican Library at St. Louis University where scholars—from high school students to university professors—can gain access to them. For the professionals, a committee could be selected to chose just which volumes—and in what priority—of the Wuenschel Collection should be included in such a repository. Even in this magnificent collection, not all texts are of real value to the serious researcher. Thanks be to God that this entire collection has been microfiched; but there lies ahead the laborious and expensive task of converting that format into a digitized one. Legal advice will be required as to which volumes may or may not be so reproduced without violating copyrights; and, in the case of more modern works, permission and arrangements must be negotiated with contemporary publishers.

Simultaneously, the international community of sindonologists must become a part of this project. God alone knows what treasures waiting to be mined already exist in texts published in French, Italian, German and Spanish to say nothing of more ancient works in Greek and Latin—some hidden away in monasteries and unknown even to those who possess them. For the non-linguist, just imagine what a priceless gift it would be to have an English translation of Ernst von Dobshütz' *Christusbilder*?

Finally, add to the above list the need to assemble an Audio-Visual Library where 35mm slides, movies, videos, audiotapes, etc. could be stored and accessed by future researchers. Have any of you ever tried to come up with a full-length reproduction of the epitaphios of Uroš Milutin depicting the Man of the Shroud in a "standing" or vertical posture with his arms crossed à la the Man of Sorrows/Christ of Pity? Not only is this cloth highly significant for both iconographic and liturgical scholars, but the danger to which it has been exposed in the recent bombings of Begrade points to the larger need to insure photographic preservation of it and all other such existing visual representations of the Shroud. How grateful we all are to Lennox Manton for his superb photographs of the Cappadocian frescoes, which have now begun to deteriorate considerably.

OTHER VALUABLE ITEMS

Many items related to the Shroud are "one of a kind"(e.g. the STURP table on which the actual 1978 testing was performed, the cloth replica shroud crafted by England's John Weston for "The Silent Witness," the pre- and post-mortem forensic sculptures of the Head of the Man of the Shroud effected by Thomas Goyne, etc.) while others are too delicate and/or too valuable to be chanced to a traveling exhibit (e.g. Richard Orareo's Boston Collection, bas reliefs of the Holy Face by Robazzo, Ferri and Bossani, the Mexican "Face of Threads" crafted from metallic wires, a wood carving of the Holy Face by Charles Eze of Nigeria, the full-size replica mandylion by Mary Whanger and one of six extant fiberglass "sculptures" of the Man of the Shroud constructed by Drs. Jackson and Jumper from the readings made by the VP-8 Image Analyzer.

THE NEED FOR A PERMANENT REPOSITORY

Like the Boston Collection, all of these items can be photographed digitally and even preserved and distributed on CD-ROMs. However, the need still remains for a permanent display site—be it a museum, art gallery, central "Department of Sindonology" on a university campus or whatever.

Truly a university—with a school of theology, one of medicine, liberal arts, and a strong school and/or alliance with a nearby institution prestigious in the hard sciences—would be the ideal location for such a repository. We are already aware what today's modern computers and laser discs are capable of providing in terms of storage of both data and images which in turn can be retrieved by scholars around the world who have access to the university's network terminals. The ideal scenario would be to convince the chosen institution to offer the first multi-disciplinary course of sindonolgy in the USA. Professors already on the faculty of its different departments could be utilized to teach as was done for years at Connecticut's Wesleyan University for the mandatory course in freshman Humanities. Some of these scholars might even be inspired to conduct further research in their own specialized fields of expertise on this the world's most-studied artifact. Even the most skeptical and "empirical" just might discover that the Shroud's initial appeal to their minds eventually results in a conversion of their hearts. And if seminary involvement is part of the larger area of inclusion, clergy and christian educators could carry the message to local judicatories and congregations while others, currently not inclined to the Faith might find as have so many through the centuries that though "they came to scoff, they stayed to pray."

EFFECTIVE & EFFICIENT "STEWARDSHIP" OF RESOURCES

All of us who are called to the apostolate of the Holy Shroud have an obligation to get beyond the linen to the Lord whose Image it bears. Thus, we have a mandate to look beyond the limitations of the present to the fullness of the possibilities for the future. Greater ecumenical cooperation and participation is the wave of the future, and all Christians—especially those of us with this privileged ministry of the Holy Shroud—should be prepared to offer their special "gift" to the larger Church family when the occasion permits.

It has become increasingly clear since the Holy Shroud's last public exposition in 1998 that this sacred linen has drawn worldwide ecumenical interest and support. As Fr. Anthony Delessi of the Monastery of the Holy Spirit in Conyers, Georgia has so wisely observed: "We Roman Catholics have been its custodians for the last five hundred years after stealing it from the Greeks (i.e. Orthodox) who performed that function for the first twelve centuries. But in truth, it belongs to no one denomination—maybe not even to Christianity. Rather, it is in actuality 'God's love letter in linen' to all mankind."

With the beginning of a new millennium and the computer technology which will be even more marvelous and utilitarian than what is presently available, we have both an ecumenical imperative and opportunity to proclaim the Shroud and its Gospel as never before. While debates as to its authenticity and relevance will continue both within the Roman Catholic Church and among the Greek Orthodox and various Protestant denominations, the window for joint exploration and study has never been more open. One does not have to raise the thorny issues of Apostolic Succession, all male priesthood, etc. in the common search for the meaning of this linen artifact left by the Lord Himself. God willing more and more Christians will come to share the insight of the Blessed Sebastian Valfré (1629-1710), an Oratorian and chaplain to Duke Victor Amadeus of Savoy, that: "the Cross receives the living Saviour and gives Him back dead; the shroud receives the dead Saviour and gives him back alive."

Even before the Jacksons and others had established links with Russia, the following quote from two Rusian Orthodox monks appeared in an issue of *Diakonia*:

> ....anything which God lifts up to inspire our search for
> inner truth commands our veneration. If the Holy
> Shroud lifts us up to a sincere search for God, it becomes
> an icon. In this sense, we might be so bold as to say that
> the crucial question about the Shroud, which must pass

beyond the Shroud and touch on the power of the resurrection itself, makes its historical authenticity secondary. We must take great care, then, not to join with those who hate the spiritual and unwisely condemn something that God, in His wisdom, may have set forth to wake a sleeping people.[1]

Both the Mass and the Office of The Holy Shroud, first authorized in 1506 by Pope Julius II, may someday become approved liturgies employed to celebrate our common ecumenical devotion to the Holy Shroud. Just such an evening office was celebrated in Atlanta to commemorate the opening of the TURIN SHROUD EXHIBIT at the Omni. The date chosen was August the 16th—the Feast of the Holy Mandylion for the Greek Orthodox—and those present included both the Greek and Roman Catholic Archbishops, the Episcopal Bishop of Atlanta, the Presiding Bishop of the African Methodist Episcopal Church and official representatives from the Lutheran Church in America, the United Methodist Church and the Southern Baptists. Such a gathering reveals how easily a traditional office can be adapted to permit joint participation when supported and approved by the larger ecumenical community. Though not a viable possibility at this moment in history, a joint baptismal service by Roman Catholics, Episcopalians and Lutherans at Pentecost of 1988 at Sacramento, California hints at a future time when even the Mass might be celebrated "at the same time in the same place" with each denomination consecrating the elements according to its own ritual and providing separate stations for reception by worshipers à la the procedure at Taizé in France. True, at the moment this is a matter of extreme delicacy, but the joint baptismal rite cited above grows out of a joint study commission of Roman Catholic scholars with their Anglican and Lutheran counterparts where issues such as the validity of priestly orders and sacraments has been recognized, though not formally approved at this time. Despite the unlikelihood of such an ecumenical Eucharist in our own lifetime, our prayers continue that the interest shared in the body and blood of the holy linen may some day also be shared in a common holy liturgy. Ecumenicity has not failed; like Christianity, it has never really been "tried."

TIMING

THE TIME IS NOW! It is not by chance that God has chosen the 20th century with its great technological revolution to be the chosen vehicle for revealing some of the mysteries of the Holy Shroud. Ironically, the very rational empiricism responsible for sophisticated skepticism and agnosticism is being used by God to "convert" former non-believers. Countless stories can be told of those who "came to scoff, but stayed to pray" in their investigation of the Shroud. Recent word from India tells us of amazement on the part of Hindus and Buddhists that Christianity is willing to submit its most precious relic to rigorous scientific investigation. Neither of these faiths can offer anything for such empirical scrutiny. In 1986 over 90 Muslim high school and college students holding a convention in Atlanta requested a group tour with discussion to follow at the TURIN SHROUD EXHIBIT so that they might learn more about Christianity. Jews have heen "completed" or "converted" as a result of their study of this holy cloth. Overseas missionaries continue to request pictures of the Man of the Shroud having learned that this "visual aid" has a profound effect on illiterates for whom reams of printed material would have no effect.

We who are part of the "Shroud Crowd" do not have to be convinced of the power of this Fifth Gospel. However, unless we take steps to insure continuing sindonological research and promulgation of the Shroud's many truths for future generations, we run the risk of having our great "treasure" buried under apathy and neglect. Unfortunately, history records that many a shroud group has come and gone over the years. Even the pioneer of American studies, the HOLY SHROUD GUILD, might someday cease to exist. Who will bear the banner of our holy apostolate for future generations of English-speaking devotees? As previously stated, my own evaluation is that a full-fledged university, complete with a seminary which serves both Roman Catholic and Protestant students as well as the larger undergraduate body, would provide both the permanency and prestige required of such a program.

But, and this is a very crucial "but," without careful planning at this moment in history our fondest dreams may be reduced to dust. As one old saw states it so well, "God provides the inspiration, but he expects man to supply the perspiration." In a more theological vein, God has abundantly provided His prevenient grace; we are now being asked to respond with our own cooperating grace. The current group of scientists whom God has used to provide so many insights about the Shroud will eventually "lose interest" after the last test results are printed in their professional journals. Oddly enough, the very confirmation of a 1st century date by C-14 testing may result in diminished interest and/or the widely-rumored decision by the Church to inhibit further testing. At best, the scientists can give us only a probability figure that the Man of the Shroud was an historical personage named Jesus of Nazareth. As there is no laboratory test for "divinity," they can never tell us that this Son of Man was also the Son of God—the Christ, our Lord and Saviour. The latter Gospel is known only to the eyes and hearts of Faith. It is we who are members of the Church who are called upon by God to proclaim the eternal meaning and divine purpose of the Holy Shroud long after the hard, empirical data which it yields has been filed and forgotten by the scientific community.

Now, when the time is right, God has called us to be "conservatives" in the best sense of that word. We are called to conserve, preserve, and promulgate the essential message of the Holy Shroud for future generations—moving them beyond the linen to the Lord. With ever more challenges like those of Danin and others challenging the flawed C-14 dating of 1998, the time will be right as never before to "recruit" the support of churchmen and academes alike to establish a permanent and on-going vehicle for the continuing study of the Holy Shroud. God can use even the hubris of the university as the choice for a permanent repository, that of contributors both large and small, and the very limitations of our own weakness—all to establish a vehicle for His Silent Witness on linen for future generations. It is our decision to choose whether or not we will accept God's call in this venture. He does not need us, but He is offering us the chance to be part of this great plan. Like Joshua, we are being confronted with the challenge of "Choose you this day whom you will serve" THE TIME IS NOW! Do we have eyes to see and ears to hear? Or, will we like the priest and Levite secure in our own faith—walk by "on the other side" once again failing to hear our Lord's "Is it nothing to you who pass by?" THE CHOICE IS OURS. HOW WILL WE RESPOND?

Footnote:

1 Archiamandrite Chrysostomos & Hiermonk Auxentios. "The Holy Shroud: The Controversy in Perspective." Diakonia, 1980, p.128

BARRIE M. SCHWORTZ

OFFICIAL 1978 STURP TEAM PHOTOGRAPHER

Barrie M. Schwortz was the Official Documenting Photographer for the STURP team during their five-day examination of the Shroud in October 1978. He is also the host and webmaster of **www.shroud.com** where many of the 1998 Dallas Meeting of American Sindonology participants' writings can be found in their entirety. Schwortz began his Dallas presentation with an overview of the Shroud of Turin Website. He also demonstrated for the first time to the public "The Virtual VP-8" Segment from the Shroud of Turin CD-ROM. This is the most dynamic and interactive portion of the disc. It allows each viewer the opportunity to manipulate the 3-D characteristics of the Shroud image.

Electronic Archiving and Distribution:

The Value of the Internet and CD-ROM Technology

Note: Verbatim transcript (from audio tape) of an extemporaneous presentation made by Barrie M. Schwortz on September 7, 1998 at the Shroud meeting in Dallas, Texas.

There are a lot of different things that I wanted to talk about today, probably far more than I have time to talk about. Then of course, last night I inadvertently showed something to a few people who then insisted I show it to everybody.

I want to give you a quick update on the digital archiving that we started talking about last year (at the September 1997 Kaufman, Texas meeting) and it's simply this: Last year, right after our meeting, Fr. Fred Brinkmann immediately sent me the Wuenschel Collection on disc. Paul Maloney and I worked out a way where he could provide his bibliography from his work by making sure it didn't conflict with his publishing contracts. Of course, Emanuela Marinelli's collection has already been archived as the Booklist page on my website. And Richard Orareo immediately handed me a printed version of his collection, which I am thrilled to hear that Fr. Kim (Albert Dreisbach) is now working on getting into a digital form. We have already integrated the Wuenschel and Marinelli collections into a single database, so we did get about half way through the process before my resources ran out and I had to stop that so we could work on the (Shroud of Turin) CD-ROM, which some of you know I am working on.

One of the great things about this meeting, and it's funny how these things work out when you are involved with the Shroud, but one of the things I was coming here to say was a simple, one word plea, Help! And then, I wound up rooming next to Mark Borkan. Thank you! So I've now found help. He happens to be an expert in Microsoft Access, the database (program) we are using for (archiving) the collections. Even though it's long distance, I'm in Los Angeles and he's in New York, and AT & T's stock will rise again, we will work together. It's wonderful to have found an ally as skilled and experienced as Mark.

I want to thank Russ (Breault) for bringing this wonderful projector (making reference to the equipment that projects an image from a computer to a large screen), because there are some of you that have given me a lot of "guff" about the Internet, Al (making reference to Alan Adler). (laughter) And I know that there are some of you who don't have (Internet) access for other reasons beyond just stubbornness!

I had brought a number of overhead projector transparencies to show my website, but thanks to wonderful Russ Breault who brought this beautiful projector, I can now do that directly from the computer.

With that in mind, for those of you who have not had access to the Internet, who don't know how it works, I'm going to very quickly show you the Shroud of Turin Website, or more accurately, some of the key areas on the Shroud of Turin Website.

Basically, this is what you encounter when you first get there, which is a Main Menu of various things that are available on the website. First, there is the Late Breaking Website News. Whenever I add something (to the site) it goes on this page first. That tells you, since the website has gotten as huge as it has, where things are.

For example, this particular meeting, if you wanted to read about it you could click on the text and, this is what a hyperlink is, it jumps you immediately to that spot (on the website). And you can always hit the back button and go back to where you were.

Now a few of the pages I want you to see are accessible from the Shroud Library. The most logical place to find information is the library, so I've created a library page on the website that covers these primary areas:

The Shroud History—note that it is blinking "updated" because we recently updated the 20th century segment, the most significant scientific years (of Shroud history) and expanded it thanks first to Ian Wilson, and also to Harry Gove and his detailed account of what occurred during the time of the carbon dating. Then I went through my archives of 22 years of STURP (Shroud of Turin Research Project) history and that has also been included. So, starting in the 1900s, you just scroll down the list and through each date, including the background of Fr. Adam Otterbein, Fr. Francis Filas, Fr. Peter Rinaldi, the Holy Shroud Guild, etc. All of that is now found in the Shroud History. So this is one of the important pages I wanted you to see.

Now, going quickly back to the Shroud Library, I want you to see what I'm told is now over 700 titles on the Shroud Booklist. And this is done in several ways. You can search it (the list) alphabetically by just picking a letter. For example, let's pick an author, say Ian Wilson, so you go to the W's by clicking on the letter. Then it immediately takes you to the W's and, if you wanted to you could scroll through the whole list. You will also notice certain book titles are highlighted and linked, so you can click on them and go directly to **Amazon.com** and virtually purchase the book online.

Now backing up to the Library again, we select probably the most important page, and that is the Shroud Scientific Papers and Articles page. This page has the complete text of many articles, well, there are forty articles currently on this page. I am going quickly to the latest one I put up by Isabel Piczek.

Now the reason I'm showing you this is because one of the problems I've had as a professional photographer for the last 28 years is the frustration of seeing my work horribly mangled when it gets into print. One of the best examples of that was the "Mapping of Research Test Points" paper that I did for STURP. The (photographic) maps were so unreadable in the printed results that very few people were able to use them. The reason I'm showing you Isabel's article here first is because Isabel profusely illustrates her articles. I'm not going to show it all to you, but I'm just going to scroll down quickly so you'll see, and maybe for the first time Isabel will see, the way it really works. It's all one huge, long page Isabel. The ability to reproduce an image on the Internet is so far superior to what it takes to do it onto a printed page, that I recreated those maps from my own mapping article for the website. And I was able to add color so you can see that certain specific data points are in red and some are in blue because they illustrate only approximate areas. This is now far more useable in this form than it ever was on the printed page.

I recently got a telephone call from the Pentagon. I know that sounds strange, but I got a call from a nuclear physicist who called me to thank me personally for putting the carbon dating paper on the website. For those who don't know what I mean, I'm referring to the carbon dating paper. Now why did I put that up there you might ask. Well, finding it is pretty difficult unless you happen to have access to a research library. And many interested scientists out there aren't going to take the time to go find it. But when you put it right there in front of them, the reason this nuclear physicist from the Pentagon called me was to tell me he appreciated my putting it there, because after he read this (and he was a firm believer in the carbon date until he read this), he then said, wait a minute, that's a preliminary set of tests! How can they claim a 95% certainty? Well, I'm just a photographer and I can't answer the question, but I told him, "thank you for calling to ask."

Of course, immediately after I told Isabel about this phone call she asked, "will he put it in writing?" Well he probably won't, he works at the Pentagon! He doesn't want to jeopardize his situation. (laughter) But on the other hand, the advantage of putting the factual information on the screen for people to see, if you present people with facts, they can make informed decisions. Up until now, the average person, not the researchers (we know where to research stuff), but the average person in the world, does most of his Shroud "research" at the grocery store checkout counter! (laughter)

And I hate to say it, but, when somebody calls me up and says, "Hey! I noticed at the grocery store checkout counter, that they've taken Jesus' blood off the Shroud and formed a serum that cures every disease known to man!" (laughter) You know, when I hear that kind of stuff, it's pretty pathetic, it really bothers me! And part of the reason that this happens is that people don't have access to (accurate) information. So this website was designed because I was tired of explaining to my friends that no, Leonardo couldn't have painted the Shroud, it was being displayed 60 years before he was born! And that's what prompted the website. That phone call! When somebody told me that "Shroud thing" I was involved with...well, Leonardo painted it!

Now another thing the website is good for is debates. A gentleman named Antonio Lombatti, who is the editor of *Approfondimento Sindone*, the somewhat anti-Shroud publication, wrote an article that appeared in the *British Society Newsletter*. Alan Whanger saw it and responded to it. It prompted an e-mail debate that went back and forth amongst some of us, and I was a party to it, until I finally wrote to everybody and said, look, that needs to be on the Internet. And so the debate between Lombatti and Whanger is on the website.

The point is, it is a place where people can debate an issue and do it in a manner where all of us can either be participants or at least, observers. It doesn't have to happen just in personal correspondence.

The last page about the website that I'm going to talk about now, is a very important page and one that I'm also very proud of. It's called the Research Registry. The Research Registry is a page where people can place a request or "want ad" for things that they're looking for (relative to Shroud research). In this case, somebody was looking for documentation and that was from Remi Van Haelst in Belgium. Here's a search for photographs and bibliography information. Now here is somebody who wanted a paper, Diana Fulbright. And Diana got it because, Gino Moretti of the Centro in Turin saw this on the website and immediately responded to Diana. I was very pleased to hear that.

Also, here is a researcher in Japan who wants to be a participant in Shroud research if somebody is willing to use his services. We've been talking about finding new blood? And we've got top-notch scientists, experts in certain disciplines, ready and willing. But they can't be participants until somebody invites them. So this website can stimulate and attract people in that direction.

A lady put up a notice trying to find a book and Richard Orareo promptly sent her a copy! Gus (Dr. August) Accetta used the Research Registry, he was the first! And people responded. The point is that the website can provide us with the resource to do that.

Another thing the website can do, and this is something Al Adler and I have been really talking about for well over a year. And with all the noise Al jokingly makes about the Internet and the website, he also realizes that this is the place for materials to be published once they've been peer reviewed. And my goal is to establish a peer review committee, listing researchers in specific disciplines that can be called upon for peer review within their area of expertise. Underline, boldface, capital letters: **WITHIN THEIR AREA OF EXPERTISE**.

Short story: Nicholas Allen published his theory that the Shroud image was formed by UV light via camera obscura using a form of photography he devised using medieval raw materials ("The Shroud is a proto-photograph"), so I included a link to Allen's website from mine. Shortly thereafter, a gentleman wrote to me from NOAA (the National Oceanographic and Atmospheric Administration). He stated that he was not a Shroud researcher, but that his field was specifically "the effects of UV radiation on the biosphere." In other words, how ultraviolet light impacts us on the surface of the planet. He stated that it was impossible for the wavelengths quoted by Nicholas Allen to have caused the "exposure," and, should they ever reach us here on the surface of the planet, there would be no life as we know it remaining. So, for that one precise, short moment, that researcher, who has nothing to do with the Shroud, was able to contribute to the body of knowledge. And because I put this response on the website and sent it to Nicholas Allen, Allen had to go back to the drawing board on that part of his theory.

So the Internet is not only a place to publish the science, but a place to attract scientists. It's the credibility that we've been missing for the last number of years. STURP was very credible when it began. When we got back we had gathered some of the very best data that researchers are still using worldwide, but in the end, the credibility was lost, in part of course, because of the carbon dating, and in part because STURP, like everybody else, was comprised of human beings. And when the cameras are pointing you in the face, sometimes the ego gets a little bigger than it needs to. So we did experience some problems along those lines.

At any rate, I was planning to come here and read everyone the riot act about cooperation and communication, but after getting here and seeing how cooperative everyone was being, I decided not to. I will suggest that, if you can get onto the website there's an editorial I wrote called "Repeating the Past" (on the Late Breaking Website News page). In essence it says that, with all the criticism of STURP, perhaps we should go back and reexamine what STURP did, because they certainly did one thing right: they are the only group in history to put together a multi-disciplinary group of experts, go to Turin and examine the Shroud of Turin for five days and nights. Nobody else has ever done that. In retrospect, we know that STURP did some things wrong, but they did that one thing very right! It was STURP having their act together and functioning as a disciplined team of scientists, with a written test plan so they knew exactly what they were supposed to do that eventually got them the permission to examine the Shroud of Turin. And they went and they performed flawlessly for five days and nights. I think that is critical for us to remember, so although we shouldn't go back and repeat the mistakes they made, we should go back and look at what they did right. If we want to be a part of whatever comes next, we better do that— or we'll be sitting on the sidelines watching someone else do it, if we don't get our act together. And this meeting is a wonderful step toward doing so.

Now, because of what happened last night, I'm going to shut the website off. I've given a few of you who have not seen the Internet a peek at it. And now I'm going to show you something completely different.

You've heard me talk for years about the Shroud of Turin CD-ROM. Many of you probably think that it's just something I'm imagining! Well, rather than just telling you about it, what I'd like to do is allow you to see a little bit of the Shroud of Turin CD-ROM. And I'm so thrilled Mr. (Pete) Schmacher is here (in reference to the man who developed the VP-8 Image Analyzer), because what I'm going to show you is what I call "The Virtual VP-8."© It is a complete simulation of the VP-8 Image Analyzer.

One of the most frustrating areas of Shroud image study is the so-called 3-D image that was detected by the VP-8 Image Analyzer. It is without question the least understood property of the Shroud image and the VP-8 is the wonderful device that allows us to examine that property. Yet few outside the inner circle of Shroud research have ever had the opportunity to operate the device and examine the Shroud image with it. In realizing this, I wanted to give everyone the same opportunity to examine the Shroud for themselves, using the VP-8. So we created the "Virtual VP-8"© Image Analyzer simulation.

Now this is on a CD-ROM, much like the Emanuela Marinelli CD-ROM that Kevin Moran showed you. From within the simulation you can select from one of four available Shroud photographs and a normal photograph of two children to examine. Once selected, the photo moves under the camera, the lights come on and it is displayed on a black and white video monitor within the display of the simulator. Then you go to the control panel and select a function, such as "gain" (which turns up and down the 3-D effect), and now you actually use your mouse to manipulate the gain at your own pace using the provided controls, just like on a real VP-8.

As a matter of fact, this is real VP-8 imagery, thanks to Kevin and Anne Moran, who were kind enough to let me come into their home and disrupt it for about 20 hours! Poor Anne was probably a little concerned that Kevin wasn't going to get to sleep at all that night. I actually videotaped, with a broadcast BetaCam camera right off the screen, my manipulations of four of my Shroud photographs on the VP-8.

Then, we took the videotape and spent eleven months designing and building it into the multi-layered interactive computer simulation you see here, so that eventually, everyone will be able to do it. And just like a real VP-8, you can turn up and down the gain, rotate the image, or tilt it up and down from flat to vertical. And any time you want, you can click on the black and white monitor screen and it opens a detailed, scrollable written description of the image currently on the VP-8 screen. The descriptions include clues of what to look for in each of these various images. You just click on it again and it goes back to the view of the source image.

Now the other thing you can do of course, is select different images. You'll see the previous photograph go out from under the camera and be replaced by the new one. And once again you select what control you want to use. This is the tilt function and you can then tilt that image of the Shroud, in this case the face.

Now of course, everybody says, "so what?" What's the big deal? Why is that significant? Well, you have to take a normal photograph (referring to the photo of two children that is part of the Virtual VP-8 simulation), and this happens to be the Moran grandchildren, which was the nearest one available so I grabbed it off the wall, and compare it to a VP-8 Shroud image. That's when you begin to understand the differences.

For example, if you use the gain control here on the kids, you will immediately notice that, instead of getting a natural relief, the kids hair is going into his head, in the facial relief his mouth is going deep in, the eyes are going deep in. Not close to a natural relief. Why, because this is an image made by light using photography, unlike the image on the Shroud. Note that I refer to the VP-8 image of the Shroud as a "relief" and not as "three dimensional" or "3-D." It's not three dimensional, which implies 360 degrees. It is a relief image.

This virtually simulates the precise way a VP-8 works. There is a camera, there are lights, there is a monitor to see the camera image on, and that is what the top monitor is, and of course, there is the green-screen oscilloscope type monitor that shows the VP-8 image.

This is one that Kevin was really happy about. He says it is one of the very best dorsal images we've been able to get. And you have to rotate the image. At certain angles it's not very good at all but at other angles it's quite good.

At any rate, I'm showing you this part of the Shroud of Turin CD-ROM to give you a sense of what we're working on and how valuable it will be when it is complete.

I want to thank everybody that's here for showing the spirit of cooperation that they've shown, the spirit of participation. And remember that the two things that will do the best towards getting us down the road in the future together is to cooperate and communicate. We now have the tools available. Not just one website anymore, but a complete network of websites.

I must point out that the Whangers (Dr. Alan and Mary) have updated their website. For those of you who have Internet access, you've got to go see this. If your familiar with Alan Whanger's polarized light overlay technique, you now go onto the website and compare the images yourself. There are a dozen different ones, it's very simple to operate and it gives everybody the opportunity to see this.

So again, I thank you for your time and I thank you for your cooperation. We have to keep this up and we have to open it up to everybody. We have to remember it's an international thing. The Shroud is not American, the Shroud is not Italian, the Shroud doesn't belong to anyone, it belongs to everyone (although we know it belongs technically and legally to the Vatican). But what it stands for belongs to everyone. And we have to remember that it's not about us. It's about the Shroud.

KEVIN E. MORAN

OPTICAL ENGINEERING EXPERT

Kevin Moran is an optical engineer who has been working with Holy Shroud researchers for twenty years and lecturing on the subject at schools, churches and industry. He has made photomicrographs of the Frei samples taken in 1978 and he maintains one of only two remaining functional VP-8 workstations. The VP-8 is the NASA device that can detect the three dimensional information encoded in the Shroud image. He analyzes photos that are sent to him to see if they are like the Shroud image. He has built test apparatus for shroud researchers and has video documented many Shroud conferences for technical review and archiving. He has appeared, with the VP-8, in 4 documentary videos including two very popular, *Unsolved Mysteries* in 1991 and *In Pursuit of the Shroud* in 1998 directed by Reuben Aaronson.

Mr. Moran has worked 40 years in industrial research for companies such as Ford Aerospace, Hercules Powder Company and Eastman Kodak Company. He now has his own consulting business Cambiano Engineering Company that designs and builds prototype instruments. His education is in engineering and physics. He has 15 U.S. patents.

Mr. Moran and his wife Anne have 7 children and 6 grandchildren and now live in Belmont, NC.

Digital Medium for Shroud Records

Introduction

Documentation of current work on the Holy Shroud has become so large that digital recording methods are a must for all current and past data, and it must be considered for all future work. Fortunately, prices have gone down on computers and recording medium, to such a low, that all workers can now afford them. About three-quarters, or more, of the people who contribute to the current literature on the Shroud have PC or Apple computers. And anyone can go to a print shop or library to get work that is on digital medium translated to hard copy. Two examples are the websites of B. Schwortz (**shroud.com**) and the Holy Shroud Guild (**shroud.org**). The clear advantage is the speed and low cost of printouts. It is proposed that all future work use digital capture and recording for raw data processing graphics, text and presentation graphics.

By 1998 over two thirds of all homes, in the USA, had personal computers. In academic work over 90% of all workers are now using computers for reports and publications. The Internet is growing at a very rapid pace. It allows anyone in the whole world to see a finished document at his or her desk in just a few minutes after the author has posted it.

All the while libraries are becoming automated with the old and new books they have had cataloged by their computer using the Machine Readable Catalog or MARC record format. They have the capacity to search their internal stack or go out to other collections or reach the Internet, for the information desired. This seamless coverage of data storage shows how mature the literature has become to those who have digital experience and access equipment.

To be sure periodicals, books, tapes, slides and all forms of "firm" medium will remain in use for a long time. But it will not be growing as fast or become as cheap as digital electronic medium. Thus it behooves us to consider this as applied to the Holy Shroud. Any digital material can always be printed and published in paper form, but it is easier to get collected and published in digital form. **The content is still the important point.**

Equipment Consideration

Most personal computers, PCs, have the 3.5" floppy disk recorder, that uses the 3.5" medium, that holds 1.44 megabytes of data. As many know these little disks fit in your pocket nicely and cost so little, about 30 cents apiece, that they can be handed out and later printed from, or added to, and handle a good sized report. With the advent of laptop computers, the 3.5" disk data, as well as other size disk data can be directly projected to the screen as is being done here today, with the video projector.

It is important to think about getting the data in digital form as it is gathered. One example is the digital camera I am showing you here that is the Kodak model DC260. This particular unit belongs to Barrie Schwortz.He uses it in his work and can put a picture on his website, (**shroud.com**)without the need of a darkroom.

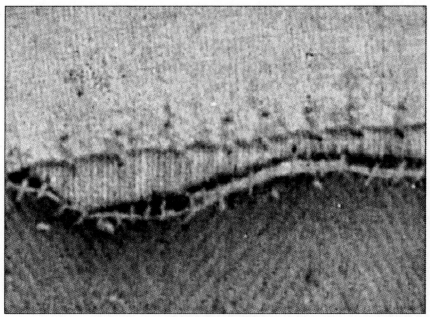

Figure 1. Close-up of gap in 1534 patch work that shows stitches.

Flatbed scanners and inexpensive cameras are available as commodity items in discount stores all over the country. I recently paid $89 for a flatbed scanner that only 4 years ago would have been $890. And it works even better than the higher priced unit. The SONY digital Mavica camera uses the 3.5" disk a its picture-storing medium. It comes in different resolution quality for $499 up to $999. An example of a Shroud detail is shown in Figure 1.The resolution of this picture is not as high as say the Kodak DC260 could show, but it is good enough to show certain stitch differences for discussion. It is a close-up photo of the Holy Shroud Guild's quarter size reproduction. But the main feature here is to show how easily I could put it into this document.

Another example is the photo-microscopic detail of a single fiber on the Frei slide Bd4 taken from the Shroud in 1978. The 35mm film was digitized at high resolution onto a Kodak PhotoCD and sent to the Holy Shroud Guild website Gallery page. But its importance will be seen in the image pixel that is sharply terminated.

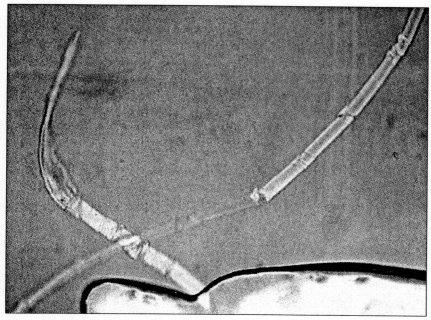

Figure 2. Body Image Pixel from Max Frei slide bd4, 1978.

Figure 2 Shows two fibers, one laying across the other, both with a slightly darker segment that is an image pixel. These random darker sections make up the body image. They are more brittle than the non-imaged fiber. These fibers are about 15 microns in diameter.

The flexibility of the use of digitally recorded text and graphics is the main breakthrough we want to call to your attention.

Software Considerations

This document is being written in Microsoft Word. It is a software product that comes under the "Office "package sold by Microsoft. But it also comes pre-installed on many new machines when you buy them.

Corel sells WordPerfect that will also combine images and text with ease. Adobe PhotoShop is the program that I use to process pictures before I put them into the Word program. But there are at least a dozen other programs that will do the same thing

The types of medium fall into two classes: Magnetic and Laser disk. Now the price of laser disk recorders has come down to under $200. This makes both the old standard magnetic disk and the new laser disk very competitive. This is shown in Table I.

This table gives youan idea of how low the cost per megabyte of data has come down as of 1998. A megabyte can easily equal 100 pages of text or 20 moderate resolution photos, or a mixture of both.

I have left out tape as a medium, not because it is not economical, but because it is not as convenient, anymore, when compared to the other forms of storage.

A very new development is the low cost of rewritable laser disks, or CD-RW as they are called. They are now only about two times the cost of the original write-once, CD-R laser disks.

Conclusion

With the low cost of digital medium, it is proposed that all future work use digital capture and recording for raw data processing graphics, text and presentation graphics. Prices will probably stabilize in the near future, but at the current cost levels, it is a bargain and certainly complements regular printing and publishing.

Medium	Capacity/ Megabytes	Price	Cost per Megabyte
3.5 floppy	1.44	$15 per 50	21 cents
Zip disk	100	$10 each	10 cents
Jaz disk	1000	$70 each	7 cents
3M disk	120	$6 each	5 cents
CD-R	650	$1	1.6 cents

Table I. Cost per Megabyte of Data

RUSSELL A. BREAULT

SHROUD OF TURIN EDUCATION PROJECT (STEP) FOUNDER

Russ Breault has been researching and lecturing on the Shroud of Turin for nearly 20 years. His lectures are carefully designed to be compelling and enjoyable while leading the audience through a dynamic, thought-provoking experience. Using over 100 slides and other media, his acclaimed presentation is called The Mystery of the Shroud: A Multi-Media Encounter.

Mr. Breault has captivated hundreds of audiences from New York to Hawaii including numerous prestigious institutions such as Duke University, Auburn University, West Point, Mercer University, Regent University, Brenau College, University of Alabama, U.S. Army Command College, and others. He has also presented at hundreds of churches across the country including such notables as Coral Ridge Presbyterian, home of Dr. D. James Kennedy.

Mr. Breault co-produced and appeared on the nationally televised documentary *Behold a Mystery* in 1991 and also appeared on *Mysteries of the Ancient World*, which ran on CBS in 1994. He has participated in several international symposia including the initial STURP conference in 1981, Paris in 1989, New York in 1990, Rome in 1993, and Turin in 1998 and Dallass in 1998. He has appeared on nationally televised talk shows including *Straight Talk* and *The 700 Club*.

An expert communicator—currently a vice-president at the FOX Family Channel, Russell has taken on the task of making Shroud information available to young people, with a specific focus on colleges, universities, and high schools. To that end, he has founded the Shroud of Turin Education Project (STEP). Through STEP he has created an award winning web site on the Shroud (**www.shroud2000.com**) that averages over 25,000 hits every month from all around the world.

Mr Breault has authored several articles on the subject and is also on the Board of Directors of the Atlanta International Center for the Continuing Study of the Shroud of Turin (AICCSST).

EDUCATION AND THE SHROUD:
FOR THE YOUNG AND FOR NEW MEMBERS

"What better way, if you were a deity, of regenerating faith in a skeptical age, than to leave evidence 2,000 years ago that could be defined only by the technology available in that skeptical age?" —Ray Rogers, Thermal Physicist

The Shroud of Turin Education Project, Inc. was established to build awareness of this most fascinating artifact amongst high school and college students as well as interested people of all ages. The primary vehicle for this is the STEP website (**www.shroud2000.com**).

By stimulating independent research, more people will learn about the Shroud, helping to build public support for more research, which in turn will enlarge the pool of information. Additionally, building general awareness gradually generates more media coverage and will enhance the ability to raise research funds.

Ultimately, whether the Shroud is authentic or not, it is the message that matters. The Shroud is a dynamic way of presenting the truths of the Gospel in a unique and compelling manner. Campus ministries and Churches in general need to recognize the potency of this "gospel on linen" and use it as a powerful tool to proclaim the message so clearly conveyed by the blood-stained image of the Shroud.

The theme used by the Shroud of Turin Education Project is simply, "Explore the Mystery." While it is the mystery that is the subject of so many recent documentaries and serves to draw people in, it is the message that grips and lasts a lifetime.

Through the website, STEP encourages students to utilize the Shroud as a research project in a variety of subjects from art, to history, to science, to medical forensics. The website currently offers a comprehensive presentation outline as a general research guideline.

The next steps on line—to offer outlines submitted by experts in the field, resources referenced so students can find them, and online publishing of student research—are ambitious but the site already offers a solid bibliography, and the section for student research papers is coming soon. Expert outlines are still on the drawing board for a future addition.

There are a large number of ways students can integrate shroud research into their curriculum. Examples of related subject areas include: Anatomy and Physiology, Blood Chemistry, Optical Sciences, Chemical Sciences, Carbon 14 Anomalies, Archaeological Procedure, Scientific Protocols, Religious Art, Legends and Folklore, Medieval art Techniques, Forensic Sciences, Relics, Secret Societies, Apologetics, Epistemology, and Methods of Torture.

Marketing will be the expensive part of the STEP project and is still in the planning stages as far as any mass implementation. Students are regularly engaged via email through the website as they access it. However until dollars are raised for a real marketing push, posters and direct mail will remain out of reach.

Websites, however, are not enough. Because most school library resources are out of date, STEP aims to devise a shroud research kit for them. This goal will require foundation money and conversion to non-profit status, which is anticipated in 2000. Grant requests will be written to secure funding for placement of a comprehensive research library in every school that requests one. Though it may also be offered for sale, money is still needed to develop packaging and marketing. With adequate funding, it will be more likely the kits will be offered free or with deep discounts. The kit would consist of three hard cover books, a recent video for classroom use, a CD ROM, a set of slides for class presentation, and a comprehensive directory showing where and how other resources can be obtained. For those interested in more in depth study, STEP offers a full day seminar.

For quick dissemination of the ever-evolving body of shroud knowledge, STEP developed The Shroud Report, a bi-monthly newsletter that is delivered to a fast growing list of e-mail recipients. The Report focuses on news updates, new documentaries, new books, CD ROMs, website updates, conferences, and other information that may be of interest to Shroud enthusiasts. All recipients sign up for the newsletter through the website.

It is a belief of STEP that the Shroud is one of the greatest tools ever created—by God or by man—to convey the central message of the

Gospel: the life, suffering, death, and resurrection of Jesus Christ. If it is a work of art, it was created as an unparalleled masterpiece to represent these truths. If it is authentic, then it is the most valuable artifact on the planet because it would contain both the image and blood of Christ. Either way, the message remains the same. Churches, both Catholic and Protestant alike should set aside their fears and biases and recognize that the mystery of the Shroud is compelling. But as one explores the evidence, one also encounters the message. It is not necessary for the Shroud to be proven one way or the other for it to be used effectively. The Shroud can never replace faith, but it can inspire it.

If Christian educators, regardless of denomination, can get beyond their bias and fear to focus on the Shroud's message, it could be used in the way God may have intended: The visual Gospel for a video and information age culture. The Shroud of Turin Education Project (STEP) is committed to that mission.

Just as Jesus asked Peter, "Who do you say that I am?" The Shroud asks the same question today to a world full of Doubting Thomases. Why not let them see the Shroud and hear the evidence and make up their own minds the way Thomas did. Perhaps they too will say, "My Lord and my God."

Excerpts from the STEP website:
...Is there a prophetic reason that the Shroud wasn't fully revealed until the 20th Century through science and photography? Interestingly, the Shroud was exhibited in 1998 at the same time that Israel celebrated its 50th birthday. This was called the Jewish Jubilee. The exhibition of the Shroud, however, was based totally on the 100th anniversary of the first photograph ever taken of it, when it was discovered that the image on the cloth is actually a negative (and becomes positive in a photo-negative). It is only by coincidence that it intersected with the Jewish Jubilee? It will be on exhibit again in 2000 to celebrate the Christian Jubilee.

...The formation of the State of Israel is considered a major fulfillment of biblical prophecy. Until 1948, the Jews had been scattered for 2500 years without a homeland. But it was prophets spoke of a time, at the end of the age, when they would be re-gathered in Israel once again. Following the Six-Day War in 1967, the Jews regained complete control of Jerusalem. This is considered another fulfillment of prophecy...The principal purpose of prophecy is to sound a warning to a lukewarm church to get its act together—to be ready and watching for His return.

...The study of iconography looks at how the Shroud image, rediscovered in Edessa in 525 AD, was the progenitor of all the iconic images of Christ that followed. Some of the common characteristics between the Shroud and many icon images are: the large hollow eyes, forked beard, a sprock of hair in the middle of forehead, a flattened nose, raised cheeks, and most pronounced is a double line across the neck which corresponds with a fold line on the Shroud. Not all icons have all the same characteristics but the pattern is clear.

STEP · PO Box 3397 · Peachtree City, GA 30269 · USA
Email: shroud2000@earthlink.net
Website: **www.shroud2000.com**

PHILLIP E. DAYVAULT, CPP

COUNCIL FOR THE STUDY OF THE SHROUD OF TURIN (CSST) DIRECTOR

Philip E. Dayvault, CPP, graduated from the University of North Carolina at Chapel Hill in 1973. With over fifteen prior years in federal law enforcement and corporate security management, he served approximately eight years with the US Federal Bureau of Investigation (FBI), both as a Physical Science Technician and Special Agent. He also has served as a sales representative, Dealer Sales Manager, or Corporate Security Manager with several international companies. In 1996, he received the prestigious Certified Protection Professional, CPP designation. He is a member of both the International Association of Professional Security Consultants (IAPSC) and the American Society for Industrial Security (ASIS). Since 1994, he has served as the Executive Director of the Council for Study of the Shroud of Turin (CSST). Also, since 1997, Mr. Dayvault has been the president of SECURITY INSIGHT, a security management consulting company located in Chapel Hill, NC, USA.

Phillip Dayvault represented CSST and Dr. Alan and Mary Whanger, the organization's founders who could not attend, at the 1998 Dallas conference. Phil has studied the Shroud for a number of years and works closely with the Whangers in their ongoing research. In addition to providing an overview of CSST's recent activities, Mr. Dayvault's Dallas presentation took a look at the research currently being done by the organization in collaboration with Dr. Avinoam Danin and Dr. Uri Baruch of the Hebrew University in Israel. CSST is the curator of Dr. Max Frei's Shroud tape samples, taken in 1973 and 1978, and has recently completed a thorough analysis of the pollens found on the samples. CSST also has a website (http://dmi-www.mc.duke.edu/shroud).

CSST—An Overview

The history of the Council for Study of the Shroud of Turin, CSST, began in October, 1994 with the convening of our first annual Board of Director's Meeting. This nonprofit scientific/educational group was formed as a means to promulgate continuing research by Dr. and Mrs. Alan D. Whanger of Durham, North Carolina. All "Shroudies" are aware of the tremendous research done by the Whangers and of their remarkable findings; which include, images of much of the Armi Christi, 28 floral images, and skeletal images that were apparently produced by some sort of radiation and coronal discharge. The founding members of CSST agreed upon a singular "Mission Statement," which reads: "To study, research, and publish the findings from the Shroud of Turin and related Relics of the Passion; and to disseminate this knowledge and promote general awareness." The members of our Board of Directors include Dr. and Mrs. Whanger, primary researchers, Dr. Thomas Langford, Duke University Provost Emeritus, Mr. James Neal, CPA, Mr. William Self, CPA, Mr. Thomas Vuke, businessman, and myself, Philip Dayvault, former FBI Special Agent and Laboratory Technician and CSST Executive Director. CSST also utilizes the services of a Legal Counsel, Mr. Robert Price. As we just held our Fourth Annual Board meeting, this mission is currently "in progress," and much has been accomplished by CSST towards meeting our goals.

In 1993, the Whangers acquired the entire Frei Collection from Mr. Paul Maloney of ASSIST, where the collection had been on loan from Mrs. Frei-Sulzer. This collection consists of "sticky-tape" slides Dr. Max Frei personally collected both in 1973 and 1978 directly from the Shroud of Turin, as well as other slides he collected from the Tunic of

Argenteuil and the Crown of Thorns. His original notes and manu-scripts, along with numerous photographs and control samples are also included in this priceless collection. To alleviate previous allegations that Dr. Frei had "salted" the tapes, CSST retained the services of a supervisory forensic examiner in 1997 who concluded that there was no evidence of tampering with the "sticky-tapes," after conducting a thorough examina-tion of each individual Frei tape.

In 1996, CSST acquired a state-of-the-art microscope system, and Olympus AX-70. This computerized research microscope will permit examination under reflected and transmitted light, in either brightfield, darkfield, polarized, phase contrast, DIC Nomarski and several fluores-cent ranges. The magnification ranges from 40-400 (4x-40x), plus 2x zoom, permitting 80-800 magnification. This microscope system will now provide the means to conduct a complete digitization of each slide, with reference points for located items, such as pollen grains, botanical bract, fibers, and Blood shards.

CSST has firmly believed in the utilization of experts in specialized fields for confirmation in that field of study. That is precisely why we sought the opinion of Professor Danin, a botanist at the Hebrew University in Jerusalem. Danin is the world authority on flora of the Near and Middle East. After our first meeting in 1995, he was able to thoroughly examine the areas that the Whangers had thought were floral images. Danin confirmed most of the images and even found a couple of others. However, when it came to pollen grains found on the Frei tapes, other expertise was needed. Danin referred us to Dr. Uri Baruch, a palynologist at the Israel Antiquities Authority. Baruch and Danin have visited CSST offices on numerous occasions and have been able to basically confirm the floral images and pollen grains which are present on the Frei tapes. **Their final conclusions indicate that the Shroud originated in the springtime in the general environs of Jerusalem, Israel.** (Note: The Whangers, Danin and Baruch, have co-authored a paper on the Flora on the Shroud—to be published early next year in a botanical journal.)

As presented at the III International Congress on the Shroud in June, 1998 in Turin, Italy, CSST is currently involved with what has become known as the "Frei Project." This is the actual digitization of each Frei "sticky-tape," or the digital recording of every recognizable or discernible artifact on each tape. Comparative studies can then be conducted and images shared with other researchers. Members of the Frei Project include Danin, Baruch, Whanger, Vuke, Dayvault and our colleague, friend and scientific advisor, Dr. Al Adler. CSST is honored to be involved in collaborative studies with various international study groups such as the Centro Espanol de Sindonologia, CES, whose forte is primary research on the Sudarium of Oviedo (Spain), the traditional "facecloth" of Our Lord Jesus. Other groups include the UNEC/Costa, who are primary researchers on the Tunic of Argenteuil (France), which is the traditional "Seamless Robe," also used in the Passion. CSST has always asserted the need for cooperative studies and its willingness and desire to participate collaboratively with other viable groups and individuals worldwide.

Another primary goal of CSST is the acquisition of a suitable "information center" which would serve as a main office for CSST functions. This would house an exhibition hall for all of the Whangers' posters and life-size photographs, as well as an auditorium for presentations to the general public, church and civic groups, etc. Also included would be a fully operational forensic research laboratory for the conduction of scientific studies on various aspects of Shroud studies. Office space would also complement the center.

Since September, 1994, CSST has been a 501(C)3 nonprofit corporation, with scientific and educational emphasis. In 1995, we made available a means for individuals to participate with their financial support and volunteer service though Associate Memberships of varying degrees. Currently we have over 150 Associate Members and this number continues to rise as more people become aware of our endeavors and the importance of Shroud studies. CSST also publishes a newsletter three times annually. The *CSST News* is sent to approximately 750 interested parties and offers information on new research, book reviews, upcoming meetings, etc.

CSST was elated last February when the Whangers finally got their recollection of nearly twenty years of Shroud research published in their first book, *The Shroud of Turin—An Adventure in Discovery*. This book has been highly recommended by reviewers and is a thorough compilation of remarkable findings on the Shroud. It should be noted that CSST retains the copyright to this book and that all proceeds go directly to CSST to underwrite ongoing research and educational activities. Information on current research being conducted by CSST, as well as some remarkable overlays can be viewed by visiting the CSST homepage: **http://dmi-www.mc.duke.edu/shroud/default.htm**. Another method for access, and somewhat easier, is to go the **www.shroud.com**—Other Organizations—CSST link.

We feel very confident about the future of American Sindonology and want to be an integral part of it. It has been an honor to be involved in the study of this most remarkable cloth known as the Shroud of Turin. We feel that although much has been done over the years, there is still much to do. CSST wants to participate and contribute in any way possible in hopes of finding out the Truth about this historical enigma of monumental proportions and importance. To the organizers of this important meeting, thank you for this wonderful opportunity to participate.

Rev. Albert "Kim" R. Dreisbach, Jr.

Founder of the Atlanta International Center for the Continuing Study of the Shroud of Turin (AICCSST)

The Rev. Albert "Kim" R. Dreisbach, Jr., an Episcopal Priest, is the founder and Executive Director of the Atlanta International Center for the Continuing Study of the Shroud of Turin, Inc. (AICCSST). Selected for Marquis who's Who in Religion, Fr. Dreisbach is the author of numerous papers, a frequent lecturer—most recently at the III International Congress held in Turin in June of 1998. He has also lectured at St. Stephen's House, Oxford, Bologna, Mount St. Alphonus in Esopus, NY, at Emory's Senior University, Atlanta, and has often appeared on national radio and TV. He also served as a panelist with author Ian Wilson and Duke's Dr. Alan Whanger on Vatican Radio following the Bologna International Symposium in 1989. A commentator and technical advisor in a segment devoted to the Shroud on CBS's *Mysteries of the Ancient World*, he also has functioned in the same capacity for NBC's *Unsolved Mysteries*, CBN's *Behold a Mystery*, and for the newly released update on the Shroud for The Learning Channel titled *In Pursuit of the Shroud*.

The Shroud of Turin:
Its Ecumenical Implications

When I first began to lecture on the Shroud of Turin, I had very real reservations as to how it would be received by the larger ecumenical community. What I have discovered in the intervening years is that the Shroud needs no such apologist. It is now, as it was on that very first Easter morning, self-authenticating. In presentations ranging from the Salvation Army to the Syrian Orthodox, from the Bible Belt to the Biretta Belt, Christians of all persuasions are beginning to acknowledge not only that the Shroud is Christianity's most precious artifact; but that it is also "the" most significant visual aid available to the religious educator for teaching about our Lord's Passion, Death, and Resurrection.

There are many "testimonies" regarding the impact on the beholder at his or her first encounter with the image(s) of the Man of the Shroud. One example will serve to make the point:

> It was in the late forties when I first saw a photograph of the vastly imposing image on the Shroud of Turin...From that moment, whatever the solution to the mystery of its origin, I had a sufficient face, and a credibly assaulted body, that seemed as far as I could advance toward the original. For me the face on the Shroud was the image that seemed no guess at all but the thing itself.
>
> At once it surpassed the variously moving guesses of artists in the Roman catacombs, the Byzantine mosaicists, Mantegna, Leonardo, Rembrandt and Rubens...Carbon dating now concludes that the linen is medieval in origin, with the corollary that the image was somehow made by an artist. But no one has shown how a fourteenth-century artist

*produced an object so complex in historical accuracy and still
so mysterious in its physical properties. Meanwhile the bat-
tered calm face on the Shroud goes on seeming a worthy cause
of the cataract of music, art, architecture and mystic rapture
that artists and saints of the past two millennia have poured
in honor of Christ and directed toward him. And all the
Christs I imagined thereafter began in the unanswerable
eloquence of the Shroud.* —Reynolds Pierce
(1990. *Clear Pictures*. New York: Ballantine, pp. 243-44)

Returning to the ecumenical dimension of this sacred linen, it became
very evident to me on the night of August 16, 1983, when local judicatory
leaders offered their corporate blessing to the TURIN SHROUD
EXHIBIT and participated in the Evening Office of the Holy Shroud.
The Greek Archbishop, the Roman Catholic Archbishop, the Episcopal
Bishop and the Presiding Bishop of the AME Church gathered before
the world's first full size, backlit transparency of the Shroud and joined
clergy representing the Assemblies of God, Baptists, Lutherans, Meth-
odists and Presbyterians in an amazing witness to ecumenical unity. At
the conclusion of the service, His Grace Bishop John of the Greek
Orthodox Diocese of Atlanta, turned to me and said: "Thank you very
much for picking our day." I didn't fully understand the significance of
his remark until he explained to me that August 16th is the Feast of the
Holy Mandylion commemorating the occasion in 944 A.D. when the
Shroud was first shown to the public in Byzantium following its arrival
the previous day from Edessa in southeastern Turkey. What made things
all the more amazing was that those who had scheduled the dedication
had no idea of the significance of the date. It just happened to be the one
night that all the various clergy had free on their busy calendars. Was it
merely coincidence, or was it yet another sign of God's larger purpose for
his Son's burial cloth?

The following January, bishops, clergy and laity of the local Roman Catholic
and Episcopal Dioceses returned to the TURIN SHROUD EXHIBIT to
sign a mutual covenant of cooperation and unity. The participants had agreed
upon the EXHIBIT as an appropriate and neutral site for the covenant's
signing rather than selecting either of their respective cathedrals.

How God may choose to further ecumenical cooperation in the future
must wait to be seen. However, we at the Atlanta International Center
For Continuing Study Of The Shroud Of Turin, Inc. pray that the
intent of that first dedicatory service may prove to be prophetic: Accept

we pray, this Exhibition of the Turin Shroud, and grant that those who look upon it may have their hearts open to things which can be seen only by the eyes of faith. By the Holy Spirit, use it to preach the Gospel of Salvation with power and grace to those who have not heard it, turn the hearts of those who resist it, and bring home to your fold those who have gone astray; that there may be one flock under one shepherd, Jesus Christ our Lord.[1]

History may provide a clue as to what the cloth's future ecumenical implications may be. After almost 2,000 years of history since its discovery in the Empty Tomb, the Shroud has been on the move both literally and figuratively. If Ian Wilson's thesis is accepted that the Image of Edessa-Mandylion-Shroud of Turin are one and the same, then the Holy Linen truly has traveled from the Tomb to Turin. In the process it has survived a flood at Edessa, the sack of Constantinople by the Fourth Crusade, and a near disastrous fire at Chambéry.

As I began to reflect upon its journey through time I also began to discover the ecumenical dimension of its travels. Could it be that, in addition to its physical preservation through the ages, God also has intended it to be an ecumenical bridge and unifier? Until the day when we can once again share One Cup and One Loaf, what could serve as a better focus for ecumenical unity than this "photograph" of the Resurrection. "To the Jew first and also to the Greek" (Rom. 1:16), the Shroud has moved from the East to the West. Is it merely by chance that in the process it has been "lifted up" so that "all" are being drawn to Him whose sacred image it bears? Is it merely by chance that those first Jewish disciples who visited the Holy Sepulchre learned of the Resurrection from this sacred linen's very emptiness—an experience so powerful that it sent them forth into all the world to share the fullness of its Gospel message? Was it by chance that an afflicted Parthian king was cured and converted by it? Was it merely by chance that our Orthodox brothers and sisters were privileged to be its custodians for nearly 1200 years, meticulously recording in their iconography and numismatics the features of our Lord which it bears? Could it be that God assigned them this very role in response to those first Greeks who approached St. Philip with the plea that "we would see Jesus" (Jn. 12:21)? Was it by chance that the Church of Rome was to be its next and faithful guardian? And is it by chance that now in the twentieth century the worldwide Protestant community is currently coming to appreciate the Holy Shroud's true significance?

Even charismatic TV evangelists like those on CBN and the Trinity Broadcasting Network have devoted hour-long programs to "The Shroud of Mystery."

History's very preservation of this Holy Cloth should alert the ecumenical community to a divine purpose which should not be ignored. Though no branch of Christianity has ever required belief in the Shroud's authenticity as an article of faith, many denominations are now coming to perceive that it can do such in the way of adding both depth and detail to a faith already held. One 6th grader after a visit to the EXHIBIT noted: "I never knew before that He hurt so much for us. I am going to try to live better for Him." A "lapsed" adult who had not darkened the doors of a church in over twenty-one years, confessed with tears in his eyes "My visit to the Exhibit has changed my life. I didn't do much with the first half, but I would like to give the second half back to God." Lest one think that he was merely overcome with the emotion of the moment, I can tell you that not only does he now serve on the governing board of his local congregation, but recently I had the privilege of writing a letter of recommendation for him to begin his formal seminary training.

Daily at the Exhibit we came in contact with many who would never attend services at a local parish, let alone even visit a church to see an exhibition devoted to an alleged "relic." For many of them the "religion" of the twentieth century is symbolized by the scientist's white laboratory jacket—certainly not the black cassock of a priest. However, quite frequently these devotees of technology discover a truth long ago known to their theological brothers and sisters. They come to scoff, but they stay to pray. This phenomenon is well described by an American Baptist minister who has astutely observed: "Maybe the greatest attribute of the Shroud is that it creates doubt in the doubter, and God doesn't need much of a toehold to get a start." Like St. Thomas before them, some of these "doubters" are profoundly moved when they discover that although Science went to test the Shroud, in reality it is the Shroud which still continues to test the scientists. We should not be surprised if God once again converts doubtful skepticism into dedicated service.

There at the Exhibit we had mimeographed forms for visitors who would care to share their reactions with us. One of these from a gentleman from Laguna Beach, California, caught my eye. He had written: "Questioned for the first time my lack of belief... profoundly moving...my knees are still weak." Only time will tell the full impact of the Shroud on this person's life, but I have a hunch that God has gotten another "toehold."

Should we Christians be amazed at much a response? I think not! From that first Easter morning the Magdalene "saw two angels in the place where Jesus had lain...one at the head and one at the feet" (John 20:21).

Could this be the very first description of the ventral and dorsal images of the Man of the Shroud? People have responded in awe to the Sacred Image which it bears. Fr. Gerald O'Collins, S.J., originally a non-believer in the Shroud's authenticity, now uses it as "a" way by which some can be led to Christ. He notes that in the Old Testament the primary emphasis was on the ear as the organ by which God was known ("Hear O Israel, the Lord our God is One" (Deut. 6:4). However, a shift in the senses occurs in the New Testament when the Beloved Disciple Mark stoops to look into the Empty Tomb and "saw and believed" (John 20:8). Are we so blind that we fail to discern that in the study of the Shroud our Lord is once again being "lifted up (to) draw all" (Jn. 12:22) to Himself? Is it not possible that once again "when the time had fully come" (Gal. 4:4)? God is using this autograph of His Son in His own Blood to make Him known as never before to a generation gifted with analytical methods heretofore not technically possible? *Mirabile dictu*, could this "polaroid of the Resurrection" and the means to reproduce same via printed and electronic media all over the world now have the potential to be even more fully appreciated than it was 2,000 years ago? Truly, such implications are staggering.

Although the linen is now legally the possession of the Pontiff and all his successors, its message is for all the world. One day at the nearby Trappist Monastery of the Holy Spirit, I was to learn this truth phrased in a way that has stayed with me through the years. Fr. Anthony Delesi said: "You know, Kim, we Roman Catholics have taken care of the Shroud for the last 800 years after we stole it from the Greeks who had been its custodians for the first 1200 years. However, in truth it belongs to no denomination—possibly not even to Christianity—for in reality it is **God's 'love letter in linen' to all mankind.**"

Certainly the Rev. Dr. James Kennedy, a Presbyterian from Ft. Lauderdale, Florida, acknowledges this truth in his wonderful sermon entitled "Save the wrappings."[2] Dr. Kennedy observes that our Lord was born in a borrowed cave, wrapped in linen swaddling clothes, and was buried in a borrowed tomb enveloped in a linen shroud. In between these two events was "the Greatest Story Ever Told."

Are not we in the twentieth century being called by God to use these final "wrappings," which God has taken such pains to preserve, to supplement our witness in reaching the hearts of those for whom He lived, died, and rose again? We would do well to heed Sir Wycke Bayliss who at the turn of the century astutely observed that there are at least two Gospel "traditions" an early one in art, and a later one of the written Word. The skill of the artist portrayed Him as The Son of Man; the pen of the writer of scripture brings us to that deeper truth that this Son of Man is also the Christ, the Son of God.

The Rev. David Scaer, a Lutheran pastor, challenges all Christians with his profound article entitled *The Shroud of Turin.- Protestant Embarrassment or Opportunity?* In addition to Protestantism's natural aversion to relics, Scaer notes that undue reliance on revelation through the written Word fails to give just due to the word made flesh in and through history. Scaer concludes his article as follows: "The Shroud of Turin may very well be an authentic link with a past that was not only sacred but real. Acceptance of the authenticity of the Shroud obviously cannot be made a criterion for orthodoxy, but a prior refusal to consider the question borders on disregard of the historical claims of Christianity. Perhaps we shall be given the same opportunity as Peter and John to see the burial garments of the Lord (John 20:6,7)."[3]

Our Lord Himself realized that His own generation sought a "sign," and He promised to leave them only one—the sign of Jonah (Matt. 12:39). Lest modern-day Christians think such speculation is too far fetched, they would do well to note that for a first century Jew the story of Jonah was a parable of Israel's "burial" in Egypt and its subsequent "resurrection" as a nation (cf. Ezek. 37:1-14); and that for writers of the New Testament, the Messiah must recapitulate the history of Israel. Remember also that the original word for "sign" used here in Matthew means "especially certain marks—a supernatural indication" (Bridget Smith, 1981, p. 61. Cf. Kittel). Those of us who believe in the Shroud's authenticity believe that not only did He keep His promise, but that this very "sign" is still with us today locked in a silver casket in Turin's Cathedral Church of St. John the Baptist. Those of us who do so believe would do well to remember that "unto whom much is given, much is required" (Luke 12:48). We of all people should give special heed to a caveat offered by the late Anglican Bishop John A.T. Robinson:

> *If in the recognition of the face and hands and feet and all the other wounds (on the Holy Shroud), we, like those who knew Him best, are led to say, "It is the Lord!" then perhaps we may have to learn to count ourselves also among those who have "seen and believed." But that, as St. John makes clear, brings with it no special blessing (20:29)—rather special responsibility (17:18-21).[4]*

That "special responsibility" is to get beyond the linen to the Lord—to see Him in the faces of the dispossessed, the victims of injustice, the poor, the neglected and all the others for whom He died. "Facts" learned about the Man of the Shroud do not guarantee dedicated service in His Name. Alas, these "facts" can become nothing more than religious erudition in pious garb unless they lead to the deepening of the student's own faith reflected in concern for and service to those for whom the Man of the Shroud came to minister.

The Holy Shroud provides a unique and wonderful opportunity for *ecumenicity* and *evangelism* to walk hand in hand. We who are called to be its advocates should not be focused on denominational converts or quotas, but rather only on the commitment and quality of those who are brought closer to the Lord through their encounter with it. Some may be called to be Baptists, some Orthodox, some Roman, Pentecostal, Presbyterian, or any one of the other multiple Protestant options. Let us trust God to lead His people where He may, even when it is not in the direction of our personal denominational preference. Let the believer discover new depth to a faith already possessed. Let the "convert" bask in the joy of a life filled with new meaning and purpose. Let all go forth to "love and serve the Lord."

Somewhere along the way the "Shroud Crowd" of the future will realize that the teachings of the Man of the Cloth are even more significant than the myriad revelations of truth that it contains. Somewhere in this pilgrimage men and women devoted to its study will rediscover a central truth long ago proclaimed by Him whose image it bears: "'I would that you were one even as the Father and I are one" (John 17:21). When that day arrives, maybe the scandal of a divided Christianity "will begin to break down its dividing walls of hostility." And on that day when Christianity is able to present one "Face" to the non-Christian world, then maybe the former will be taken more seriously by those who use its very fragmentation as an argument against acceptance of its teachings. Like St. Peter, we who serve the apostolate of the Holy Shroud can then proclaim, "Gold and silver have I none, but what I have I will certainly give you" (Acts 1:6).

What we have is a unique piece of linen which bears upon it an even more unique and significant gift for all the world: **An ecumenical bridge of cooperation for the present; a potential gift of grace for ecumenical unity and evangelism for the future.**

Note: All Biblical quotes are taken from the Revised Standard Edition.

Footnotes:

1. The Evening Office of the Holy Shroud. Privately printed Order of Service for the Official Dedication of the Turin Shroud Exhibit, Tuesday, August 16, 1983 at the Omni International, Atlanta, GA.
2. Save The Wrappings. The Rev. Dr. James Kennedy. Undated audio cassette produced by Coral Ridge Ministries, P.O. Box 5555, Ft. Lauderdale, FL 31310..
3. The Rev. David Scaer. "The Shroud of Turin: Protestant Embarrassment or Opportunity?" Concordia Theological Quarterly, January 1979.
4. The Rt. Rev. John A.T. Robinson. "The Shroud of Turin and the Grave Cloths of the Gospels." Proceedings of the 1977 United States Conference of Research on the Shroud of Turin. Bronx, NY: Holy Shroud Guild. 1977. p. 30.

II

FURTHER EXAMINATION
OF THE
Shroud of Turin

ADDITIONAL PAPERS
SUBMITTED FOR PUBLICATION
1998 DALLAS CONFERENCE

DONALD J. LYNN

AMERICAN SHROUD OF TURIN ASSOCIATION FOR RESEARCH
(AMSTAR) FOUNDING MEMBER

Mr. Lynn has been involved in Shroud research since 1976. He was a member of the original Shroud of Turin Research Project that performed the scientific examination of the Shroud in Turin in 1978. His involvement in the Shroud's scientific analysis was primarily in the areas of digital image processing and image analysis. At that time he was a Supervisor in the Image Processing Laboratory of the Jet Propulsion Laboratory (Pasadena, CA), with responsibility for all space and astronomical image processing activities within the Image Processing Laboratory of JPL. Mr. Lynn has given over 250 lectures on the Shroud of Turin, the 1978 examination, and the ongoing research.

Mr. Lynn earned a Master of Science degree in Nuclear Engineering from UCLA, and a Bachelor of Science in Mechanical Engineering from the University of Illinois. He has been involved with advanced science and technology projects for over forty years, including various projects involving optical and nuclear radiation.

160

COMMENTS ON SHROUD RESEARCH

THE FOLLOWING IS A RE-CREATION, WITH SOME EMBELLISHMENTS, OF
EXTEMPORANEOUS COMMENTS MADE AT THE MEETING OF AMERICAN
SINDONOLOGY HELD IN DALLAS, TEXAS, NOVEMBER 6-8, 1998.

Thank you for asking me to say a few words, but I really came to listen and not to speak. Having basically retired from scientific endeavors, I find that my role has evolved from an active researcher to more of a very interested spectator. I try to stay abreast of new developments as best I can by staying in touch with Barrie Schwortz and his wonderful Shroud web site, and by reading regular Shroud publications, but I am definitely in a passive mode.

I also had a very selfish reason for wanting to attend this conference, and that is to see old friends like Bob Bucklin, Kim Dreisbach, Al Adler, Gil Lavoie and Mike Minor whom I haven't seen for some time. So any comments I make today are definitely "off the cuff" and I apologize for any omissions or misconceptions.

It is very strange to stand up here and think of myself as one of the "old timers" in Shroud research, when almost twenty-five years ago, I was one of the new faces who was bringing new technology, in the form of digital image processing, to the investigation of the Shroud of Turin. Now, I am very pleased to see so many new faces at this conference, and to hear new ideas and new areas of research and education that are being proposed and explored.

Thanks to the work of Al Adler and others, we believe we know the mechanism by which the frontal and dorsal body images are recorded on the Shroud. The next obvious unknown is the image transport mechanism. Many theories have been proposed, but none have been demonstrated to satisfy all of the characteristics of the images on the Shroud. In this area, I am especially excited by the radiographic work done by Gus Acetta. He has produced images which more closely resemble the images on the Shroud than any I have seen so far. And I especially admire his willingness to be the guinea pig in this investigation. Gus, I don't know how far you are going with this, but I think you are definitely on the right track.

I am also impressed by the work done by Dan Scavone and Kim and others in pursuit of the history and provenance of the Shroud. I am totally amazed that you people can dig through ancient writings in unintelligible (to me) languages and find obscure references that may pertain to the history of the Shroud. The current gap in the provenance of the Shroud is definitely a question which must be pursued in order to determine whether the Shroud of Turin is truly the burial cloth of Jesus Christ. So I heartily encourage you to continue to dig into these areas where I am completely lost.

Thank you Barrie for getting Dr. Grundfest interested in applying his multispectral imaging system to the Shroud. He can do in minutes what we could only partially do in many hours during the 1978 investigation. This technology can be especially useful in quantifying chemical changes in the Shroud over time—a critical question in the matter of conservation. These data would also be useful in analyzing spatial and temporal variations in the images and the background cloth as they relate to the image transport and recording mechanisms.

I am also pleased to see that there is great interest in investigating the correlation between the stains and particulate matter on the Shroud and that on other artifacts that are believed to have been involved in the passion and death of Jesus. I don't know whether valid DNA comparisons or other microbiological correlations can be accomplished, but there is much to be gained if the evidence on the Shroud can be correlated with that on artifacts which have provenance back hundreds of years prior to the thirteenth century.

Lastly, but definitely not least, work must continue on understanding the 1988 Carbon 14 test results. We can complain all we want about how the actual tests deviated from the original protocols, or how the statistical analyses of the data were in error, but the fact is that these reputable scientists obtained these results using internationally accepted techniques. The theories of Garza-Valdes and Kouznetsov have promise, but it must be shown why the age-dating techniques used on the Shroud samples gave results that indicated a thirteenth century origin.

Although, with what we know now, we can never "prove" that the man whose picture is on the Shroud is Jesus Christ, in order for the Shroud of Turin to be the authentic burial cloth of Christ, all of the circumstantial evidence must be consistent with that hypothesis.

Before I sit down and shut up, I want to commend the work being done by Barrie and others on greatly enhancing our ability to communicate information, and to facilitate feedback and interaction between researchers and other interested parties.

Also, as I said in the beginning, I am thrilled to see new faces bringing new energy and new ideas to this investigation. I believe that there is much more information that can be gleaned from the Shroud of Turin, and it can only be obtained by using new ideas and new perspectives.

I speak from experience when I say that you will personally get far more out of this experience than you put into it. It can literally change your life, and it will if you let it.

THE BLOOD IMAGES ON THE HOLY TUNIC, THE CLOTH OF OVIEDO, AND THE HOLY SHROUD

ORIGINALLY PRESENTED AT THE "SCIENTIFIC ROUNDTABLE ON THE HOLY TUNIC" HELD IN ARGENTEUIL, 14 NOVEMBER 1998.

The Holy Tunic, the Cloth of Oviedo, and the Holy Shroud are all alleged to be authentic relics associated with the Crucifixion of Christ. All of them bear blood images of what appears to be those of clotted wounds. Any scientific evidence linking these three sets of images to one another strengthens the historic arguments for accepting the authenticity of all three of them.

Using a polarized image overlay technique, Whanger[1,2] has shown that the shapes of the patterns on the Holy Shroud and the Cloth of Oviedo are strongly congruent. This congruence for the dorsal head wounds on the Shroud is strong enough to challenge the accuracy of the reported radiocarbon date for the Shroud.[3] Using this same technique, Whanger has shown a strong pattern congruence for the flog marks on the Shroud and those that have been retained on the Holy Tunic.[2] Marion has also demonstarated this same Tunica/Shroud pattern correspondence.[4]

Although some extensive work has been done tracing the historic background of the Holy Tunic,[5] the scientific investigations have been meager and are summarized in a small pamphlet by Parcot.[6] However, the formation of Teichmann's hemin crystals (a microscopic test) and an earlier type of peroxidase test are sufficient even by today's standards[7] to serve as evidence of the presence of blood. This identification should be further confirmed using modern chemical, spectroscopic, and immuno-logical techniques to relate the particular characteristics of this blood to that on the Shroud and the Sudarion.

More extensive scientific studies have been carried out on the Cloth of Oviedo.[8,9,10] These studies include a wide variety of hematological tests, chemical tests, immunological tests, photographic studies, textile studies, microscopic examinations, image comparison studies, and even simulation studies to test models for the formation of the blood wound patterns. These studies could be further extended by applying some of the spectroscopic techniques employed in the Shroud investigations.

The very extensive scientific studies carried out on the Shroud of Turin have been summarized in several scientific review articles.[3,11,12,13] The blood image investigations include medical forensic studies, microscopic studies, chemical studies, immunological tests, various spectroscopic studies, image studies, and photographic studies. The overall conclusion was that the blood images were transferred to the cloth by its being in contact with a wounded human male body consistent with the historic descriptions given for the Crucifixion of Christ, but that the body images got on the cloth by some other type of non-contact projective process following the blood transfer process.

The most interesting conclusion drawn, in agreement with the earlier speculations by Vignon and Barbet, was that the blood images are not those of fresh wounds, but represent the images of the exudates of clotted blood and it was futher demonstrated that these clots were from an individual who suffered severe trauma prior to death. This is most easily seen in the ultraviolet fluorescence photographs of the blood marks.[14] They all show a clear serum ring about every wound typical of the process of clot retraction that every blood wound undergoes as clotting progresses.

This simple study should be specifically carried out on the Tunic and Oviedo blood marks to further link them to the distinctive blood image characteristics of those on the Shroud. Some already available photographs show hints that these clot retraction rings are there. These tests could be readily done today using digital cameras, low energy portable UV sources and some simple filters in less than an hour's testing time. With different exciting sources and appropriate filters, it might even be possible to demonstrate that it is traumatic blood as on the Shroud.

Once this simple visual test links the three cloths, then one can consider the more complicated forms of spectroscopic tests and eventually attempting the more uncertain task of linking their mitochondrial DNA patterns. The Shroud and the Sudarion have already been shown to have the same blood type, and more recently[15] they have been related by pollen analysis.

References:
1. Whanger and Whanger, "The Shroud of Turin," Providence House Publishers, 1998.
2. Whanger, "Scientific Roundtable on the Holy Tunic," Argenteuil, November 14, 1998
3. Adler, ACS Symp. Series, 625,223,1996.
4. Marion, "Scientific Roundtable on the Holy Tunic," Argenteuil, November 14, 1998.
5. Le Quere, "La Sainte Tunique D'Argenteuil," de Guibert, 1997.
6. Parcot, "La Sainte Tunique d'Argenteuil," L'Auteu, 1934.
7. Saferstein, "Forensic Handbook," Prentice-Hall, 1982.
8. Guscin, "The Oviedo Cloth," Lutterworth Press, 1998.
9. Moreno, "El Sudario De Oviedo," Grafinat, 1998.
10. Almenar and Garrido, "El Sudario Del Senor," Univerisdad de Oviedo, 1994.
11. Schwalbe and Rogers, Anal. Chim. Acta., 135, 3, 1982.
12. Jumper, et. al., ACS Adv. in Chem., 205,447,1984.
13. Adler, in "Sindone Cento Anni Di Ricerca," Istituto Poligraphica, 1998.
14. Miller and Pellicori, J. Biol. Photog. Assoc., 49,71,1981.
15. Danin, Whanger, Baruch, and Whanger, "Flora on the Shroud of Turin," Missouri Botanical Garden Press, 1999.

Further Spectroscopic Investigations of Samples of the Shroud of Turin

©Alan D. Adler, PhD., and Russell Selzer, Department of Chemistry, Western Connecticut State University; Frank DeBlase, Texaco Additives International R&D. All rights Reserved.

Originally presented at the "III Congresso Inter. Di Studi Sulla Sindone" held in Torino, 5-7 June 1998.

Introduction

The June 15, 1980, issue of *Applied Optics* reported a series of Spectroscopic observations carried out by STURP (Shroud of Turin Research Project) directly on the Shroud of Turin at its repository site in Turin.[1-4] Additional studies[5-11] and reviews[12, 13] supported the conclusions of these initial reports that the images on this cloth are not paintings. In particular, the body images were identified as an oxidation product of the cellulose of the linen cloth, and the blood images were shown to be consistent with blood-derived material, mainly exudates from clotted wounds. However, an opposing view held that these were painted images.[14-17] The body images were ascribed to iron oxide held to the cloth by a gelatin binder and the blood composed of the same "paint" with the addition of cinnabar (HgS) and traces of calcite ($CaCO_3$) to the paint.

A radiocarbon dating of samples taken from the Shroud reported a mid-14th century date,[18] seemingly settling the authenticity issue.[13] However, it is now argued that since it was not old enough to be authentic, it must be a painting. Unfortunately, a detailed protocol[19] for sampling the cloth to assure both precision and accuracy recommended by a convened meeting of consultants was not followed. Only a single sample was taken from a rewoven edge in a water-stained area a few inches from one of the burn marks incurred in the historically recorded 1532 fire. This location was near the bottom of the frontal body image on the edge where a large section of cloth is missing below the seamed so-called side strip. No historic record exists accounting for this missing material and how or when this damage occurred. The nature and/or extent of the repairs undertaken here are also unknown.

Therefore, the possibility exists that this selvage edge might be linen not original to the shroud.

The selection of this single suspicious sample site is a sufficient reason to doubt the accuracy of the radiodate. This spectroscopic investigation was therefore undertaken to determine whether any evidence can be obtained to support such doubts.

Samples

At the time of the on-site STURP investigation of the Shroud, sticky tape samples were collected from designated areas of interest on the cloth for off-site chemical studies.[11] There are problems in utilizing these tapes as sample sources.[11] The cloth has been folded and or rolled many times. This mechanical action has transported loose materials from one area of the cloth to another. In particular, the blood images, being composed of material that is clearly attached to the cloth, have begun to fracture with time and have migrated everywhere. [11] Further, many artist's copies of the Shroud have been "sanctified" by being pressed to the original thereby transferring artistic materials to the Shroud surface by contact.[20] These and much other confusing adventitious materials have been observed by both set of opposing investigators, though differing interpretations have been attached to their presence. [11-13, 14-17] Dealing with this problem, including extracting samples from these tapes and distinguishing between different sample types by their typical characteristics under reflection, fluorescence, polarization, and phase contrast microscopy has been detailed previously. [11]

Since a preliminary study indicated that reliable spectra could not be directly obtained from specimens on the sticky tapes, fiber samples were removed from the tapes and their identity as to type verified by the methods previously described in the chemical study.[11] Five fibers representing non-image areas in the vicinity of the feet, the waist, and the head of the frontal image were collected from their designated sample tapes. Similarly, four waterstain fibers from the head and knee areas, four scorch fibers from the knee area, two serum coated fibers from the edge of the lance wound, two image fibers from the finger area, two backing cloth fibers from the area adjacent to the radiodate sample area, and two blood globs (particles unattached to fibers) from the lance wound area were also isolated for investigation.

The administrators of the radiodate sampling, L. Gonella and G. Riggi, kindly provided three threads from the radiocarbon sample for our study. Two were warp threads from the outer and inner edges of the trimmed sample and the third was a weft thread from the middle of this sample.

Five fibers were taken from each of these samples for comparison with those collected from the sticky tapes. Interestingly, under microscopic investigation, these samples resembled exaggerated versions of the water-stained specimens. They were non-fluorescent, unevenly colored from dark yellow to splotchy brown, roughly surfaced (even showing patchy encrustations in spots) and showed a very strong and variably multicolored birefringence patter. Considerable microdebris was also evident.

Two blood simulacra were also prepared as controls. Finely ground iron oxide (Fisher Chemical) and cinnabar with a small amount of calcite (WCSU Geology department collection) were suspended in a 5 percent gelatin solution to provide a sample of "mineral" blood.[17] A traumatic clot exudates simulacrum was approximated[11, 13] by mixing three drops of whole blood (finger stick) with three drops of a bilirubin/human albumin diagnostic standard (Sigma Chemical). A sample of each of these was applied to a salt plate (for FTIR analysis) and also to the outside face of a 1 cm silica cuvet (for UV-VIS analysis) and allowed to dry as films. Dried whole blood (finger stick), bilirubin (Sigma), and human hemoglobin (Sigma) samples were also employed as controls.

Methods

FTIR: These spectra were acquired on a Bomen MB120 Interferometer equipped with an optical side port option. A global source (operating temp. 1300°K) was employed with the system alignment optimized to give maximum energy in transmission mode. Interferometer modulation is accomplished via the standard Bomem "wishbone" modulator, using a corner cube stray light rejection interferometer and a KBr beam splitter. The side port parallel beam exit sampling option of this instrument was coupled to a Spectratech IR-PLAN microanalysis system equipped with a narrow band liquid nitrogen cooled detector. The interferometer is controlled by a 80386 PC with a 80387 math coprocessor and 220 MB hard drive. A DSP data acquisition card provides real time Fourier Transform data for spectral collection and alignment procedures for monitoring single beam spectra rather than voltage. Galactic Industries Lab Calc version 2.1 software was used for collecting all data, performing alignment procedures, carrying out spectral arithmetic operations, and plotting. Transmission spectra were collected from 4011.6 to 739.8 cm^{-1} at 8 cm^{-1} resolution, 64 scans, and using triangular apodized double-sided interferogram data with zero filling. The redundant aperturing provision of this system was not employed. Control experiments established that keeping the source aperture constant and wider than the objective aperture gave more consistent replicate spectra with less low frequency baseline diffraction distortions from aperture edges.

The IR-Plan is equipped with a Reflacromat 10X condenser, 15X objective Cassegrain optics, and an Olympus DPLAN 10X objective for use only in the visible viewing mode. The Cassegrain optics was adjustable to compensate for the refractive index of the two 2 mm thick NaCl windows used throughout the study. The windows were hand polished to suppress interference fringes in the spectra. Prior to sample analysis a protocol was established to reproducibly align the condenser optics to provide the brightest and most uniform radiation at the plane of the sample location and thereafter all adjustments were made only with the objective optics.

The mounted specimen was first located in the viewing mode and then the objective was adjusted to produce the best optical image of the specimen. This focus was employed in taking the IR spectra as control experiments showed that only this focus could provide reproducible spectra of a sample without distorting the relative intensities of the high vs. low frequency patterns of the spectrum. The objective knife-edge aperture system was then adjusted so that the specimen completely filled the aperture and then the single beam spectrum was taken under a gentle nitrogen purge. Without modifying any adjustments, the stage was then moved to a clear area of the mounting windows and a background spectrum was collected. From these stored single-beam spectra, the absorbance spectrum of the specimen was calculated and plotted on an HP DeskJet 500C plotter.

UV-VIS: A Perkin Elmer Lambda 3B UV/VIS Spectrophotometer coupled to a Perkin Elmer R100A recorder was used to collect the simulated blood control absorbance spectra from 400 to 650 nm. The tungsten visible source and a scan rate of 60 nm/min were employed.

SEM: An AMRAY 1645 Scanning Electron Microscope equipped with a LaB6 electron source was used for this analysis. This instrument is equipped with a Noran Voyager energy dispersive spectroscopy system utilizing a Norvar window on a SiLi detector, which has 10 mm^2 spatial resolution and 133 eV spectral resolution. Instrument conditions were held constant at 20 KV, spot size 3 or 4, aperture size 200 µm, and a working distance of 24 mm for the fibers. Magnification was mostly between 1000 and 3000X, with a partial field

Continued on page 184

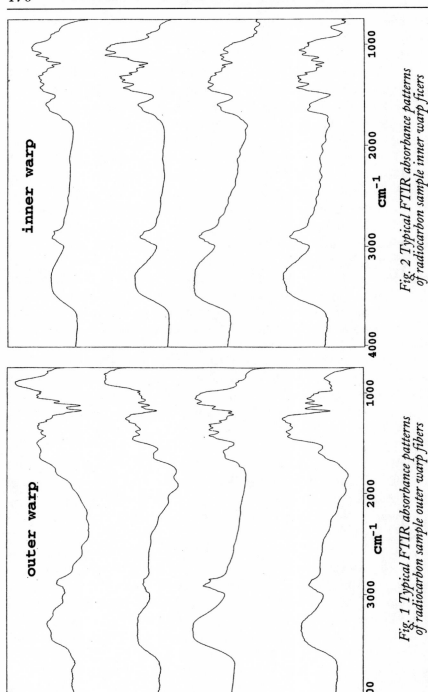

Fig. 2 Typical FTIR absorbance patterns
of radiocarbon sample inner warp ficers

Fig. 1 Typical FTIR absorbance patterns
of radiocarbon sample outer warp fibers

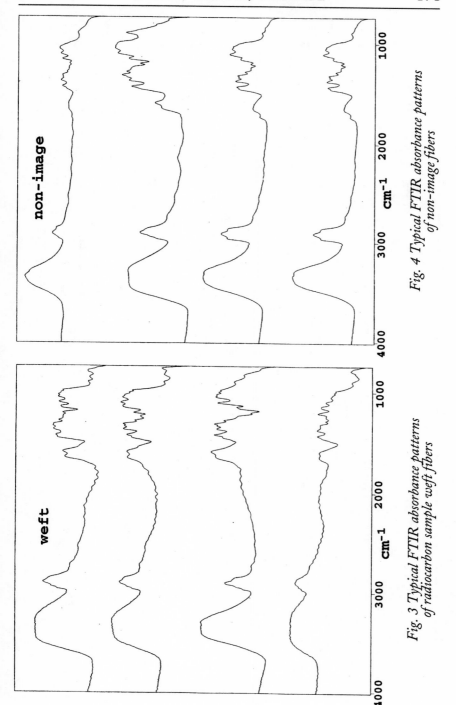

Fig. 4 Typical FTIR absorbance patterns
of non-image fibers

Fig. 3 Typical FTIR absorbance patterns
of radiocarbon sample weft fibers

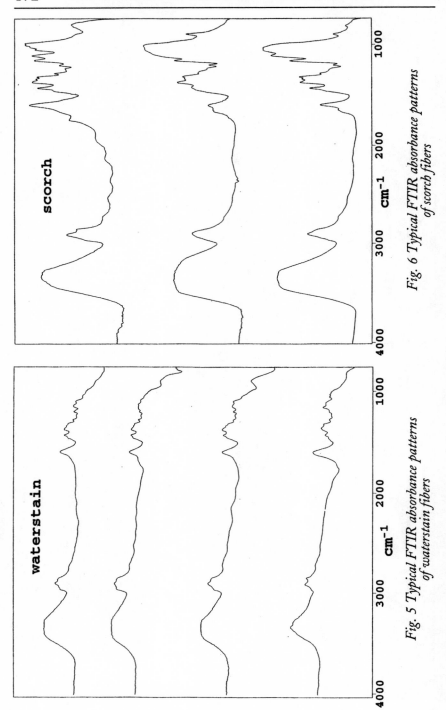

Fig. 5 Typical FTIR absorbance patterns
of waterstain fibers

Fig. 6 Typical FTIR absorbance patterns
of scorch fibers

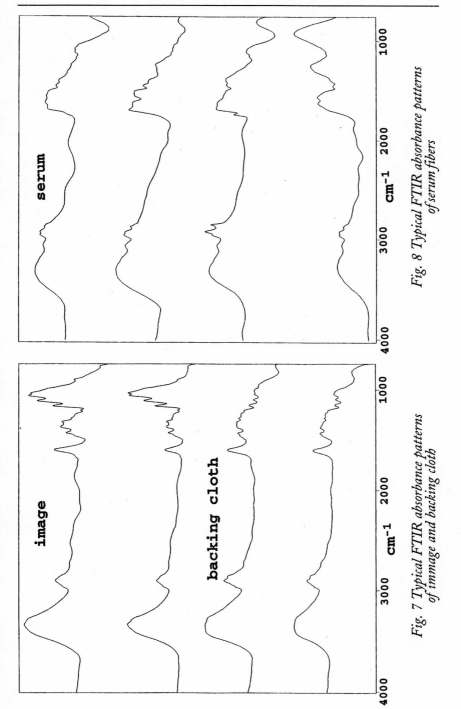

Fig. 8 Typical FTIR absorbance patterns
of serum fibers

Fig. 7 Typical FTIR absorbance patterns
of immage and backing cloth

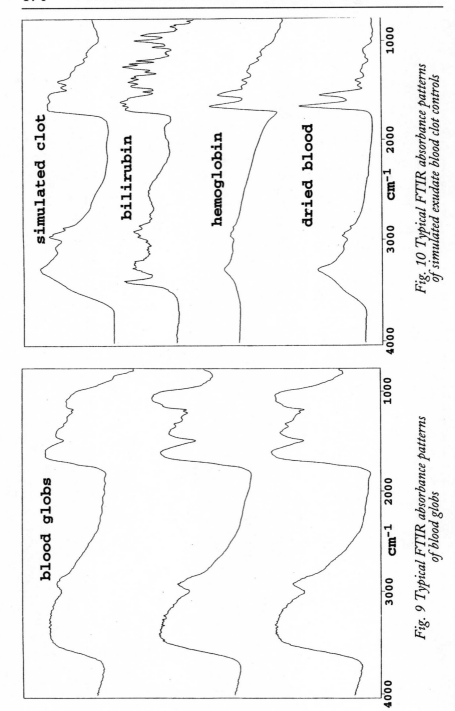

Fig. 10 Typical FTIR absorbance patterns of simulated exudate blood clot controls

Fig. 9 Typical FTIR absorbance patterns of blood globs

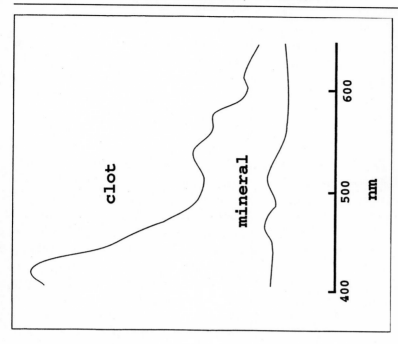

Fig. 12 Comparison of UV-VIS absorbance spectra of simulated exudate blood clot and mineral blood controls

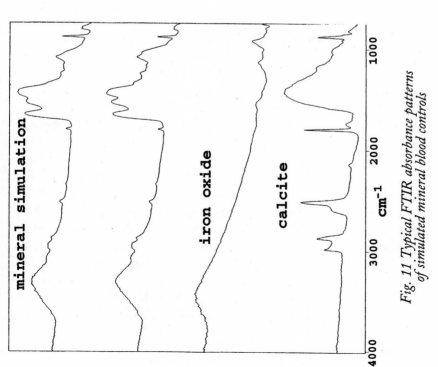

Fig. 11 Typical FTIR absorbance patterns of simulated mineral blood controls

collimation of the beam to restrict it to within the bounds of the fiber samples or the individual particles seen within them. Samples were prepared by applying the specimens onto double sticky tape placed on a sample stub that was then positioned within the instrument sample chamber.

Results

FTIR: Typical spectral absorption patterns for each fiber type and the blood samples are displayed in figures 1 through 11 and clearly show distinctive differences indicating differences in their chemical makeup. It should be noted that there is more variation in the patterns of the radiocarbon samples representing an area of a few square centimeters than in those of the non-image samples taken from areas a whole body-image length apart. The backing cloth pattern is readily distinguishable from the other patterns. Using the software to identify specific peak frequencies further demonstrates differences in chemical composition.

Comparison to the tabulated data on carbonyl frequencies[21] is most revealing. The position (given in cm^{-1}) and relative intensity of the peaks in the carboxylic acid salt region (1650-1540) and conjugated ketone region (1680-1640) show an apparent progressive oxidation-type pattern with the non-image (1593, 1643) the weakest, then water stained (broad 1697, weak 1640), then image (strong 1694, 1645 shoulder), then scorch (1591, broad 1645), and finally the radiocarbon pattern (1590, 1643, both strong). This can be compared with the progressive thermal oxidation pattern seen in the scorch fibers displayed in figure 6. Note, there is no evidence of the typical amide pattern (1695-1630) associated with proteins on any of these foregoing fibers; specifically, not on the image fibers, nor on the radiocarbon fibers. However, this amide pattern is clearly seen in the serum fiber samples (complex pattern 1694-1566) and in the blood samples. This is in complete agreement with the previously published chemical investigation[11] and does not support the painting hypothesis. The peak patterns and relative intensity patterns in other regions of the spectra are also consistent with the conclusion that the spectral patterns of these fibers are all distinguishably different from one another. Note this is specifically true for the radiocarbon fibers and the non-image fibers from the bulk of the cloth, thereby demonstrating that the area selected for the radiocarbon sampling is atypical and is not clearly representative of the rest of the Shroud.

The spectral pattern of the blood globs from the sample tape is in good agreement with the spectral features of the various blood controls. Some of the more distinctive features of the bilirubin pattern are even weakly evidenced in the serum fiber spectra (note, these fibers are yellow colored) and was further confirmed by overlaying control spectra. Unfortunately, the only really distinctive features in the mineral simulated blood control, other than the protein peaks, are provided by the calcite present, as the iron oxide and mercuric sulfide spectra are weak and broad featured. However, these distinctive calcite peaks are clearly not evidenced in the blood globs. Therefore, the conclusion that the blood images are derived from blood clot exudates and are not mineral pigments is further confirmed. [5, 11, 13]

UV-VIS: The near ultraviolet-visible spectra of the two simulated blood controls are displayed in figure 12. The peak position pattern and relative overall absorbance ratio of the blue to red region of the spectrum of traumatic clot exudates sample is in excellent agreement with the previously reported spectra of Shroud blood specimens and also the spectra taken from the examination of the whole cloth blood images. [2, 5] The spectrum of the simulated mineral blood showing only two broad weak peaks at 470 and 514 nm is in complete disagreement with these previously reported spectra.

SEM: The typical weight percent elemental composition patterns of the various Shroud fiber types are given in table 1. Again, it should be noted that a great deal of variability was evidenced in the radiocarbon samples. Some of the patchy encrustations were so thick as to mask the underlying carbon of fibers whose continuity were clearly obvious in the microscope images. As this is a surface-analysis technique, this is not unexpected. Microdebris identifiable as particles of gold, iron oxide, and mercuric sulfide were also seen in these samples. The trend in weight % C compared to the opposite trend in "mineral" content of the radiocarbon samples (even compared to the waterstain fibers) clearly indicates that the radiocarbon sampling area is a strongly contaminated "waterstain" area.

Discussion

There is insufficient evidence to conclusively demonstrate the presence of any adventitious linen in the radiocarbon sample area. However, there is a clearly evident chemical compositional difference between this

Table 1. Typical Weight % Element Composition Pattern of Shroud Fiber Types

Sample	C	O	Na	Mg	Al	Si	P	S	Cl	K	Ca	Fe	Cu	Au	Hg	Ti	Mn
Warp	21	49	8.3	0.9	2.0	1.6	0.4	0.6	3.1	4.3	8.5	0.6	0.1	0.0	0.0	0.0	0.3
Warp	33	43	6.7	0.1	1.1	1.4	0.0	0.4	2.5	3.4	6.1	1.4	0.0	0.5	0.4	0.0	0.0
Weft	22	48	6.6	1.0	0.2	1.6	0.2	0.6	1.9	4.3	12	0.5	0.3	0.9	0.3	0.1	0.0
Waterstain	66	27	0.6	0.0	0.0	0.1	0.0	0.0	0.5	0.1	0.1	5.5	0.1	0.0	0.0	0.0	0.1
Non-image	93	3.2	1.7	0.0	0.1	0.1	0.0	0.0	1.5	0.1	0.4	0.4	0.1	0.0	0.0	0.0	0.0

sample area and the non-image areas of the cloth. In fact, the FTIR data for the radiocarbon sample, in a sense confirming its inappropriate physical location, shows physical characteristics of both the waterstain and scorch regions of the cloth. To what extent this affects the observed date is not at all obvious. Nevertheless, the accuracy of the reported date is justifiably suspect. Further, comparison of the dorsal head wounds on the Shroud with a similar pattern of wounds on the 7th century Cloth of Oviedo confirms the inaccuracy of the reported radiocarbon date. [22]

These new findings support previous conclusions that the body image chromophore is an oxidation product of the cellulose itself and that the blood images are derived from clotted blood wounds.[1-13] They do not support the painting hypothesis.[14-17] The microdetection of artist's materials in the debris might seem to support the painting hypothesis. However, as neither of the X-ray examinations of the whole cloth produced any evidence for the presence of mercury in the blood images at the macroscopic level,[8, 9] it seems more reasonable to attribute the presence of artist's materials to the historically recorded practice of sanctifying copies of this image by pressing them to the original. [20]

The Shroud of Turin is a complex object, defying oversimplified explanations of the mechanism by which it was produced. As no acceptable laboratory test exists that can give us the identity of the man whose image is portrayed, science can never authenticate the Shroud. However, future research could reveal to us the mechanism of image productions, providing a basis for a properly planned conservation program.

Acknowledgements
We wish to express our indebtedness to Melanie Behrens for technical assistance and to Lucas Adler of LA Engineering Computer Services for aid in preparing the figures.

References
1. E. Jumper and R. Mottern, "Scientific investigation of the Shroud of Turin," *Appl. Opt.* 19, 1909-1912 (1980).
2. S. Pellicori, "Spectral properties of the Shroud of Turin," *Appl. Opt.* 19, 1913-1920 (1980).
3. J. Accetta and J. S. Baumgart, "Infrared reflectance spectroscopy and thermographic investigations of the Shroud of Turin," *Appl. Opt.* 19, 1921-1929 (1980).

4. R. Gilbert and M. Gilbert, "Ultraviolet-visible reflectance and fluorescence spectra of the Shroud of Turin," *Appl. Opt.* 19, 1930-1936 (1980).

5. J. Heller and A. Adler, "Blood on the Shroud of Turin," *Appl. Opt.* 19, 2742-2744 (1980).

6. J. Jackson, E. Jumper, and W. Ercoline, "Correlation of image intensity on the Turin Shroud with the 3-D structure of a human body shape," *Appl. Opt.* 19,2244-2270 (1984).

7. V. Miller and S. Pellicori, "Ultraviolet fluorescence photography of the Shroud of Turin," *J. Biol. Phot.* 49, 71-85 (1981).

8. R. Morris, L. Schwalbe, and J. London, "X-ray fluorescence investigation of the Shroud of Turin," *X-ray Spectrometry* 9, 40-47 (1980).

9. R. Mottern, R. London, and R. Morris, "Radiographic examination of the Shroud of Turin—a preliminary report," Materials Eval. 38, 39-44 (1980).

10. S. Pellicori and M. Evans, "The Shroud of Turin through the microscope," *Archaeology* 34, 34-43 (1981).

11. J. Heller and A Adler, "A chemical investigation of the Shroud of Turin," *Can.; Soc. Forens. Sci J.* 14, 81-103 (1981).

12. L. Schwalbe and R. Rogers, "Physics and chemistry of the Shroud of Turin," *Anal. Chim. Acta* 135,3-49 (1982).

13. E. Jumper, A. Adler, J. Jackson, S. Pellicori, J. Heller, and J. Druzic, "A comprehensive examination of the various stains and images on the Shroud of Turin," *ACS Adv. in Chem.* 205, 447-476 (1984).

14. W. McCrone and C. Skirius, "Light microscopical study of the Turin Shroud I," *Microscope* 28, 105-113 (1980).

15. W McCrone, "Light microscopical study of the Turin Shroud II," *Microscope* 28, 115-128 (1980).

16. W. McCrone, A. Teetsov, M. Andersen, R. Hinch, H. Humecki, B. Majewski, and D. Piper, "Microscopical study of the Turin Shroud III," *Microscope* 29, 19-38 (1981).

17. W. McCrone, "The Shroud of Turin: Blood or artist's pigment," *Acc. Chem. Res.* 23, 77-83 (1990).

18. P. Damon, D. Donahue, B. Gore, A. Hatheway, A. Jull, T. Linick, P. Sercel, L. Toolin, C. Bronk, E. Hall, R. Hedges, R. Housley, I. Law, C. Perry, G. Bonani, S. Trumbore, W. Woelfli, J. ambers, S. Bowman, M. Leese, M. Tite, "Ra-

diocarbon dating of the Shroud of Turin," *Nature* 337, 611-615 (1989).

19. G. Harbottle and W. Heino, "Carbon dating the Shroud of Turin," *ACS Adv. in Chem.* 220, 313-320 (1989).

20. L. Fossotti, "Copies of the Holy Shroud," *Shroud Spectrum Inter.* 13, 23-39 (1984).

21. D. Lin-Vien, N. Colthup, W. Fately, and J. Grasselli, *The Handbook of Infrared and Raman Characteristic Frequencies of Organic Molecules*, (Academic Press, Boston, 1991), pp. 117-146.

22. A. Adler, "Updating recent studies on the Shroud of Turin," *ACS Symp. Series* 625, 223-228 (1996).

ALAN D. WHANGER, M.D.

CO-FOUNDER COUNCIL FOR STUDY OF THE SHROUD OF TURIN (CSST)

Alan D. Whanger, M.D., is a Professor Emeritus from the Duke University Medical Center in Durham, North Carolina, USA. He received the AB and MD degrees at Duke University and has done further postgraduate training in general surgery, tropical medicine, psychiatry and geriatrics.

His life-long interest in photography led him to an immediate interest in the Shroud of Turin when he first saw a photograph of the face in 1977.He and his wife, Mary, began serious research on the Shroud in 1979 when they were challenged to do exacting comparisons between the face of the Man of the Shroud and early Byzantine icons of Jesus. They eventually developed the Polarized Image Overlay Technique by which similar or congruent features of two images may be exactingly observed and quantified. By this means, they were able to show that various icons of the fifth and sixth centuries were based so accurately on the Shroud image that the icongraphers had to have had direct access to it.

Much of their work has been with image comparison and recognition, using thirty or so high-grade photographs of various aspects of the Shroudmade from those of Guiseppi Enrie. They have identified the images of a number of non-body objects that were placed on and around the body at the time of enshroudment, and have demonstrated that the images were formed between 24 and 36 hours after death by two types of radiation.

They have presented numerous papers at professional meetings, and their work has been presented in various television productions on all of the major networks. He has co-authored two books, *The Shroud of Turin an Adventure of Discovery*, with his wife Mary and *Flora of the Shroud of Turin* with Mary and Israeli botanists A. Danin and U. Baruch.

In 1994, he and Mary founded a non-profit corporation, Council for Study of the Shroud of Turin (CSST) to facilitate and expand their research and educational efforts. Some of the research can be seen on the CSST website at **www.shroudcouncil.org**.

Radiation in the Formation of the Shroud Image—The Evidence

Originally presented in Turin Italy at the III Congresso
Internazionale di Studi sulla Sondone

How the image got on the Shroud of Turin has long been a major question for many. This was the primary question of the 1978 STURP studies on the Shroud. A wide variety of mechanisms have been proposed, none of which adequately explains all of the findings on this remarkable object. There are a large number of ways that one can produce some type of image on cloth, but extensive testing has eliminated most of these as a possibility with the Shroud. The chemistry of the image is well known—the chromophore is composed of oxidized and decarboxilated cellulose molecules. The physics of the image is well known also—it is extremely superficial, and its density is directly proportional to the distance between the body and the Shroud. This characteristic encodes three-dimensional information into the image. There is image on the Shroud in places that could not possibly be in touch with the body, but not further than about 4 cm from the body. It has been increasingly speculated that some type of ionizing radiation would be necessary to produce such images. There has been little evidence from the Shroud itself shown for what this may have been like.

Interestingly, there have been speculations along these lines for a long period. Colonel P.W. O'Gorman published an article in 1940 in which he theorized a combination of four different agents: namely, oxidizing vapors, radioactive substances, electrical radiation, and sudden radiance. In 1981, astrophysicist A.A. Miles postulated a corona discharge hypothesis. Physicist Oswald Scheuermann felt that the image is the product of corona discharge and wrote a book reporting a great deal of experimentation that he had done. In 1981, physical chemist Giles Carter noted the possible image of the bones in the apparently long fingers of the right hand as well as possible teeth images. He published a paper in 1984 hypothesizing x-rays in the formation of the Shroud image. He was told by a radiologist that his observations were not correct, and did not pursue the issue further. Interestingly, in 1982, both theologian Father Francis Filas and my wife and co-researcher Mary commented that they thought the proximal part of the right hand showed the bones. I dismissed that idea, feeling that the apparent finger length was due to corona discharge off of the extensor tendons on the back of the hand.

I began serious Shroud research in 1979 when I was challenged to determine whether a famous sixth century icon of Christ had been painted from the Shroud of Turin, as one its owners contended. I began searching for a technique to accurately compare two different images. Finding no useful technique, my wife and I finally developed one of our own, which we call the Polarized Image Overlay Technique. To use this technique, we project two images, one on top of the other, onto a lenticular screen through polarizing filters whose planes are at right angles one to the other. By viewing the superimposed images through a third rotating filter, one can shift back and forth from one image to the other and compare the images in minute detail. The points of congruence (matching or highly similar markings) between the two can be diagrammed and tabulated. Forensic criteria can then be applied to determine the significance.

To appreciate the incredible details and comparisons that this dynamic image analysis technique enables one to see, one needs to use the filters oneself or view the process on videotape. Two examples will document the usefulness of this technique. The first is a Byzantice gold tremissis coin struck by Justinian II in 692, whose coins were the first to bear a depiction of Jesus. This depiction, which is 8 mm high, has 185 points of congruence with the Shroud face, and is a direct copy of the face on the Shroud. Forensically, only 45 to 60 points of congruence are needed to determine that the faces are the same.

Second is a comparison of the bloodstains on the Shroud of Turin with those on the Sudarium of Oviedo, the traditional face cloth of Jesus. With these, even on side-by-side comparison, the marked similarity of the bloodstains on the back of the neck is easily seen. The overlay technique shows about 120 congruent bloodstains between the two cloths, clearly indicating they were both in touch with the same individual. Since the Sudarium has been in Oviedo, Spain, since the eighth century, obviously the Shroud is at least that old.

After we had developed our Polarized Image Overlay Technique in

1982, we contacted Father Frank Filas, who claimed that he had identified tiny letters and a design over the right eye, which he thought might indicate the presence of a Jewish coin, a lepton of Pontius Pilate, similar to one he had been given. He supplied us with photographs of his coin, and photographs and a computer enhancement of the image over the right eye. We did a detailed overlay comparison of the Filas coin and the Shroud image, and tabulated 211 points of congruence between the two, and only 86 discordant points. This showed both that indeed there is an image of an identifiable coin over the right eye of the Shroud image and that Father Filas has been given a coin that is a die-mate of the one whose image is on the Shroud. Forensically, only fourteen points of congruence are needed to declare two fingerprints, larger in area than the coin, to be identical. Those who claim that the images over the eye are simply weave pattern, random images, or imagination fail to appreciate the principle of statistical probabilities.

When observing the overlay comparison of the computer-enhanced image over the right eye and the Filas coin, Dr. Alan Adler made the important observation that the image on the Shroud comes off of the irregular surfaces and high points on the coin, which is characteristic of corona or electrostatic discharge. This is major evidence from the Shroud itself, and helps to explain many of the characteristics of the image. For many years, we have worked closely with German physicist Oswald Scheuermann, who has done extensive studies with corona discharge off of a wide variety of objects. His studies have helped us to understand what these type of images look like. They are faint; partial off of irregular surfaces and margins; may be either positive or negative or some of both, depending on the distance between the object and cloth or photographic film; may come off of any kind of material; and are attenuated in air. Those on the Shroud are frequently imbedded among other images. Scheuermann has produced a number of detailed images on linen similar to those on the Shroud.

Research engineer and high-voltage specialist Dr. Igor Benson felt that the Shroud images are characteristic of electron corona. He pointed out that in a high-energy field, one may get corona discharge off of all the objects in that field. This would explain why there are images typical of corona discharge off of all objects that were enshrouded with the body. Benson did a simple experiment to estimate how much energy might be required to produce an image on linen similar to that on the Shroud. Using a coin with an area of one square centimeter, he first heated it electrically and then touched the hot coin to linen. At 100 watt-seconds, the coin burned a hole through the linen, at 50 watt-seconds it made a very accurate scorch, and at 25 watt-seconds it formed scarcely any image. Then using a high-voltage transformer, he used 50 watt-seconds to generate corona discharge and varied the time of exposure. The image was clearest at 1/10 second, and showed tiny details at good resolution, virtually the same size as the letters on the Shroud. By estimating the body size and the distances involved, Benson estimated that to produce images like those on the Shroud by electron corona would take about 11,000 kilowatts at one to two hundred million voltage for one-tenth of a second or less. This is approximately the power of a lightning bolt. His colleagues at the high-voltage laboratory firmly turned down any thought of testing this hypothesis.

I gave little credence to the x-ray speculations about the image until 1992 when I first tried the image enhancement technique called continuous directional derivative in the Y-vector. To use this, one projects the positive and negative images of the hands and arms on top of one another and then puts the two images slightly out of vertical alignment. Not only does this enhance the images, but it also produces a very dramatic 3-D effect. It was immediately apparent to me that I was clearly seeing the bones in the fingers and the palm of the hand (the phalanges and the metacarpals). I have had considerable clinical experience in reading x-rays, but I took a photograph of this to a professor of skeletal radiology who agreed that indeed the bones are visible. I got x-rays of my own hands in the same position as those on the Shroud, and it became readily apparent that we were seeing the knuckles and the base of the thumb on the Shroud image. For more detailed comparison, I obtained a photograph of surgeon Dr. Pierre Barbet's x-ray of an amputated hand with a half-inch spike driven through the wrist in the space of Destot, the only place where a nail could be driven through without breaking any bones. Using the Polarized Image Overlay Technique, we showed the clear presence of the x-ray appearance of the individual bones in the hands and the wrist. At the site of the nail, there is a gap in the unbroken wrist bones on the Shroud, indicating that the space of Destot was indeed the site of the wrist nailing. The ligaments would have been torn by the nail, and the gap did not close when the nail was extracted. The blood stain is quite visible where the nail exited the skin on the back of the wrist.

Most importantly, this shows that the image on the Shroud is in part an autoradiograph. This means that there is x-radiation, or some similar type of radiation, coming from within the body causing the image of the skeletal system to be revealed on the Shroud.

At the suggestion of the radiologist, I used the same enhancement process on the head. Again, there was the dramatic emergence of a 3-D image, plainly showing many features of the underlying skull, including the margins of the eye orbits, the nasal bone, the nasal passages, the maxillary sinuses, the mandible, and twenty-four teeth with their roots. Both the images of the hands and of the head have been seen by a number of radiologists and physicists, none of whom have had any difficulty seeing the autoradiographic appearance. Similar examination has shown that images of some of the bones of the right foot and of the vertebral processes are visible on the Shroud.

This clearly indicates that the x-radiation originated equally in every part of the body. It was alleviated, as only the skeletal features close to the surface can be seen on the Shroud. Importantly, if one follows the image of the teeth from the center laterally, one suddenly sees the image of the beard, showing that the images on the Shroud are complex and were formed by at least two types of radiation, x-radiation from the depth of the body and corona discharge from the surface of the body and everything in the field.

In 1984, chemist Giles Carter published a basic paper on his correct speculations on the autoradiographic features of the head, and included research on the production of images on linen by means of x-radiation. He noted that the presence of iron in the fabric served to enhance the image from x-radiation.

Ordinary autoradiographs such as those made with radioactive material show rather fuzzy images. This is what one would expect, as radiation from amy point tends to extend in all directions. The reason that the Shroud image is needle sharp and anatomically correct is that all of the radiation had to have been vertically directed or collimated, as shown by physicist John Jackson and others. How this could have occurred is another of the great mysteries of the Shroud.

One of the other great mysteries is where the radiation came from. Theoretical physicist Thaddeus Trenn started with observations and evidence from the Shroud itself, namely, the body abruptly disappeared from within the still-wrapped cloth with the production of free electrons and x-radiation. He speculated that if the strong force that holds the nuclei of the atoms together were overcome in a process that he calls "weak dematerialization," then the atoms would disappear with the freeing of the electrons from their orbits resulting in an electrical energy release and x-radiation. The protons and neutrons that make up the nucleus would be freed. Basically, this would be illustrating the conversion of matter into energy, an interchangeable process popularized by Einstein. This same process would release a flux of neutrons, the impact of which on nitrogen produces the element carbon 14. This is the very element used to measure carbon dating. Any addition of carbon 14 to a material being carbon dated would produce a date younger than the actual age of the specimen. The implications of this in the face of the erroneous carbon dating results of 1988 are considerable.

In conclusion, I feel that we have clear and substantial evidence from the Shroud itself that the image is formed by at least two types of ionizing radiation: x-radiation coming from the depths of the body showing the more superficial skeletal system, and electron corona or electrostatic discharge from the surface of the body and all of the other objects that had been placed within the Shroud. The body-wide front and back distribution of the x-radiation would seem to indicate that it originated in each molecule of the body. The corona discharge would indicate a high-energy field surrounding the body. Limited experimentation would indicate a very narrow range of the amount of energy between what would incinerate the cloth and what would produce no image. About one-tenth second exposure time gave the clearest image. Corona discharge is blocked by blood, and there is no image under the bloodstains on the Shroud. Understanding that images made by corona discharge are faint, fragmentary, and comes off of irregular surfaces, high points, and margins of objects helps one to better understand, perceive, and appreciate the images, especially the non-body images, that are on the Shroud.

The non-body images indicate a Roman mocking and crucifixion of a Jew in Jerusalem in the manner described in the Scriptures, in the spring of probably AD 30. The radiation-produced images of many objects put in the Shroud with the body indicate the highly unusual nature of the crucifixion and entombment. The images of the crown of thorns and of a few of the Greek and Latin letters on the title or titulus indicate that the man whose image is on the Shroud is indeed Jesus of Nazareth. The disappearance of the body from within the Shroud between twenty-four and thirty-six hours after death with the release of controlled corona discharge and x-radiation producing minutely detailed images on the linen speaks of a unique event in human history. The evidence requires that we expand our range of possible explanations to include a Resurrection, even though that transcends our scientific capacities. The late Father Francis Filas concluded many of his Shroud presentations with the phrase "Reality is not destroyed by lack of explanation." The Shroud and its mysterious images challenge us to use our best abilities to understand it more fully, but the Shroud leads us on beyond itself.

AUGUST D. ACCETTA, M.D.

SOUTHERN CALIFORNIA SHROUD CENTER FOUNDER

August David Accetta is a native Californian. As a graduate of California State University at Long Beach, he achieved the honor of great distinction in the field of physiologic psychology and pre-medicine. He later attended Marquette Medical School in Milwaukee, Wisconsin, where he pursued the field of obstetrics and gynecology. His post-graduate training (residency) was received at UCLA and Kern Medical Center, where he sub-specialized in urological gynecology and pelvic surgery. He has been in private practice in Newport and Huntington Beach, California, for more than 11 years.

August founded the Shroud Center of Southern California on May 18, 1996. His interest in the Shroud dates back to 1975 but he did not get active in research until 1995. Since that time, most of his research together with his co-researchers has been in the area of nuclear medical imaging. At this conference, August will be presenting his fourth paper regarding nuclear medicine and the Shroud.

Nuclear Medicine and
Its Relevance to the Shroud of Turin

Hypothesis

If indeed a corpse created the image we see on the Shroud, then the source for the energy received by the cloth may be from the molecular bond energy and/or nuclear forces within the body in some way interacting with the cloth. The closest practical tool we have to study this today is nuclear medicine.

Introduction

The Turin Shroud bears an image of an apparent crucified man, chemically the result of some dehydrative, oxidative, and subsequent carbonyl conjugative process of cellulose, the origin of which is heretofore enigmatic.[1] Many properties of the Shroud are however understood quite well. For example, it is clearly understood through the work of STURP and others that the Shroud did in fact wrap someone at some point in time and that it is not the product of some medieval artist.[2]

The Shroud image suggests quite strongly the presence of many skeletal details e.g. carpal and metacarpal bones, some 22 teeth, eye sockets, left femur, left and possibly right thumbs flexed under the palms of the hands, as well as soft tissue and soft tissue injuries; all presumably originating from some form of radiation emitted from the body enshrouded.[3]

No scientific human model has been satisfactorily utilized to offer elucidation of the origin of this quality image. Many have postulated image formation theories, e.g. Pellicori-Germans "latent image" and Jackson et al. direct contact experiments which he concluded had quite negative results and have effectively been ruled out.[4] Others have suggested diffusion.[5] Schwalbe and Rojers, however, failed in the properties not limited to sharpness and clarity of the image.[6] Later researchers, such as Giles Carter and Thaddues Trenn, have studied radiation biology in a theoretical framework and have achieved promising results in terms of image superficiality and clarity.[7]

The human radiation model seems to offer the greatest application to the Shroud image thus far.

Materials and Methods

Tc-99m is a metastable (i.e. 99 "m") isotope that decays with a six (6) hour halflife yielding a single gamma ray at 140 kev. (There are low energy characteristic x-rays, 20 kev and below, that are not detectable by our cameras.)

We used a gamma camera with a 3/8-inch thick, wide field, sodium iodine crystal, which is ideally suited to the 140 kev energy of Tc-99m MDP. The energy resolution is 9.8% and sensitivity is 135 cpm/microcurie. The collimator used was a long bore ultra high resolution, yielding a system resolution of 7.5 mm @ 10 cm and 11 mm @ 15 cm. The long septal length preserves resolution at depth with 11 mm @ 15 cm.

The Tc-99m or MDP binds to bone by chemisorption. Approximately 50% of the injected Tc-99m MDP or HMDP is taken up in the bones.

High quality images depend upon an optimum target to background ratio. Thus the percentage of Tc-99m MDP compound that binds to protein and red blood cells greatly affects the quality of the bone scan. Tc-99m MDP is more satisfactory for bone than other compounds due to low protein binding and rapid clearance from soft tissue and blood by renal excretion. At two hours post injection, about 10% of administered Tc-99m MDP is protein bound. At four hours post injection, 3% of the injected per liter dose of Tc-99m polyphosphate is bound to RBC's and 0% of Tc-99m MDP or HMDP is bound.

We did timed sequence scanning in order to manipulate this predictable bioavailability to optimize our soft tissue to bone ratio (background to target). The early images during the first 15 minutes had a high soft tissue and blood component. Later, as the blood level and soft tissue concentration diminished, most of the photons came from bone. The last images were showing primary bone photons with most of the soft tissue contribution attributed to low angle scattered photons.

(The following sequence was originally tied to a slide presentation)

- First, we demonstrated that a human model can be used to generate images resulting from emitted radiation that resemble the image on the Shroud.

- Second, we demonstrated that this radiation when captured by a vertical collimator can yield the verticality parallel seen on the Turin image.

- Third, we demonstrated that the nature of the emitted radiation is such that it produces an image void of a sharp outline such as that on the Turin Shroud.

- Fourth, we demonstrated that the resulting radiation image is void of any light focus such as the Shroud.

- Fifth, due to the nature of the collimator, no side images are observed though the radiation is being emitted circumferentially.

- Sixth, the fact that soft tissues, skeletal information, as well as pathology in these tissues can all be imaged concomitantly using the nuclear medicine model, demonstrated the parallel to the Shroud where the same is observed.

- Seventh, we demonstrated that the thumb flexed under the palms of the left and right hands can be imaged (precluding the need of any so called contact method), which parallels the Shroud. In addition, the V-P-8 image of the hands demonstrates the underlying thumb similar to that of the Shroud.

- Eighth, we demonstrated that the nature of the emitted radiation was volumetric in that the image generated had higher density shading (higher number of pixels) towards the center or midline of extremities, digits, and torso, then fell off in intensity laterally. This differential dosimetry should and in fact does yield a Z-axis relief (or isometric projection) when scanned by V-P-8 photodensitometer.

- Ninth, isometric projection (V-P-8) of our generated images, yielded a striking similarity to the V-P-8 image of the Shroud at the fall off of the left fingers. Knowing this is due to a 75-80% drop in signal intensity on our image, its relevance to the same phenomenon on the shroud should not be overlooked and seriously considered to be a function of a similar effect i.e. a dosimetric sudden fall off of signal or radiation.

Conclusions

The human radiation model we used generated a number of characteristics which parallel the image on the Turin shroud. It must be noted that these researchers in no way are claiming that they reproduced any of the exact characteristics of the Shroud image. Rather, those characteristics that are similar can potentially help to better explain those seen on the shroud as well as point to the probable general origin of its image.

Summary
The radiation model described in this study characterized much of what we see in the Shroud image in terms of the behavior of radiation being emitted from a human source. We believe the nuclear medicine model is the best currently available to aid in our understanding of the Shroud image. We feel our results effectively demonstrated plausibly that the Shroud image resulted from an organized emission and/or organized collection of radiation from the body and/or cloth respectively.

Note for Future Studies
Though we obtained quite analogous results with respect to arm, hand, and leg images, the head image was highly distorted on V-P-8 (i.e. not yielding a conforming relief of a natural face). The author believes this distortion arose from the volume of radiation emitted from the distal two-thirds of the head. This can be studied in a future experiment by subtracting out this radiation, which we plan to do in the near future.

References:
1. Heller and Adler, 1981. "A chemical Investigation of the Shroud of Turin." *Journal of the Canadian Society of Forensic Sciences* 4 (3): 81-103.
2. Heller, J. H. and A. D. Adler, 1980. "Blood on the Shroud of Turin," Jackson, John P.l, 1989 *Shroud Specturm International.*
3. Whanger A. and M. Whanger 1985. "Polarized Image Overlay." *Applied Optics* 24 (6): 766-772.
4. Jumper et al. *Archaeological Chemistry* III, pp 447-476.
5. Schwalbe and Rogers, 1982: 35. Jackson, Jumper, and Ercoline, 1984: 2264.
6. Schwalbe and Rogers, 1982: 32-33. "Physics and Chemistry of the Shroud of Turin," *Analytica Chimica Acta,* 135: 3-49.
7. Carter, Giles F. 1984. "Formation of Images on the shroud by X-rays: A New Hypothesis." *ACS Advances in Chemistry* No. 205: *Archaeological Chemistry,* pp 425-446.

Neutron Flux and the Resurrection

We have to recognize above all, when we consider the interaction between the Turin Shroud and the body once wrapped in it, that we are dealing with two extremely complex systems, one of which—the body—is almost totally unpredictable as a purely physical system. Consequently we cannot attach to this interaction well-defined and controlled laboratory condition.

We also have to realize that, the fact that only the surface of the fibrils of the Shroud is lightly scorched, probably should not be interpreted to mean that the thermal energy of whatever caused the scorch was weak. This fact, rather, indicates a built-in time element: the scorch happened too fast to have taken more effect. Fast removal of the source might be indicated, and also a lack of thermal equilibrium.

IN OTHER WORDS WE MAY BE DEALING WITH A TOTALLY UNFINISHED PHENOMENON.

The unknown elements reasonably described above put a terrific strain on scientific descriptions of the interaction between the Turin Shroud and source X (the only way we can name the body in scientific terms), in Y time length, with Z intensity, since most part of the potential intensity may have been removed and rendered beyond measurement.

To this we have to add that we may not rely on any instruments generating energy, particles, velocity etc. No generators, no detectors, no accelerators, no nuclear reactors, no electrodes, no emulsions, nothing we can think of to introduce a control. We are up against unknown, raw nature.

If atoms are falling apart in source X it can only happen through radioactive decay if we want to involve only the laws of science. A radioactive decay means that unstable atomic nuclei spontaneously give forth excess energy by emitting a particle or a photon, by capturing an electron, or by fissioning. Nuclear fission means the dividing of atomic nucleus into parts of pretty much the same mass. This is usually restricted to heavier nuclei. When whole atoms are involved, it means at least fission, but more likely atomic explosion, if we don't want to take fission barriers into account.

Now we may have free protons, free neutrons and free electrons available. We still don't know and so it seems cannot know the time element involved, but we cannot talk about a slow nuclear disintegration. Rather the opposite: a very fast nuclear disintegration. We may have fast protons, neutrons and electrons at hand.

Incredibly strict, pre-planned laboratory conditions would have to exist to cause the free neutrons to neatly join the C-12 nuclei and step them up to C-14. All other interactions would have to be neatly eliminated.

Since it has a half-life of 12-13 minutes, a lot of different reactions can take place. This, of course, depends also from the kinetic energy the neutron has upon formation. If it does not decay first into a proton, electron and anti-neutrino, most likely it will join the nucleus of hydrogen atoms. This is a likely happening between source X in our case and the Shroud, in the humid atmosphere which must have existed there. If it is some other, more complex atom which the free neutron may join, a charged particle may be ejected, a proton or an alpha particle most likely. Even fission may be caused by the intruding neutron. Then again, because of its long half-life, with proper kinetic energy, it may just go through the cloth of the Shroud without an interaction and disintegrate into the proton, electron and anti-neutrino.

Some of the free neutrons may join carbon nuclei, it cannot be excluded. But in order that this phenomenon would exist through the entire substance of the Shroud even in non-uniform degree, an enormous amount of free neutrons would have to be available, a small percentage of which would assist in the making of the C-14 isotopes. How could one check that without destroying the entire Shroud and subject it to the doubtful carbon testing? A well controlled neutron flux belongs into the lab only.

Free protons, or alpha particles, create powerful radiation. Since protons have an indefinite lifetime, they either would just go through the cloth and react somewhere else, or they would cause fission, ejecting neutrons or ejecting electrons and cause ionization. Since we have to assume that a great number of free protons are present, either there would be a massive fissioning phenomenon or a very heavy ionization of the Shroud. As for free electrons, their mass is very small compared to the proton and neutron and electron tracks show a lot of scattering. They quickly lose energy in collisions and are scattered out of the beam of mono-energetic electrons, their range is small.

Free electrons absorb and emit virtual photons. Orbital electrons absorb and eject real photons when they change quantum states. In order for electron radiation to design a whole frontal and dorsal image of a full grown man (I doubt they would do that anyhow) an enormous amount of uniform photons would have to exist at once.

Even though the basic building blocks of matter, the protons and electrons are subject to indistinguishability, which means that all protons and all electrons look the same, we have to still consider that some of the protons and electron, which have indefinite lifetimes, may still be around out of Source X if the neutron flux hypothesis holds.

Would the neutron flux hypothesis hold? The laws of particle physics indicate that probably it would not hold, but we cannot know it for sure unless we substitute source X with its value, its true identity, which is the rising Body of Christ. Then we are up against the whole theology of the Resurrection, up against it momentarily, but helped by it actually.

It would react as an equation when it is finally solved. We said before, "If atoms are falling apart in source X it can only happen through radioactive disintegration." How else would protons, neutrons and electrons separate?

When we substitute X with its value, it reads: "If atoms are falling apart in the rising Body of Christ it can only happen through radioactive disintegration."

The Body of Christ, according to Biblical evidence and according to the medical evidence of the very Shroud, was saved from the breaking of any of his bones. It also was saved from putrefaction even to the slightest degree, as again medical science testifies, examining the Shroud image. Now, however, we say that is underwent radioactive disintegration.

Again, the Shroud itself testifies that the body must have left it with speed, judging by the untouched blood-marks, etc. Considereing this, we have to admit that the radioactive disintegration was not and could not have been a slow disintegration, but a very fast one, which qualifies it for fissioning or even nuclear explosion. Do we see that on the calm man on the Shroud?

The theology of the Resurrection, identifying Christ, tells us, that there cannot be a resurrection, unless it means the returning to the fullness of life, the fullness of power, death ending in life, vivification, entropy turned around.

"By an extraordinary working of power, Christ rises up clothed in infinite Power." (Durrwell) Even about the bodies of risen man St. Paul says, *"sown in weakness, shall rise in power."* (1 Cor. 15:43)

"Gone is all subjection to any law other than that which belongs to his own new life." (Durrwell)

"The fullness of life is restored (to Christ) and this totality does not leave anything behind." (A.M. Henry)

The total restoration and coming into full power is the essence of a resurrection. Unless radioactive disintegration would be given an unlikely new twist, I doubt it can possibly describe the process of the Resurrection, but rather exactly the opposite.

One is free, of course, to dismiss the Resurrection of Christ, but then source X will remain the forever unknown value in an unsolvable equation. I would rather believe that the methods of C14 testing are not valid, not only in the case of the Shroud, but simply not valid in general and valid only in certain specific cases.

The neutron flux hypothesis is one example, when the Shroud selects its own science and cancels an imperfect match.

The theology of the Resurrection will select for us its own science. It will read:

Gamma radiation would originate out of the Body of Christ due to radioactive decay. If these would be absorbed by nuclei in the Shroud, particles would be ejected out of atoms and the nuclei could be split.

X-rays would be produced by the Body of Christ if electrons would be ejected out from the inner orbits of atoms within the Body of Christ and electrons from the outer orbits would fall into the vacated inner orbits. The Body of Christ would be ionized. The X-rays would hit the Shroud and cause ionization there too.

Ultraviolet radiation would originate out of the Body of Christ if, in its atoms, electrons would be jolted from a close in to a far orbit. This would leave those atoms in an excited and chemically highly reactive state. Higher frequency ultraviolet rays out of the Body of Christ would cause burns and irradiation of the Shroud, the lower frequency ones would cause certain surfaces of the Shroud fluoresce or emit visible light.

Visible light waves would proceed out of the Body of Christ if electrons within its atoms would be jolted a few orbits out and thus would emit photons of the wavelength of visible light. High intensity visible rays would burn the Shroud. If a stupendous amount of uniform photons would be created at once there is a slim chance of image formation, but not by light itself alone.

Infrared radiation would be generated by the Body of Christ due to thermal agitation generated by vibrational oscillations within the molecules and the atoms of the Body. In excess, this would be harmful to the Body of Christ and it would burn the Shroud. If the infrared radiation is not in excess, its radiation would spread evenly all around and it is doubtful that it would create an image with distinguishable details.

Micro and radio waves would be created by the Body of Christ by excitation of molecular rotations—and by thermal agitation respectively. No image making properties there.

If we again expose these statements to the scrutiny of theology, namely that there cannot be a resurrection described by the scientific statement unless they also describe a "coming into power," a vivification, a "fullness of life," a "return to life" and, therefore, entropy turned around, then we can see if there is a match between the scientific statements and the theology of the Resurrection.

We can immediately see that gamma radiation, X-ray, micro and radio waves can be disregarded.

The Infrared range should present some degree of match, but in its present form it just does not. The low frequency Ultraviolet rays and Visible Light rays lend a vague match, but they are an imperfect match, leaving many insurmountable difficulties indicating that, in their present form and unaided, they could not create the image.

All the particulate radiations, electron, beta, alpha, proton, neutron, and ion are produced by source X only through radioactive disintegration. If we again substitute for X, the Body of Christ, the Body would have had to go through radioactive disintegration. This theory is on a direct collision course with the properties of a resurrection.

The conclusion we can draw, is that some kind of radiation resembling the electromagnetic type from the low ultraviolet to the high infrared radiation frequencies, must have been at work. However, this process cannot be described very well through the physics of the baryon-oriented universe. Another structure of the cosmos and physics is needed to describe it.

Avinoam Danin, Ph.D.

Professor of Botany
Hewbrew University of Jerusaelem

Dr. Avinoam Danin, is a Professor of Botany at The Hebrew University of Jerusaelem, Israel, and studies plant taxonomy, phytosociology, phytogeography, and ecology of the vegetation in the Near East.

His interdisciplinary research involved the distribution of higher plants, microorganisms, other organisms, and their relations to the environment. He described in this area more than 30 taxa new to science. Many of these taxa are confined to smooth-faced rock-outcrops which function as a refugium for relict mesophytes in desert areas.

His knowledge of the flora of Israel and its distribution was used in several forensic investigations. The most important of them was detecting the origin of the Shroud of Turin at the vicinity of Jerusalem.

His studies of biogenic weathering of rocks by various organisms enabled him to contribute to the study of palaeoclimates and the protection of ancient monuments in Mediterranean countries.

URI BARUCH, PH.D.

ARCHAEOBOTANIST
ISRAEL ANTIQUITIES AUTHORITY

Dr. Uri Baruch is an Archaeobotanist with the Israel Antiquities Authority in Jerusalem. A native of Israel, he obtained a master's degree in Prehistoric Archaeology at the Institute of Archaeology of the Hebrew University of Jerusalem with a specialization in Palynology (pollen studies). He later obtained a Ph.D. in archaeology with his dissertation on the palynology of sediments in the Dead Sea. He has lectured at several universities, and was head of the Multidisciplinary Research Division of the Israel Antiquities Authority for five years. He has engaged in numerous archaeological excavations and published over 30 papers in the fields of archaeobotany and palynology.

Floristic Indicators for the Origin of the Shroud of Turin

©Avinoam Danin, Ph.D., Uri Baruch, Ph.D. All rights Reserved
This paper was presented at the 3rd International Congress on the Shroud of Turin on 6 June 1998 in Turin, Italy.

Introduction

Minute plant parts and pollen grains were incidentally observed on the Shroud of Turin by Dr. M. Frei in 1973 when he was asked for an opinion by the church about accuracy of earlier photographs (Frei 1982). Applying methods he developed in his forensic investigations, Frei used transparent sticky tapes approximately 5 cm long which he pressed into the linen of the Shroud using pressure of his thumb to assure collecting of small particles for microscopic examination. The location of his sampling sites in 1978 utilized a grid devised by Prof. Baima Bollone and Dr. Aurelio Ghio and is fully documented photographically by Barrie Schwortz (Schwortz 1978 and 1998) and partially in Weaver (1980: p. 750). Comparing the pollen grains he found on the Shroud with pollen grains he obtained from living specimens in Israel, Turkey, Cyprus, France, and Italy, Frei (1982) concluded that the Shroud with its pollen must have originated in the Middle East. His untimely death in 1983 prevented him from completing the examination of his collection of 1978. Preliminary studies of his material by Maloney (1988) revealed a wealth of additional pollen grains as well as other plant parts.

Images of plants were detected on the Shroud by Scheuermann (1983) and by Whanger and Whanger in 1985 on photographically enhanced prints of negatives from photographs by Enrie in 1931. The Whangers tentatively identified the plant images by comparison to 1:1 illustrations of plants in *Flora Palaestina* (Feinbrun 1978; Zohary 1966, 1972). Although covering much of our findings, the Whangers' (1989) manuscript was not accepted for publication, possibly because it was submitted only a year after the radiocarbon 14C dating of a corner of the Shroud led those who did it to declare that the Shroud is a 13-14 century forgery (Damon et al., 1989). Later studies (Adler, 1996) proved that the chemical make-up of the single linen sample sent to three distinguished laboratories for carbon dating differed distinctively from that of most of the Shroud. Other ways of dating, such as by comparing the blood stains morphology on the Shroud with those on the Sudarium of Oviedo (Adler, 1996; Adler, Whanger, and Whanger 1997), prove its age to be at least from the 8th century CE Dating from earlier dates are fully reported by Whanger & Whanger (1998).

The first author became involved with the interpretation of plant images he saw on the 1:1 enhanced photos of the Shroud at the Whangers' collection at Durham, North Carolina in 1997. The second author in February 1998 checked microscopic slides derived from the Shroud, sampled by Frei, which are in the custody of The Council for Study of the Shroud of Turin (CSST).

In the present paper we wish to report our preliminary findings and discuss their chronological and spatial significance for the study of the Shroud of Turin.

Methods

Palynology

Microscopic slides sampled by Dr. Max Frei in 1973 and 14 of the 27 slides he sampled in 1978 were studied microscopically at 100 to 800 power magnification. In determining the pollen grains from the Shroud, U. Baruch compared grain morphology with control specimens, collected and determined by A. Danin in 1996 & 1997, and his own control collection. The samples were studied using an Olympus AX-70 computerized research light microscope.

Plant image detection

Plant images were studied at the first stage using 1:1 prints derived from third generation approved Giuseppe Enrie (1931) negatives and printed for high contrast (Whanger & Whanger 1998). The findings were later compared to the negatives of Secondo Pia (1898) displayed in Museo Della Sindone and Archivio di Stato, both in Turin. They were also compared to a 25% life size colour photograph of the Shroud (Miller, 1978) and to the fluorescence photos assembled by Miller (1978). Finally, on June 4, 1998 the first author observed a few of the images on the Shroud itself, using a pair of binoculars from a distance of ca. 4 m, at the exposition of the Shroud of Turin. Plant name nomenclature follows Feinbrun-Dothan and Danin (1991) and Danin (1998).

Results

Pollen

Table 1 presents results of re-determination of microscopic slides which were determined by Frei (1982). The rest of the slides reported by Frei (l.c.) are not in the possession of CSST at present. Of the 34 pollen grains reported at the specific level by Frei (1982) only 3 are recognized as such (*Gundelia tournefortii*, *Ricinus communis*, and *Lomelosia [Scabiosa] prolifera*) by the present authors. All Frei's determinations are correct at the higher taxonomical level, however, the differences in our perception will be discussed later.

Table 2 presents the results of pollen determination of the 1973 tapes and 14 of the 27 sticky tapes sampled by Frei in 1978. The most frequent type of pollen of all 168 grains studied is that of *Gundelia tournefortii* which accounts for 33.3% of the grains investigated and identified. The second most frequent is the Cistaceae type (13.1%). Although Dr. A. Orville Dahl determined several clustered pollen grains which he identified as likely those of *Cistus creticus* from tape 6Bd (Whanger 1996), we can not approve or disapprove this determination until pollen of the suspected Cistaceae are removed from the sticky tape and determined under a microscope with higher resolution.

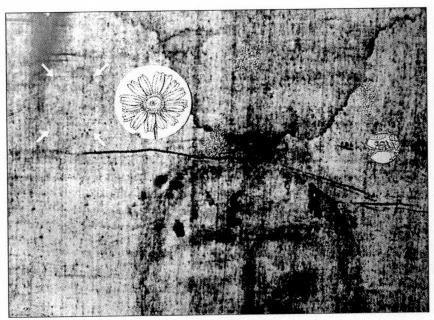

Fig. 1 Images of Chrysanthemum coronarium *and* Pistacia lentiscus *on the Shroud with adjacent drawings from* Flora Palaestina *(Koppel, 1972 and 1978).*

Plant images

Images of opened flowers, flowering buds, inflorescences, leaves, spiny bracts, stems, and fruits have been observed on photos of the Shroud and on the Shroud itself. An example of an inflorescence of a plant from the Asteraceae (Compositae), best fitting in size and morphology to that of *Chrysanthemum coronarium*, is presented in Fig. 1. Hundreds of additional flowers and inflorescences were discovered on the enhanced photos of the Shroud. We shall restrict ourselves in the present paper to only three species which are the most significant.

An image of an inflorescence of *Gundelia tournefortii* was observed at the area of the right anatomic shoulder (Fig. 1). Discovered first on Enrie's enhanced photos it was later seen again at the same location in Enrie (1931) and Pia (1898) negatives in Turin, and in Miller (1978) colour photo.

Fig. 2 Floral images on the shroud, with a thorn of Gundelia tournefortii *adjacent to a Gundelia image, and a drawing from* Flora Palaestina *adjacent to one of the* Zygophyllum dumosum *images (Koppel, 1972)*

Images of *Zygophyllum dumosum* leaves were observed at the man's chest area, above the boundary of the water stain (of the fire extinguishing at the church in Chamb(rcy, France, 1532). The leaf of *Z. dumosum*, which starts to develop in winter, is succulent. It has a sausage-like petiole and two flat thick elliptic leaflets (Figs. 2, 3). In summer the two leaflets dry and fall. The six-months-old sausage-like leaf slowly shrinks during the summer. Following the first rain the one-year-old leaf swells and resumes its full size. By that time new leaves, each with two leaflets start to grow. The images on the Shroud are of two pairs of young but full-sized leaves and a few sausage-like older leaves (Fig. 2). The large top-left leaf in this figure was first observed on Enrie's (1931) enhanced photograph and later on his negatives, on Pia's (1898) negatives, on Miller's (1978) colour photograph, on Miller's (1978) fluorescence photo, and finally on the Shroud itself.

Fig. 3 A stem of Zygophyllum dumosum *displaying leaves from the present year (with two leaflets) and leaves from the previous year or years (without leaflets). Specimen gathered in the Judean (Sinai) desert by A. Danin.*

A peduncle carrying three fruits of *Pistacia lentiscus* (Fig. 1) was observed in all the five media listed above for the *Zyophyllum dumosum* leaf. In addition there are more than 300 spots, at same size as these three fruits, most of which have an attached line which looks like a pedicel. Many of these spots, interpreted as fruits as well, are attached to branched lines which resemble peduncles of *Pistacia palaestina* and *P. atlantica* (as illustrated by Huber, 1972).

Chronological notes

Being the most frequent pollen type on the Shroud (Table 2), *Gundelia tournefortii* may serve as a quasi-calendar for indicating the season when its spiny flower-carrying inflorescence was laid on the Shroud. According to Feinbrun-Dothan and Danin (1991) *G. tournefortii* blooms from March to May. Danin's field observations of 1998 could extend the blooming time to February in the warm parts of its area in Israel. This definite calendar dictates the origin of *Pistacia* fruits. All the three species do not bear fruits between February and May. Therefore these fruits were originated from a preserved source and were not picked up directly from local trees and shrubs.

The phenologic status of *Zygophyllum dumosum* indicated by the presence of leaves from two years and from flowers (Fig. 3) may be found in the eastern Judean Desert between January and April.

The wide temporal range of blooming in Israel is a result of high diversity of habitats in this part of the world.

Spatial notes

Gundelia tournefortii is restricted to the Middle East. *Zygophyllum dumosum* is endemic to Israel, West Jordan, and Sinai. The three *Pistacia* species mentioned above have a wider distribution area, and since their fruiting time does not coincide with the flowering time of *Gundelia tournefortii* they have no significance as distributional or chronological indicators (cf. Discussion).

Discussion

The two plant species that are part of the Shroud, evidenced by pollen grains incorporated among the linen threads and by their images, indicate that it came from the Middle East. The most likely area where flowering stems of both *G. tournefortii* and *Z. dumosum* could be laid fresh on the Shroud is the vicinity of Jerusalem. Pollen grains of *G. tournefortii* at a density of 11-14 grains/5 cm2 could not derive from dispersal by natural agents (e.g. wind)(Fig.4). In the rare cases where pollen grains of this species were found as part of the "pollen-rain" (Baruch 1993), they never reached a density of more than 1-2 grains/400 cm2. The inevitable conclusion is that the pollen containing inflorescence or inflorescences had been laid on the Shroud, prior to the formation of the plant images sometime in the remote past.

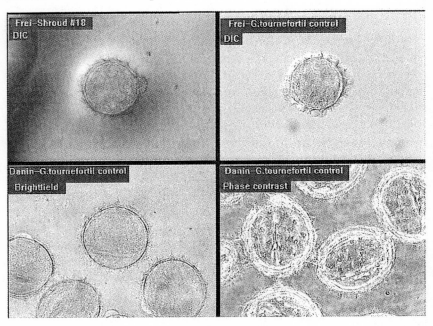

Fig. 4 Pollen grains of Gundelia tournefortii. *Upper left is a pollen grain under tape taken from the Shroud in 1978 by M. Frei. Upper right is a control pollen grain under tape obtained by M. Frei. Lower left are* Gundelia *pollen grain controls under tape gathered by A. Danin. Lower right are* Gundelia *control pollen grains under a cover slip examined by phase contrast, gathered by A. Danin.*

There can be hardly any doubt that the plant images presented here form a genuine part of the Shroud. The proof we have that they are not artifacts caused in the processes of photographic enhancement of Enrie's (1931) negatives, is that the images were discovered also on Enrie's negatives, the photos made by Pia (1898), and those of Miller (1978). The three sets of photographs are separated by up to 80 years. They were taken with different cameras, with different optical quality, using films with different emulsions and different spectral characteristics. They were developed under different darkroom conditions, and yet the same sets of images were observed in the photos of all three generations. This fact, together with other non-body images, not mentioned here, prove that the images are not artifacts, but part of the nature of the Shroud.

The images of the *Zygophyllum dumosum* leaf and the three *Pistacia* fruits were seen on the Shroud even without photographs.

The images of *Zygophyllum dumosum* leaves on the Shroud are of turgescent ones indicating that fresh plants were laid on the Shroud (Fig. 2). The distribution maps of *G. tournefortii* and *Z. dumosum* have area of almost common boundaries along the Jerusalem-Hebron area in Israel and the Madaba-Karak area in Jordan. On the earth map both areas are in a small locality—the Holy Land. Further investigations may enable us to use additional plant indicators for restricting the area in the Holy Land from where the Shroud started its journey.

Fruits of the three species of *Pistacia* are not available on plants during the season indicated by *Gundelia tournefortii* and *Zygophyllum dumosum*. Therefore, these fruits should have been brought in from a storage. The present day practice (as was told by a spice-merchant in the market of the Old City of Jerusalem) is that the *Pistacia* fruits (BUTUM in Arabic) are picked up when ripe in September, dried and preserved by this way to be sold the year round. They are used as a condiment for cakes and as a component of spices (e.g., Za'atar).

The differences in determinations of pollen grains between us and M. Frei (1982) derive from the knowledge and perception of the pollen flora of the study area. It seems that M. Frei was not aware of the possibility that many of his determinations at the specific level could not be accepted by palynologists today. At present, with the great increase in our knowledge of the Middle Eastern palynology, palynologists familiar with the local flora will be highly reluctant to determine a Chenopdiaceae pollen grain as *Anabasis aphylla*. This is because generally Chenopodiaceae pollen grains can not be determined to a specific level. Frei was correct, however, in his determination of *Gundelia tournefortii*, which became one of our leading indicators.

Acknowledgments

We thank Dr. A. Adler for his enlightening conversations during the preparation of the manuscript; Dr. A.D and Mrs. M.W. Whanger, Mr. P.E. Dayvault, and Bishop J. Barclay for the critical reading of the manuscript. Thanks are due to Mrs. Tamar Soffer for drawing the maps and to the Israel Academy for Science and Humanities for using of few of the drawings from *Flora Palaestina*.

Table 1. A list of comments made by Uri Baruch on Max Frei (1973) pollen determination

Slide#	Frei's label	Baruch's comment
MS01	*Anabasis aphylla*	OK, but *Anabasis* type
MS02	*Alnus glutionsa*	Empty
MS04	*Acacia albida*	OK, it is *Acacia* but not with species level
MS05	*Artemisia sieberi*	OK but for *Artemisia* sp.
MS06	*Atraphaxis spinosa*	OK for a generic level.
MS07	*Capparis ovata*	*Capparis* sp., + non *Capparis*
MS08	*Carduus*	*Cedrus*, + *Carduus* type!
MS09	*Carpinus betulus*	at the present status - not identifiabe
MS10	*Cedrus libanoticus*	OK, but *Cedrus*
MS11	*Corylus avelana*	at the present status - not identifiable
MS13	*Echinops glaberrimus*	OK but should be *Echinops* sp.
MS15	*Fagonia mollis* (Danin's)	looks like *F. arabica* control
MS16	*Fagus sylvatica*	inconclusive material
MS17	*Glaucium grandiflorum*	Echinops; the *Glaucium* is not found
MS18	*Gundelia tournefortii*	OK
MS20	*Haplophyllum tuberculatum*	OK, but species can not be determined
MS21	*Helianthemum vesicarium*	Cistaceae; the slide is not clear enough
MS23	*Hyoscyamus reticulatus*	Only generic level is tangible
MS26	*Linum mucronatum*	Only generic level is tangible
MS31	*Paliurus spina-christi*	either *Paliurus* or *Ziziphus*
MS32	*Peganum harmala*	Can not be confirmed

Table 1. Continued

Slide#	Frei's label	Baruch's comment
MS34	*Sarcopoterium spinosum*	Can not be confirmed
MS35	*Prosopis farcta*	OK
MS38	*Reaumuria hirtella*	Species can not be differentiated
MS39	*Ricinus communis*	OK
MS41	*Scabiosa prolifera*	OK + Centaurea solstitialis type, + Tubiliflorae Type
MS42	Scirpus	Cyperaceae OK
MS43	Secale	Gramineae OK
MS45	Suaeda	OK as Chenopodiaceae
MS46	Tamarix	OK as *Tamarix* spp.
MS47	Taxus	Uri can't confirm

Table 2. Results of examination (by U. Baruch) for pollen grains found in sticky tapes derived from the Shroud of Turin sampled by M. Frei in 1973 and 1978 (updated after Danin et al, 1999).

Pollen Determinations	Pollen Grain Number	Total ID Pollen
Acacia sp.	1	0.3%
Anabasis type	1	0.3%
Artemisia sp.	3	1.0%
Atraphaxis sp.	1	0.3%
Capparis sp.	1	0.3%
Carduus type	1	0.3%
Cedrus sp.	2	0.6%
Centaurea solstitialis type	3	1.0%
Centrospermae	1	0.3%
Chenopodiaceae	1	0.3%
Cistus incanus-type	1	0.3%
Cistus salviifolius-type (?)	2	0.6%
Cistaceae	23	7.3%

Table 2. Continued

Pollen Determinations	Pollen Grain Number	Total ID Pollen
Corylus sp.	1	0.3%
Dryopteris (?)	1	0.3%
Cyperaceae	1	0.3%
Echinops sp.	4	1.3%
Fagonia sp.	1	0.3%
Gramineae	6	1.9%
Gundelia tournefortii	91	29.1%
Haplophyllum sp.	1	0.3%
Hyoscyamus sp.	1	0.3%
Linum sp.	1	0.3%
Olea sp.	2	0.6%
Ononis type	2	0.6%
Papilionacea	5	1.6%
Pinus sp.	1	0.3%
Pistacia sp.	2	0.6%
Plantago (?)	1	0.6%
Pteranthus (?)	2	0.6%
Quercus (deciduous) [?]	8	2.6%
Quercus (?)	3	1.0%
Ricinus (?)	2	0.6%
Lomelosia prolifera	1	0.3%
Tamarix sp.	4	1.3%
Tubiliflorae	8	2.6%
Umbelliferae	13	4.2%
Total identified	204	65.2%
Unidentified grains	109	34.80%
Total	313	

References

Adler, A.D. 1996. "Updating recent studies on the Shroud of Turin." *ACS Symp*. 625: 223—228.

Adler, A.D., Whanger, A.D., and Whanger, M.W. 1998. "Concerning the side strip of the Shroud of Turin." *Actes du IIIeme Symposium Scientifique International du CIELT, Nice, 1997*. Imprimerie de la Neuvelle Clemacy, France. P. 103.

Baruch, U. 1993. "The palynology of Late Quaternary sediments of the Dead Sea." Ph.D. thesis, The Hebrew University of Jerusalem (in Hebrew with an English abstract). 273 pp.

Damon, P. et al., 1989. "Radiocarbon dating of the Shroud of Turin." *Nature* 337: 611-615.

Danin, A. 1997. "Pressed flowers, where did the Shroud of Turin originate? A botanical quest." *Eretz Magazine* 55: 35-37, 69.

Danin, A. 1998. *Wild plants of Eretz Israel and their distribution*. Carta, Jerusalem. 212 pp.

Danin, A., Whanger, A., Baruch, U., and Whanger, M. 1999. *Flora of the Shroud of Turin*. St. Louis, Missouri. Missouri Botanical Garden Press. 52 pp.

Feinbrun-Dothan N. 1978. *Flora Palaestina* part III. Israel Acad. Sci. Human. Jerusalem. 481 pp.

Feinbrun-Dothan N. 1986. *Ibid*, part IV. 463 pp.

Feinbrun-Dothan, N. and Danin, A. 1991. *Analytical Flora of Eretz Israel*. Cana, Jerusalem. 1040 p.

Frei, M. 1982. "Nine years of palinological studies on the Shroud." *Shroud Spectrum International*. 1(3): 1-7.

Heller, J. and Adler, A. 1981. "A chemical investigation of the Shroud of Turin." *Canadian Soc. of Forensic Science Journal* 14(3): 81-103.

Huber, E. 1972. "Plates 436 and 437" in Zohary, M., *Flora Palaestina*, part 2. Israel Academy of Science and Humanities, Jerusalem.

Koppel, R. 1972. "Plates 363 and 439" in Zohary, M., *Flora Palaestina*, part 2. Israel Academy of Science and Humanities, Jerusalem.

Koppel, R. 1978. "Plate 589" in Feinbrun, N., *Flora Palaestina*, part 3. Israel Academy of Science and Humanities, Jerusalem.

Kupicha, F.K. 1975. Gundelia. In: *Davis' Flora of Turkey*, Edinburgh, University Press. 5: 325-326.

Lavoie, G.R. 1998. *Unlocking the secrets of the Shroud*. Thomas More, Texas. 224 pp.

Maloney, P.C. 1988. An interim progress report on the photo-inventory/ survey project, the Max Frei sticky tape collection on loan to ASSIST.

Scheuermann, O. 1983. There is an image caused by radiation on the Shroud of Turin after all! proof by experiment (unpublished).

Schwortz, B.M. 1978 and 1998. Shroud of Turin Image Library: Max Frei (Custom CD-ROM containing 50 documenting photographs from the 1978 STURP study; cf. www.shroud.com).

Weaver, K.F. 1980. "Science seeks to solve the mystery of the Shroud." *Nat. Geogr.* 157(6): 730-751.

Whanger, A. D. 1996. "Pollens on the Shroud: a study in deception." *Shroud News* 97: 11—18.

Whanger, A.D. and Whanger, M.W. 1989. Floral, coin, and other non-body images on the Shroud of Turin. (Unpublished manuscript).

Whanger, M.W. and Whanger, A.D. 1998. *The Shroud of Turin, an Adventure of Discovery*. Tennessee, Providence House Publishers. 144 pp.

Zohary, M. 1966. *Flora Palaestina*. Part 1. Israel Acad. Sci. and Humanities, Jerusalem. 367 pp.

Zohary, M. 1972. *Ibid*. 489 pp.

The Frei Collection
Digitization Project

Originally presented at the III International Congress on the
Shroud, Turin, Italy, June 6, 1998.

The Dr. Max Frei Collection consists of 27 "sticky-tapes" he personally collected from the Shroud in 1978. Forty-one slides containing individually dissected pollen grains collected from the Shroud in 1973 are also included. The collection further includes 7 tapes from the Tunic of Argenteuil, and 6 tapes from the Crown of Thorns (Notre Dame), taken in 1979. Control samples, original notes and correspondence, miscellaneous photographs and a manuscript make up the rest of this invaluable collection.

Dr. Max Frei, a botanist by profession, also served as the head of the Zurich Police Department's Crime Lab and was expert at determining the presence of dust and other particulate matter at crime scenes via the collection of "sticky-tapes." The method of "sticky-tape" collection which he invented is, in part, what makes this collection so important. He would pull off a strip of 1.5 cms. clear adhesive tape, Sello brand, approximately 7-10 cms. long, place it on the surface and would then knead it into the fabric to collect any minute particulate matter in-between the threads and fibrils. His work and subsequent studies were never completed, in that he died in 1983. In 1988, his widow and son, wishing for Dr. Frei's studies to be continued, released the full custody of the Collection to the ASSIST group, to which they had previously loaned 5 samples to Mr. Paul Maloney for examination. In 1993, Dr. and Mrs. Whanger became the sole custodians of the Frei Collection.

This is important evidence for many reasons, but primarily because it is *original*, it came *directly* from the Shroud and other Relics, it *was authorized* by the Church, and the tapes were *personally taken* by Dr. Frei. Each Frei "sticky tape" collected in 1978 was photo-documented by

Barrie Schwortz, the official documenting photographer of the 1978 Scientific Examination. Dr. Frei took these samples from predetermined sites located on a grid designed by Prof. Baima Bollone and Dr. Ghio. The provenance of the collection is intact in that we know where it has been and who has had access to it. Even Dr. Walter McCrone, a noted Shroud skeptic, examined the 1978 tapes in 1988 and declared that they were consistent with other evidence from the Shroud and concurred they had in fact originated from contact with the Shroud. In 1997, CSST engaged a senior forensic microscopist to examine the entire collection of tapes for the presence of tampering. His final report indicated that there was no evidence of physical tampering with the Frei Collection. Part of the reason for seeking this exam was to answer the allegation that the tapes had at one time been tampered with or "salted" with pollen grains. That issue is now settled.

The people involved in this project are numerous, but primary project members and their expertise include; Dr. Alan Adler, heme chemist; Dr. Alan Whanger, primary Shroud researcher; Dr. Uri Baruch, Israeli palynologist; Dr. Avinoam Danin, Israeli botanist; Mr. Tom Vuke, microscope system integrator; and myself, Philip Dayvault, comparative microscopist. Other forensic experts with the North Carolina State Bureau of Investigation and several professors of local universities have also offered their assistance. We also seek assistance from our international colleagues in Italy, Spain, and France and we look forward to collaborative studies with them.

The collection is kept in a bank vault in Durham, NC and when it is brought out for cursory exams, it is secured in a safe at the CSST office. The premises are alarmed for intrusion and equipped with a high sensitivity smoke and fire detection system. All examinations are videotaped for documentation purposes. All people present must sign a registry book or be noted in it. The entire collection can offer a tremendous amount of information for worldwide scientific studies. But it must first be completely archived and digitized with the use of a computerized microscope system. Digitization, in lay terms, is the process of converting data into computer language.

After the tapes are scanned under various magnifications and lighting modes, the data will be instantly retrievable from the databank for cross-comparisons and study. This scan will permit the determination of what is actually on the Frei tapes. Evidence could further confirm Dr. Frei's important research, as well as further corroborate the research of Dr. and Mrs. Whanger, and Drs. Danin and Baruch. For example, years ago Dr. and Mrs. Whanger identified the images of 28 flowers on various areas of the Shroud. Since beginning his collaborative work with CSST in 1995, Dr. Danin has reviewed these findings and has basically confirmed the identity of these floral images. As a world expert on the flora of Israel and the Near-East, Dr. Danin speaks with authority. Also, another colleague, Dr. Uri Baruch, a palynologist at the Israeli Antiquities Authority, visited CSST in February 1998, and personally reviewed some of the Frei tapes. His findings and identifications of numerous pollens also basically confirmed the work done previously by Dr. Frei, Dr. and Mrs. Whanger, Mr. Paul Maloney and Dr. Danin. I refer you to the next presentation by Dr. Danin for more of these remarkable findings.

The equipment utilized in this project is the Olympus AX-70, a state-of-the-art research microscope system consisting of a motorized stage, remote controls, digital camera, video camera, two-35mm cameras for prints and slides, all connected to a color video printer. This was acquired by CSST in September 1996. The scope magnification varies from 20 to 400, plus a variable 2x zoom, allowing maximum 800 magnification. The available illumination is either transmitted or reflected light, with brightfield, dark field, polarized, DIC, phase contrast, and fluorescence in several wavelengths, i.e. Ultraviolet, Blue Violet, Blue and Green.

Right now, one of the most important agendas is to scan the slides at a relatively low power to seek the location of the numerous pollen grains. We anticipate Dr. Baruch's return to help with the actual identification and/or confirmation of them. Both his and Dr. Danin's studies have helped confirm the historical provenance of the Shroud, already placed at some time in its history in the general environs of Jerusalem. Other items of evidentiary value include numerous fibers (linen, cotton, and wool), and botanical materials which could be instrumental in possibly associating various Relics of the Passion, i.e. the Sudarium of Oviedo, the Tunic of Argenteuil, the Cloak of Trier, and the Crown of Thorns. Studies are under way to examine the existing STURP tapes, and we are hopeful for cooperative studies with other tapes or sample collections from the Sudarium and the Tunic.

Further studies will, no doubt, lead to the need for further confirmation. Hopefully, another much-needed scientific examination will be forthcoming in order to answer some of the new questions. We anticipate collaborating with other serious researchers in order to find out all we can about this remarkable collection, and its important relevance to the mystery of the Shroud.

The Professional Arts and the
Principle and Practice of Conservation—
Restoration vs. the Turin Shroud

Conservation-Restoration

By conservation-restoration it is generally meant to put back into sound order a product of human activity. These can be industrial articles that merely have to be restored to working order or art works that have no functional purpose, only aesthetical.

While the product of art fundamentally differs from any other manmade object with its aesthetic merit and its influence on the future, it still visibly manifests that it can only be a human product. Is the Turin Shroud in any way a human product? Because if it is not, do we really know what conservation principles could be safely applied to it?

An uncut marble from the quarry has a chemical composition that can be tested and analyzed by scientific instruments. A statue made from the marble has exactly the same chemical composition, but the marble underwent a radical transformation.

The arts gratefully accept the assistance of science in the preservation of art, namely the use of:
- polarizing microscope
- spectrometry of emission in the ultraviolet band
- spectrometry of X-ray fluorescence
- X-ray microfluorescence
- X-ray diffraction
- infrared absorption spectrography and chromatography

However, the final authority to determine if something is or is not a painting belongs to the professional arts.

Numerous people from around the world, best represented by noted microanalyst Dr. Walter McCrone, believe that a medieval artist had the genius to have painted the Shroud of Turin. Yet, McCrone made the statement, "The Shroud is not a question for art experts." What airtight logic!

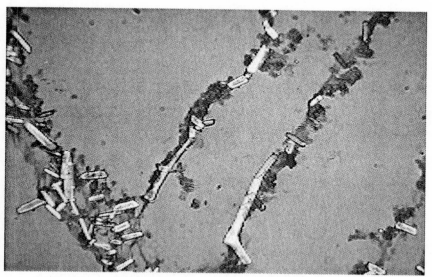

Is this a painting? No. It is a sponge under the microscope.

This is not a painting either. It is the tip of a human nose.

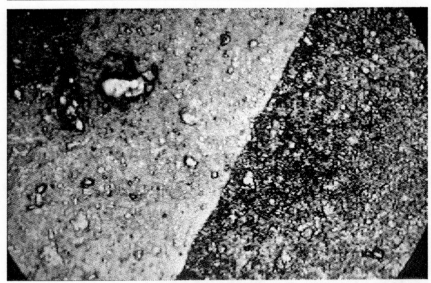

Now, this is truly a painting. Is it beautiful? Not particularly. Paint particles are not the painting.

Under lesser magnification this is obviously a part of a painting showing the brush technique of Rembrandt. Suddenly the pigment particles become the painting, the unique territory of the professional arts.

The previous illustration showed a detail of the helmet in the painting to the left. A work of art presents style, technique, a historic milieu and an influence on the future. If all these together do not exist, the object of our discussion is not art. The professional artist has to be trained in all these disciplines.

Can the trained artist tell us whether or not the Shroud of Turin is a painting or artifact? I have created large works of art in 486 buildings around the world like the below 280 sq. meter stained glass I installed recently. I can assure everyone, the Turin Shroud is not a painting or artifact made by us. I gave the many reasons for that in earlier papers.

Today, let us look at some of the mistakes the proponents of the Shroud's painting theory are making. It is important, because if the Shroud would be accepted as a painting, it would have to be preserved and eventually restored as a painting, and that would be the end of it.

The claim was made that the Shroud was painted with greatly diluted glue tempera. Glue erratically reacts to atmospheric changes. Therefore, it is used only with chemical stabilizers. If none found on the Shroud sticky tapes, it is not a glue paint medium. In very diluted form the medium does not permanently hold the paint particles. Also, this medium remains absolutely water soluble. The Shroud could not have been boiled, hosed down or handled and still retain the image. In case of highly diluted medium, one does not have to dislodge paint particles. They are loosely attached. Because of the unpleasant qualities of this medium, this technique seldom was used for fine art, except on Egyptian wall paintings inside of protected tombs in a very dry climate.

Dr. McCrone claims it was glue tempera which was the technique used on medieval paintings. This is highly incorrect. In the Middle Ages glue tempera was only used on the lesser kodex illustration. This medium cannot be used for realistic representations, as the Shroud's image would be, only for flat, decorative styles in art. The medium of fine art paintings in the Middle Ages was egg tempera.

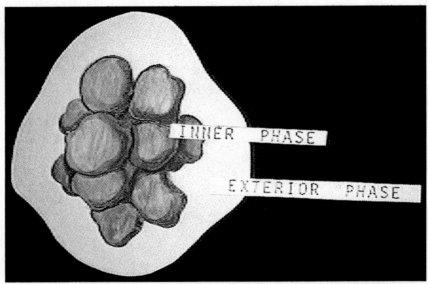

In case of glomerates, the paint mediums surround the paint particles. The paint particles, which are always in the center of the glomerate, are called the inner phase; the colloidal binder outside is called the exterior phase. The yellow substance supposedly found by McCrone inside of glomerates simply could not have been the paint medium.

Paint media and varnishes yellow and darken with age and one can see its effect on the Shroud, said our microscopist. This is wrong. The aqueous colloidal mediums used in the Middle Ages maintain their airy, light colors even in decay. Therefore, whatever is that yellowed on the Shroud cannot be a medieval paint medium. Only the oil-paint mediums and some varnishes yellow.

Old paint cannot be compared with modern paint. The refractive indices and the structure of old paint radically and erratically change. Some opaque paints become transparent and the underlying tracing lines show through.

Dr. McCrone stated that the fire of 1532 would not have changed the color of vermilion because the Shroud was folded. The change of color on both, vermilion and red ochre, would have taken place to different degrees from layer to layer, and we would see a checkerboard effect on the Shroud.

Our microscopist takes his knowledge of medieval paint techniques from old books, such as Cennino Cennini, and Eastlake. There is great professional doubt about the identity of some of the pigments, materials and methods described in old texts. Some of the pigments are either not recognizable or obsolete and the methods are no longer in use and forgotten. The word sinopia or sinoper, used by McCrone for instance, is not in use today and Venetian red is just an arbitrary term used for the unknown sinoper. Eastland, writing in 1847, due to similarly unsure identification of old texts, describes old techniques of art, examples for which do not exist.

As a convincing proof that Shroud–like monochrome paintings with red ochre were commonplace in the 14th century, Dr. McCrone shows in his book this monochrome fresco at the Palace of the Popes in Avignon, France.

Every artist from 25,000 BC until today, including myself, paints the composition on the wall or even on canvas first in monochrome colors, red ochre or verdaccio,light green. In the Middle Ages the muralists did not prepare a full size cartoon as we do today. They plastered the whole wall to be painted. Then made a full-scale sketch of the composition in monochrome, red or green earth. When that dried, the wall was wetted and replastered, a piece of it a day. The same design underneath was copied in full color on the topcoat.

If for any reason the work was terminated before the second stage in color, or the two coats of plaster separated due to detachment, the preliminary, monochrome step remained exposed on the wall. It has nothing to do with the Turin Shroud.

This painting by Andrea Orcagna is indicative of the artistic style of those Dr. McCrone speculates could have painted the Shroud image.

Dr. McCrone named in his book several candidates in the 14th century who, according to his judgment, could have painted the Shroud image. Lippo Memmi, Pietro Cavallini, Taddeo Gaddi, Andrea Orcagna, Agnolo Gaddi and Simone Martini. I don't think they are candidates for painting the Shroud.

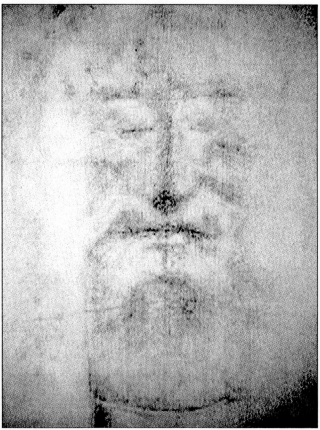

The modern imitators do not show success either and the Craig and Bresee image needs no comment from me.

The Conservation and Restoration of Paintings

Why is it so important to determine whether or not the Shroud is a painting? Because if it would have been a painting, it would have to be conserved, preserved, and ultimately restored as a painting. Let us see the consequences of that:

Dirt on paintings is anything which exists in addition to the surface established by the original artist. Dirt can be removed by cotton balls slightly dampened in water or chemical solutions. The Turin Shroud should not be cleaned, because the debris on its surface represents important historical information.

Some paintings suffer the detachment of the paint particles or peeling of the paint film because of natural aging of the adhesive substances in the paint mediums. The adhesives of the ground decompose due to atmospheric humidity, differences in thermal expansion, rhythmical vibrations or impacts. To correct this, paintings are relined from the back with a new canvas and new adhesive, applied with heat and pressure, which will reattach the loose paint or ground.

If we would believe, against the laws of nature, that loose paint particles and medium glomerates are responsible for the image on the Shroud, what protects it from a future time when a backing canvas would be attached to it with adhesive penetrating its surface?

Finally, in order to save some paintings, their decaying support is discarded and the separated paint film is re-installed on a new support. If one would succumb to the belief that paint film is responsible for the image on the Shroud what would protect the Shroud from restoration as a painting in some future age?

Would the promoters of the painting theory take the responsibility for the dangers their irresponsible research presents to the Shroud?

The professional arts strongly state, the Shroud is not a painting or manmade artifact. The Shroud is much, much more than what anyone of us could even start to understand and this should caution the conservators of today and of the future.

PETER M. SCHUMACHER

INVENTOR OF THE VP-8 IMAGE ANALYZER

"Pete" Schumacher is an electronics engineer, entrepreneur, and inventor. Pete was introduced to image processing in 1972 when he worked in the production development of the VP-8 Image Analyzer. He was issued three patents, circa 1981, for a video image marking and processing system, a system for multiple-video-image analysis, and a system for large format vide capture. These patents included devices and software. He has developed means of obtaining and processing video images for multi-spectral aerial video imaging, machine vision, medical image cross-modality studies, microbiology imaging, and various research applications.

Mr. Schumacher developed the first desktop geographic information system and the first raster-to-vector converter for video step-and-repeat imaging. His work enabled the development of the first color, three-dimensional, video-cartographic system in 1986. His research has included a six-week residency instruction in radiology, years of traveling the globe installing video image processing equipment, and training groups of students and instructors on its use. He worked on the development team for a digital output video camera in 1989.

More recently, Mr. Schumacher has taught courses in video imaging technology for large-area video "traffic incident management systems" and their associated analog and digital communications networks. His work as a sales engineer involves solving a variety of imaging problems in many diverse applications.

IMAGE PROCESSING AND PHOTOGRAPHY: UNIQUE RESEARCH FROM THE SHROUD OF TURIN

Photography and the Shroud of Turin

In 1898, Secundo Pia made the first photographs of the Shroud of Turin. The process included emulsions on glass plates. The emulsions hardened where exposed to light energy. Secundo Pia focused his lens on the Shroud of Turin, closed the lens, installed the glass plates, and opened the lens for a short period of time. The light, reflected from the Shroud, passed through the lens. Photons landed on the emulsions, and the lens was again closed. This is the common process of conventional photography. It is the same now, as then. However, the products resulting from Shroud photographs are unique.

When Pia's plates were developed, the photographic negatives made the subtle details on the Shroud much more vivid, and much easier to "interpret" by the human visual system. The actual image on the Shroud of Turin is very "faint" (low in contrast). It is difficult to orient oneself, relative to the image, if the observer is in close proximity to the cloth. Even if the observer is close to a full-scale positive color photographic image of the cloth, viewing details is difficult. However, photographic negative images of the Shroud are more easily interpreted. Details are easier to see.

This does not mean that the Shroud of Turin is a photographic negative. However, the products (negatives) of the conventional photographic process, applied to the Shroud of Turin, are unique relative to the products of photographs of other known objects. This includes photographs of art objects, such as, drawings or paintings.

It might be possible to produce, purposefully fabricate, modify, or alter the image of an object so that, when photographed, the resulting negatives would begin to resemble Shroud negatives. However, the Shroud of Turin is at least 650 years old, by any consideration. No modification, fabrication, or alterations of the physical reactions are required in taking a Shroud photograph. The methods used are the same used in making any other photograph. Yet, the results of Shroud photographs have these unique characteristics. The photons rebound from the cloth, pass through the lens, harden the emulsion, and the result exists. No image studied, made prior to photography, or made after its invention, produces the same results as those observed relative to the Shroud of Turin image.

One would think that an artist's goal is to make an image that is clearly and easily interpreted by the human visual system. One would not think that an image of low clarity and faintness of detail would be created at least 550 years in advance of the invention of a method (photography) to view the "subtle" details. It is important to note, no photographic enhancement method, such as "dodging," "push-processing," or "nonuniform illumination," is needed to produce these unique results in a conventional photographic negative of the Shroud of Turin. It is reasonable to question how, and why, an artist might fabricate a work that responds so differently, when photographed, compared to all other "artistic works." It is not reasonable to suggest the artist could "predict the outcome" (photo-negative) of the work before any reference to a specific "outcome" had been established. The artist would have to fabricate the image to produce those specific results without any reference by which to perform "quality control" of the work. Then, the artist would produce only one known work of this type, protect the method so no other works of this type could be produced, and be without fame for the talents, skills, and processes required. Artistic copies and artists' illustrations of the Shroud do not produce the same results when photographed. Even purposefully fabricated works, knowing what the outcome of photography should be and knowing the photographic process that will be applied, fail to produce the same results.

Consider the following: The Shroud of Turin induces a result through photographic imaging that is unique, compared to all other photographic results taken from other objects created during the period from before Christ to well after 1350 A.D., and even to the present day. It is the "data" existing on the Shroud of Turin, which induces the unique photographic results. Therefore, the Shroud image, itself, is unlike any other object or image known to exist.

Image Analysis

In 1972, the VP-8 Image Analyzer was invented. I was responsible for taking the design to production and delivery. I designed and documented the production units. For six years, I installed the units and trained operators. I became familiar with many different types of images and applications for this image-processing instrument.

In about 1976, I delivered and installed a unit at the hone of Captain Eric Jumper, USAF. Captain John Jackson, USAF, was present. I dutifully installed the system, and verified the calibration. I then trained Jumper and Jackson in the operation of the system. What happened next was extraordinary to me. The results were, to say the least, "unique."

Jackson placed an image of the Shroud of Turin onto the light table of the system. He focused the video camera of the system on the image. When the pseudo-three-dimensional image display ("isometric display"), was activated, a "true-three-dimensional image" appeared on the monitor. At least, there were many traits of real three-dimensional structuring in the image displayed. The nose ramped in relief. The facial features were contoured properly. Body shapes of the arms, legs, and chest, had the basic human form. This result from the VP-8 had never occurred with any of the images I had studied, nor had I heard of it happening during any image studies done by others.

I had never heard of the Shroud of Turin before that moment. I had no idea what I was looking at. However, the results were unlike anything I have processed through the VP-8 Analyzer, before or since. Only the Shroud of Turin has produced these results from a VP-8 Image Analyzer isometric projection study. Recently created, purposefully fabricated images fail to produce the same results, even when the "artist" knows the process and the outcome before creating the image to be processed.

The VP-8 Image Analyzer is an analog video processing device. The "isometric display" is generated on a cathode ray tube, like that of an oscilloscope. It is like a home television set, except the scanning and positioning of the video image is controlled by electrostatics (voltages), rather than by electromagnetism (currents). The picture is monochrome, like black and white television. However, the isometric image is "shades of green" rather than "shades of gray," due to the type of the cathode ray tube used.

The isometric display uses the changes of brightness, as they occur in an image, to change the "elevation" on the display. If something is bright, it goes up. If something is dark, it goes down. If it is some gray shade in-between, it produces an "elevation" in between something very bright and something very dark.

The isometric display was never intended to produce a "real-three-dimensional" display. A snow-covered peak would look like a high, flat surface, while a rock sitting on top of the snow would look like a deep hole in the high surface. Light reflecting from a stream at the bottom of a valley would appear to be a high elevation, perhaps even higher than the snow on the peak of the mountains. Dull rocks and dark vegetation would appear to be lower than the water of the stream. In other words, objects are not as tall or short, high or low, as their reflectance of light might indicate. There is no correlation between reflectance and altitude.

The purpose of the isometric display was to make it easier to follow patterns of changes in shades of gray within an image. Particularly, the light pattern changes in reflection of light from soils and vegetation near a fault line were of interest. Following patterns of soil types and vegetation types was also of interest. But in no case was there ever any indication on the isometric display of how high or low, how tall or short something was.

In looking at the facial area of the ventral image of the Shroud of Turin, one observes a generally proper "ramping" of the nose, a "rounding" of the face, and "shaping" of the lips, eyes, and cheeks. The isometric display is mapping responses to light energy, but the result induced by the image is altitude-relevant, or "elevation relevant." This is a unique response.

The elevation result is induced over the entire ventral image and appears to be somewhat in presence on the dorsal image. What is important to note is the similarity of the isometric display response to the actual shape of a person. There are many deviations caused by "Shroud noise," such as stains on the cloth, the weave of the cloth itself, and other easily identifiable sources. But the basic image information is readily observed as a relatively accurate "three-dimensional" body image.

The VP-8 Image Analyzer can vary the elevation scale (Z axis) relative to the X and Y axis scale. The VP-8 cannot change the linearity of the Z axis response, unless the unit is un-calibrated or the camera is improperly operated. A change of 10 percent in the incoming light level will produce an elevation change of 10 percent on the Z axis. It is a direct, linear function. The VP-8 can change the image polarity from bright-is-up to bright-is-down, but this is simply changing photographic response from negative to positive polarity. Therefore, a photographic positive or negative can be used, if the isometric polarity control is properly selected.

The Shroud image induces a response in the isometric display of a VP-8 Image Analyzer that is unique. Each point of the Shroud body image appears at a proper "elevation." Is this due to the distance the cloth was from a body inside it? Is this due to the density of the human body at various points in the anatomy? Is it a result of radiant energy? These questions cannot be answered by the VP-8 Image Analyzer. However, the related theories can be rightfully posed. The isometric results are, somehow, three-dimensional in nature. The displayed result is only possible by the information ("data") contained in the image of the Shroud of Turin. No other known image produces these same results.

If one considers the Shroud image to be "a work of art" of some type, then one must consider how and why an artist would embed three-dimensional information in the gray shading of an image. In fact, no means of viewing this property of the image would be available for at least 650 years after it was done.

One would have to ask (assuming this is a "natural result" in some style or type of art), "Why isn't this result obtained in the analysis of other works?" Or, if this is a unique work, "Why would the artist make only one such work requiring such special skills and talent, and not pass the technique along to others?" How could the artist control the quality of the work when the artist could not "see" gray scale as elevation? Did the artist predict the outcome before the outcome could be defined? Would an artist produce this work before the device to show the results was invented?

The VP-8 Image Analyzer's isometric display is a "dumb" process. That means it does one process on whatever "data" is sent to it. In that regard, it is quite like Secundo Pia's photography. The photons come from the image through a lens, onto the sensitive material in a television camera. The photons are converted to electrons, causing more voltage to be present where the picture is bright and less voltage where it is dark. The isometric display plots out bright and dark as elevation. Like a photographic negative, the process is not "involved" in the result. It is simply photons in and voltage out. The Shroud image induces the three-dimensional result. It is the only image known to induce this result.

It might be possible to fabricate, alter, enhance, or modify an image, or imaging process, to produce roughly similar results. But, the Shroud image is at least 650 years old, and perhaps nearly 2000 years old, and it is the only image that will induce these results by simply scanning it into a "dumb" processor. An artist today would have the advantage of being able to view the VP-8 image-processed result of his work. He could perform "quality control" on the work. And, he would have the information of how to create an input that would produce the result. But, VP-8 Image Analyzers were not available in 1350. In fact, the VP-8 prototype didn't exist until 1972. Yet, the result is here today.

The Shroud image has brought forth a flood of "explanations" as to what is seen. There are "conclusions" as to the cause, composition, and method for Shroud image formation. Most of these "explanations" or "conclusions" are used to further theories as to the Shroud's "authenticity" or its "trickery." Photogrammetric analysis can be quite simple in explaining why some of these theories and conclusions are impossible. I have heard no sound, valid, scientific or artistic explanation as to how the Shroud image can be fabricated through any known means or technology.

Iron pigment is simply not possible for image formation. Iron pigment, no matter how thin the mixture, will produce a specific spectral signature that is not present on the Shroud in the image areas, or anywhere else on the Shroud, in sufficient total area of presence to cause formation of the image. Iron pigment, when evenly surface-illuminated, would produce the same reflectance response, thus producing a flat elevation on the VP-8 isometric display. This result is not observed on the Shroud.

Iron pigment is more reflective than transparent. When an iron pigment is exposed to light, more photons will be reflected than will pass through the iron pigment to the other side. Some photons will be absorbed. Therefore, if an iron pigment image is lit from behind, it will "block" (absorb and reflect) more of the light than it will allow to pass to the other side. This would result in a much higher contrast photograph of the iron pigment image. This would be as if the image was illuminated from behind the "canvas," while photographing from in front of the "canvas." So, the result would be a more clearly defined, more detailed, photograph. However, when illuminated from behind, the Shroud image is not clearly visible. It is not discernable. However, in the same back-lit photographs, blood stains, water marks, and other features that absorb and reflect more light than they allow to pass, are more clearly visible, as would be expected.

Density slicing is another function of the VP-8 Image Analyzer. This is a process of grouping light-reflectance levels. For example: an aerial photograph might show fields of wheat, a lake, and several strips of ground that have been plowed for planting. Each of these individual features in the aerial photograph will have generally similar reflectance values. The VP-8 density slicing function can be used to select the range of reflectance values that generally represent selected features within an image. For our example, we could assign the color red to represent the group of reflectance values in the aerial photograph where wheat is known to exist. The VP-8 would automatically color all the portions of the image "red" where wheat is likely to exist. The same could be done with the group of reflectance values indicating the lake. The color green could be assigned. Then, everywhere a reflectance value occurred, that was associated with the group of reflectance values representing the lake, it would be colored green. All water surface areas in the image would, most likely, be shown in the color green. We might assign the color cyan to all the reflectance values associated with the plowed ground and thus indicate the probable location of all ground that has been plowed for planting.

Density slicing conventional top-lit photographs of the Shroud shows no uniform reflectance areas over the Shroud, as would be anticipated with evenly illuminated iron pigment areas of proper expanse. Using various observation methods, I could see no "dabbing patterns," as might be expected from the application of a pigment and binder. The "dabbing process," and the "iron pigment theory," are posed together as a definitive conclusion on the "trickery" side of the "explanations pile." Simple results of simple tests, such as back-lighting the image, prove such theories are incorrect. More complex tests also prove they are incorrect. Microscope examinations of the threads shows no pigment, no binders, no "bleeding of chemicals" between fibers, and no fiber discoloration to match iron pigment. The very microscope slides used to make the assessment that the Shroud image is made with iron pigment prove that no binders are in place on the fiber strand shown as example. Spectral response tests prove there is no "signature" at the appropriate wavelengths for iron pigment reflection. And, density slicing tests do not show large areas of even illumination indicating pigments and binders in the Shroud image area. Yet, such "theories" are published as fact, in spite of the many test results proving it cannot be so.

People have noticed subtle patterns in the Shroud image. Some see coins. Some see flowers. One must use extreme caution in coming to conclusions based on such general spatial observations. Caution is especially warranted if the patterns observed stem solely from studying monochrome images. It is essential to determine that the "pattern" is free of "noise." If the pattern is part of the "image" on the Shroud, then stains, dirt, shadows of creases, shadows between threads, or other non-image contrast sources should not be part of the "pattern(s)" used in the analysis. An "investigators' database," for coordinating all investigations, would help verify results and "confirm" various observations. The patterns described could very well be what they "appear to be" to those who are able to "see them." There is probably a limit to the resolution of the Shroud image, related to the cloth structure, the size of threads, and so on. A geographic information system (GIS), spatial database, could be applied to studies of the Shroud of Turin. I hope that such a database becomes available to all investigators, very soon. It could be used to aid in the study and verification of observed patterns, and contribute to all other investigations of the Shroud.

There are other unusual attributes of the Shroud image. The fingers, shown in the Shroud image, seem to extend beyond the "fleshy outline" of the fingers on our hands. In fact, the image appears to reveal the bones associated with the palm of the hand. In addition, there is darker shading in the area of the palm that would be associated with the location of our thumbs, were we to bend our thumbs onto our palms. Is this the thumb being "exposed" behind the palm, as if in an X-ray image? There are other areas of the image where it appears the shading of the image is associated with the internal body structure (i.e. bones). Does that mean the Shroud image is an X-ray? The observation does seem to prompt an explanation. Is it not sufficient to simply acknowledge the observation and not "jump to a conclusion?" I have no explanation. I do not believe the Shroud image is an X-ray, any more than I believe it is a photographic negative. I do not believe the Shroud is a gray-scale, three-dimensional image, either.

If we can avoid jumping to conclusions, we are free to describe what we observed, by using our experiences and our vocabulary. These references are made in the hope that common terms can be understood by many more people, having similar experiences and vocabulary. The Shroud image exhibits some attributes which appear similar to the attributes of photographic negatives; appear similar to a true three-dimensional gray scale encoded image; and, appear crudely similar to the results of X-ray images.

If, however, I suggest an observation that "the Shroud image seems crudely similar to an X-ray," and one assumes from that statement that the Shroud image is an X-ray, my freedom to describe what I have seen is taken away. A false conclusion is the result. If I say, "The Shroud appears more easily comprehended, and reveals more detail, in the photographic negative form," and one assumes I mean the Shroud image is a photographic negative, they have jumped to a false conclusion. Since we do not know, and we do not comprehend, the method-of-origin of the Shroud image, it is easy to jump to conclusions. Doing so may limit our ultimate comprehension of the simple truths of our observations. A "simple truth" may be far more important than any potentially flawed assumption. We are, however, forced to work within a limited vocabulary. It was okay to simply state the Shroud was "like a photographic negative" at the time of Secundo Pia. Today, however, we know there is much more information and detail in the Shroud than is represented by its comparison to a simple photographic negative. Today's comparisons will undoubtedly be outdated, and considered as "naive" tomorrow.

I cannot explain, nor can I confirm, the results of the Carbon dating tests. I can only claim that the image on the Shroud of Turin required a human body that had been tortured as Christ was tortured, and murdered as Christ was murdered. I can claim that the body is not there, but the image is there. And, I respect the many other investigations that suggest the history of the Shroud is much more ancient than the carbon tests may suggest.

However, the "subject" of the Shroud of Turin is clearly Jesus Christ. That is obvious to all. No matter how it was made or when it was made, the Shroud of Turin is about Jesus Christ. And, personally, I believe it to be the burial cloth of my Lord and Savior, and the image to be His image. The Good News is, He is risen. We have the image, but not the body. Thanks be to God!

Conclusion

The Shroud of Turin is a unique item, with a unique image upon it. The image on the Shroud of Turin induces results in common photographic processes that are unique, relative to all other "art works" studied. Furthermore, the Shroud image induces results in an isometric "brightness model" of the image that is unique compared to all other "art works" and "objects" studied. It is very unlikely that the properties of photographic negatives were understood in the fourteenth century. It is equally as unlikely that three-dimensional modeling of gray scale information was understood in the fourteenth century.

Therefore, it is most unlikely that the Shroud of Turin is a work of fabrication, or "trickery," or "forgery," of any type. No method, no style, and no artistic skills, are known to exist, that can produce images that will induce the same photographic and photogrammetric results as the Shroud image induces. This comparison includes photographic and photogrammetric studies of bas-reliefs, paintings, sculptures, etchings, and other forms of art. The Shroud image exhibits some properties of photographic negatives, some properties of body frame (skeletal, internal) imaging, and some properties of three-dimensional gray-scale encoding.

It is "none of these," and represents portions of "all of these," and more. Much more will be uncovered in future investigations. The Shroud of Turin is, in my opinion and belief, the burial cloth of Jesus Christ. There is no way I will ever prove it. Such proof is not within my grasp. I can, however, prove what it is not.

MARY W. WHANGER

CO-FOUNDER COUNCIL FOR STUDY OF THE SHROUD OF TURIN (CSST)

Mary W. Whanger received the AB degree in Religion at Duke University, Durham, North Carolina, and has further training in elementary education, home economics, written and clerical skills. Her main focus has been as homemaker and mother, with much volunteer service on the local, Conference, and Jurisdictional levels of the United Methodist Church.

She first became aware of the Shroud of Turin in 1977 when her husband, Alan, became intrigued through a photograph of the Shroud face. This interest led to the beginning of serious research in 1979 when he was challenged to do exacting comparisons between the face of the Man of the Shroud and early Byzantine icons of Jesus. From the beginning, Alan has been the primary researcher and Mary his assistant. They eventually developed the Polarized Image Overlay Technique by which similar or congruent features of two images may be exactingly observed and quantified. By this means, they were able to show that various icons of the fifth and sixth centuries were based so accurately on the Shroud image that the iconographers had to have had direct access to it.

Much of their work has been with image comparison and recognition, using thirty or so high-grade photographs of various aspects of the Shroud made from those of Guiseppi Enrie. They have identified the images of a number of non-body objects that were placed on and around the body at the time of enshroudment, and have demonstrated that the images were formed between 24 and 36 hours after death by two types of radiation.

They have presented numerous papers at professional meetings, and their work has been presented in various television productions on all of the major networks. Mary was primary author of their book, *The Shroud of Turin an Adventure of Discovery*, and was co-author of the book *Flora of the Shroud of Turin* with Alan and Israeli botanists A. Danin and U. Baruch.

In 1994, she and Alan founded a non-profit corporation, Council for Study of the Shroud of Turin (CSST) to facilitate and expand their research and educational efforts. Some of the research can be seen on the CSST website at **www.shroudcouncil.org**. Mary is editor for the news-letter *CSST News*, which is published triannually.

Non-Body Objects Imaged on the Shroud

Originally presented on 6 June 1998, Turin, Italy, at III Congresso Internazionale di Studi sulla Sindone

While the body images on the Shroud of Turin are more easily seen and therefore have naturally been the major focus of attention, there are also images of many other objects on the Shroud. These non-body images help to date and locate the origin of the Shroud and to understand it more fully. Some images are of objects that are found on the body and others are of objects that were placed beside the body.

For nearly twenty years, my husband Dr. Alan Whanger and I have been involved in major research about the Shroud, much of it analyzing the non-body images in minute detail. To do this, we obtained nearly thirty high-grade photographs of the Shroud produced from second- and third-generation negatives made from Enrie's 1931 photographs. Most of these photographs are life size, and a number have been enhanced to increase the contrast and thus show the images more clearly. Also, we have used our Polarized Image Overlay Technique, which we invented for the purpose of comparing images. This is done by projecting two images, one on top of the other onto a lenticular screen, through polarizing filters that are placed with horizontal and vertical planes at right angles to each other, and then looking at the images through a third polarizing filter which is rotated to allow the images to fade one into the other. By this means one may make detailed, exacting, reproducible, and quantifiable comparisons between two different images. This technique has made possible the identification and verification of various objects, and counters the suggestions of some that the images are simply the product of imagination or of the weave pattern.

Many images of flowers are present on the Shroud, and these will be discussed by Professor Avinoam Danin. Also, there are images of two Pontius Pilate lepton coins, one over each eye. The identification and implications of the coin over the right eye will be discussed by Dr. Alan Whanger. I will, therefore, not speak to these, except to say that there is evidence for corona discharge in image formation, and to acknowledge that the pioneering work of physicist Oswald Scheuermann in producing images off of many different types of objects by electron corona discharge onto both cloth and photographic film has been crucial to our work in finding and identifying the various images discussed in this paper.

Most objects whose images are on the Shroud correspond very accurately to known first century objects. In some instances, such as the flowers, the images are of objects that are not specific to century. There is much evidence in art through the centuries that these images were much easier to see early on than they are today. For example, flowers congruent with those whose images are on the Shroud were portrayed in numerous works of art from the third through the tenth centuries depicting Jesus. These depictions of Jesus are highly congruent with the Shroud face image, and the depictions of flowers are accurate as to placement, but not as to species. Many flower depictions are stylized, and those on coins are too small to have the shapes of the different varieties. Objects corresponding to many of the other off-the-body images were depicted frequently in medieval art. These depictions indicate that at the time they were produced the images on the Shroud were quite clear and were the basis for the artistic productions. Also, many of the objects whose images are on the Shroud correspond accurately to numismatic and archaeological evidence.

Let's look now at the images of some of these objects. The first four—the head phylactery, the arm phylactery, the amulet, and the crown of thorns—we feel show acts of mocking the man whose image is on the

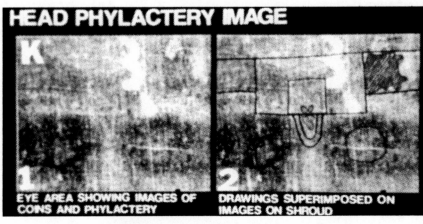

The head phylactery image with superimposed drawings

Shroud. The first two because the phylacteries have been damaged and placed on the body incorrectly. The amulet because it is an outrageous object to be placed on a Jew. It was the custom of the Jews to place in the tomb with the body all objects that were in touch with the body at the time of death or that had on them the lifeblood. With the exception of the flowers, this could account for the presence of all the non-body objects.

A structure on the Shroud which also may be seen on many of the early icons is what looks rather like a three-sided box (the top side is missing) above the nose just above eyebrow level, with a V-shaped image extending from the base of the box down over the bridge of the nose. In 1983, when Dr. Robert M. Haralick was doing his three-dimensional computer image analysis of the Enrie 1931 photographs, we asked him to pay particular attention to the area where the box is found. He found strong evidence for a three-dimensional non-body object, a three-sided box with a V. Remembering God's command to the Hebrews in Deuteronomy 6:8 to "bind them (God's words) as a sign on your hand, fix them as an emblem on your forehead," we wondered whether the box might be a head phylactery (tefillin). A search in the Duke University library yielded a book by Dr. Yigael Yadin with a photograph of the only intact head phylactery so far found dating to the first century, opened to show the four Scripture packets. Careful comparison of the dimensions of this first century phylactery with the dimensions of the three-sided box on the Shroud showed them to be an almost exact match, as did subsequent comparison using our Polarized Image Overlay Technique. We were able to identify on the Shroud image the four compartments for the Scripture packets. The two center compartments are seen as oval areas that nearly exactly correspond to the two center Scripture compartments of the first century phylactery, but the compartments are empty. Could this finding plus the V at the bottom of the box indicate that the phylactery had been torn open and the Scripture packets spilled out? Comparison studies show that the tip of the V, if folded up, reaches to the top of the phylactery and the width covers the empty compartments. Phylacteries are made of leather and do not tear easily. It would require a sharp knife wielded with considerable force to do such damage. Haralick also confirmed our earlier finding of the presence of a larger, apparently flat rectangular base underneath the box and a band from each side of the rectangle extending around the head, apparently to tie the phylactery in place, as we also found markings on the back of the head consistent with the ritual knot.

The image of the arm phylactery may be seen at the elbow of the left arm. It had been put on upside down, and also had been torn open. The image of the ritual knot is seen next to the phylactery, and there are what appear to be stains of tiny rivulets of blood in the interstices of the knot. The strap which was wound around the arm seven times and then around the hand had come loose, and its approximately ten-foot length hangs away from the elbow and down by the left thigh and then up and under the forearm, with the end visible on the abdomen.

Scheuermann was the first to discern some type of object, perhaps an amulet, in the middle of the upper chest. Alan made photographic enlargements of the area until it became apparent that there are tiny figures of a man and a woman in a circular area, the man seated with a raised spear-like object in his right hand and the woman seated opposite, with legs folded underneath her, holding some type of scepter over her shoulder. After reviewing the photographs of hundreds of Roman and Jewish amulets, it became clear that Tiberius Caesar liked to have himself depicted seated with a spear across from a goddess, with the oval-shaped sign of Capricorn between their heads. We were not able to find an exact match for the image on the Shroud, but overlay comparisons with a similar amulet showed them to be similar indeed, and also revealed the presence in the Shroud image of the oval sign between the heads of the two figures. Hanging down from the amulet image on the Shroud appear to be images of two long string-like objects, consistent with tassels or fringes taken from the hem of the cloak customarily worn by Jewish males.

MODEL OF CROWN OF THORNS OVERLAID ON SHROUD IMAGE ON THE RIGHT SHOULDER

There is an image of a circular structure that is composed mostly of the thorn *Gundelia tournefortii*, the identification of which plant will be discussed by Professor Danin. This, we feel, is the crown of thorns, placed in the Shroud on the right shoulder. It is illustrated by these drawings of *Gundelia* taped together to form a cap-like structure. Both the size and the position of the thorns are good matches for the blood stains on the head, front and back.

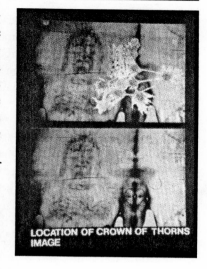

LOCATION OF CROWN OF THORNS IMAGE

There is an image of a six and one-half inch long spike, one of the crucifixion nails, about one-half inch square with a larger head. It is near the right thigh on the dorsal image half of the Shroud.

An image of a Roman *hasta* or thrusting spear may be discerned on the dorsal half of the Shroud near the edge on the anatomic left side. The blade of the spear is about level with the head of the man. The upper part of the blade disappears into a water stain. A narrow neck joins the blade to the shaft. The width of the spearhead fits the wound in the chest, and the length of the blade is correct for penetrating the right auricle of the heart.

We found the image of a sponge tied to what appeared to us to be a long stick or pole. Danin has identified the "stick" as an Arundo donax reed. The image of the sponge has within it small circular areas, each with a central depression, looking something like tiny bagels. We found on overlay comparison that these tiny "bagels" are actually the stomata or pores of a sponge. This photograph shows part of both the front and back of the Shroud—front and back images of the sponge and of the spear.

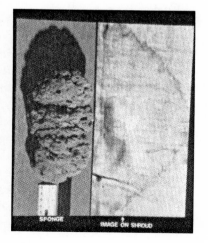

SPONGE   IMAGE ON SHROUD

Tom Flaherty pointed out to us markings that he thought might be consistent with a piece of wood, and suggested that this might be the handle of a large hammer. Careful examination revealed not only the handle but also a large hammerhead, the shape of which is consistent with drawings of first century implements.

Because we had found the images of a nail and of a hammer, we began to wonder if there might also be the image of something used to remove the nail. Further searching revealed the curved margin of the jaws of a large pair of pliers.

There are additional objects whose images we have found on the Shroud, but which I will not be able to show because of the limitation of time. Based on images on the Shroud, these models show how they may have been placed around the body at the time of enshroudment. These objects include two scourges of the type used to keep prisoners moving on the way to crucifixion, two sandals, a scoop or large spoon or trowel in a box and two brush brooms used for gathering bloody dirt, a pair of dice, and several letters on the titulus. We feel there may also be partial images of the cloak, the tunic, and two other nails.

This painting of the "Arma Christi" was made about AD 1360, and is an example of many European paintings with similar content made during the next two centuries. The depictions closely resemble the objects imaged on the Shroud.

DEPICTION FROM 1360

"Arma Christi"

This presentation has necessarily omitted much about the non-body objects imaged on the Shroud. We would be happy to talk with anyone who wishes and to show you additional photographs. We also have videotapes.

For a more complete presentation, I would like to recommend to you our book, *The Shroud of Turin—An Adventure of Discovery*, published earlier this year. It is the story of our research of the past almost twenty years, and is illustrated with 65 photographs.

It is our strong hope that detailed imaging of the entire Shroud will be done, and soon, and also that the taking of additional sticky tape samples from certain areas will be permitted. This would enable clarification of the images, confirmation of those that have been correctly identified and correction for any others. And possibly the finding of images of additional objects which would further confirm the uniqueness of the Shroud as the most remarkable archaeological artifact in existence and its authenticity as the burial shroud of Jesus.

Death by Crucifixion on the Shroud

Originally presented at the III Congresso Internazionale di Studi sulla Sindone, held in Torino, June 5-7, 1998

The asphyxiation or suffocation theory as the cause of death due to crucifixion was first propounded by LeBec in 1925 followed by Hynek in 1936 who provided his observations while a soldier in the Austro-German army where soldiers were punished by hanging them above their heads by their arms with their feet just off the ground. They had extreme difficulty breathing out, severe muscle contractions and spasm and died violently of asphyxiation. Barbet, was apprised of a prisoner at the Dachau concentration camp who was hung with his hands directly above his head and had to raise himself up by his hands in order to breathe because the air was locked in inspiration. When he could raise himself no longer, he died of asphyxiation.

There is no doubt that if Jesus was suspended with his hands directly above his head there would be difficulty breathing but *not if the victim is suspended with his arms spread apart to create an angle of between 65 to 70 degrees.* We confirmed this with our suspension studies detailed below. Even Barbet concludes that Jesus was suspended at an angle of about 70 degrees. This is also borne out on the photo of the cadaver he suspended on a cross in his book *Le cinq plait du Christ* and on the crucifix sculpted by Villandre according to Barbet's specifications shown in his book, *Doctor at Calvary.* It is interesting that Dr. P.J. Smith, the surgeon friend of Barbet disagreed with his asphyxiation theory in appendix two of *Doctor at Calvary.*

Dr. Moedder, the Austrian radiologist, attempted to confirm the asphyxiation theory by suspending medical students by the wrists with their hands above their head less than 40 inches apart on a horizontal bar. He reported that orthostatic collapse occurred within six minutes.

His experiments merely confirmed that asphyxiation occurs if a person is suspended by the hands directly above their head within 40 inches from each other without anchoring the feet to the cross. It also demonstrates that Jesus was not suspended with his hands above the head less than 40 inches apart since He was suspended on the cross for a number of hours.

Barbet added two additional hypotheses as further *a priori* evidence that death by crucifixion was due to asphyxiation.

His second hypothesis was the so-called *bifurcation pattern* of the wound image on the back of the hand. Barbet indicated that this represented two positions that Jesus had to assume on the cross in order to breathe. He would have to push up with his feet in order to expel the air from his lungs. Blood would flow thus creating one of the arms of the bifurcation. Then he would drop down, creating the other arm of the bifurcation; repeating this sequence over and over until he died. The problem with this theory is that the so called bifurcated pattern is located on the back of the hand—not on the front. This would not be possible because the back of the hand is nailed firmly against the patibulum of the cross. The hand and wrist are heavily endowed with vast networks of blood vessels being constantly fed by major blood vessels on both sides of the hand. The beating heart would be constantly extruding blood through the wound. This would create a large blood smudge all over the hand, wrist and down the arm. Every movement on the cross would result in episodes of oozing and over several hours there would be a substantial blood collection.

Moreover, during our suspension experiments with human volunteers, as described below, volunteers suspended on the cross, were requested to push themselves up as if to breathe (as indicated by Barbet) by pushing against the seatbelts that held the feet to the stipes of the cross while concomitantly pulling up with the hands that had been attached to the patibulum of the cross by leather gauntlets. *At no time did the wrists change their angle; the arms bent at the elbows leaving the wrists in the same position.*

His third hypothesis derived from the breaking of the legs of the two thieves known as the *crurifragium* or *skelokopia*. The crurifragium was not applied to Jesus because he was already dead. Barbet proposed the hypothesis that this prevented the victims on the cross from raising themselves in order to breathe and they would die of asphyxia. This speculation by Barbet was not true in fact. First of all, there is evidence by Haas, from the Giv'at ha Mivtar Excavation that of the tibia and fibula bones of the crucified 7 A.D. Jew, had been broken yet their reconstruction of the position on the cross placed the body in a maximal, lifted position where the arms are parallel to the patibulum. Although Zias and Sekeles disagrees with Haas' interpretation because the breaks are at different angles and believe they must have occurred after death is completely incorrect from a forensic point of view, because there may have been more than one blow struck at different angles. The ritual of crurifragium was the *coup de grace* blow performed at a time when the victim was near death to hasten death by causing severe traumatic shock. Moreover, fractures of the bones of the lower extremities may also cause death by fatty embolism. According to some authors, the breaking of the legs was also performed to prevent the victim from crawling away following removal from the cross so that wild animals could devour them. Both Graves and Podro and Seneca have indicated that crurifragium was used as a form of punishment.

Discussion

Barbet's hypothesis that asphyxiation is the cause of death in crucifixion is deeply entrenched in the minds of Shroud devotees despite all of the logical reasoning to the contrary. Therefore, a series of suspension experiments were designed with the objective to settle this problem once and for all.

A very sturdy cross was constructed with the stipes measuring 92 inches high and the patibulum measuring 78 inches wide. The stipes was placed on a secure base secured with reinforced angle iron. The patibulum was designed as follows: in order to provide for different arm lengths, a linear series of holes with which to affix the hands were drilled through each arm of the patibulum. This was important because if a single hole was provided for all volunteers, there would be a significant disparity in the results because the longer the arm length, the less the angle with the upright. The hands were provided with special leather gauntlets used to secure the hands to the patibulum without constricting the wrists and compromising the blood supply. An opening in the gauntlet was provided at the level of the base of the middle fingers so they could be placed over the bolt that corresponded to the arm length of the volunteer. Each hole was drilled in a slightly downward direction from front to back so that the bolts could be inserted from back to front in an upward direction to avoid slippage by the gauntlets.

Following a physical examination, human male volunteers between the ages of 20 and 35 were employed. Resting values were obtained which included, a 12-lead electrocardiogram, pulse rate, blood pressure, auscultatory examination, vital capacity and ear oximetry values, arterial blood gases, and venous blood chemistries. A gauntlet was firmly tied on each hand and heart monitoring electrodes were placed on their chests and attached to a stress testing apparatus which monitored the electrical patterns of the heart, monitored the heart rate with digital readouts, and provided electrocardiogram strips automatically, each minute. A blood pressure cuff with double transducers was placed on the arm and attached to an Infrasonde electronic blood pressure unit and a Water's Ear Oximeter probe was attached to an ear and connected to an instrument that records the oxygen concentration of the blood at all times. Each volunteer was instructed to inform us of any breathing difficulties, pains of any kinds, muscle cramps, or any other problems. They were also requested not to attempt to lift the body up at any time by straightening their legs. Each volunteer climbed up on a stool, placed their outstretched arms along the patibulum to line up the holes in the gauntlets with the respective holes on the patibulum corresponding to their arm length and bolts were inserted into the appropriate holes through the back of the patibulum then through the holes in the gauntlets. The table was carefully removed allowing the volunteer to be fully suspended. A modified seat belt was then utilized to secure the feet flush to the upright of the cross. An emergency crash cart complete with a defibrillator, cardiac medications and intubation equipment was on hand to provide for the patients' safety. Individuals were stationed to the right and left of the volunteers in case of an emergency. During the period of suspension, the following information was accrued and tabulated: visual inspection was made for muscle twitching, chest excursions, color, sweating, etc., and subjective information including pain, breathing problems, psychological feelings, etc. were also recorded. A heart-lung evaluation including examination of heart and lungs with a stethoscope, periodic arterial blood gases, ear oximeter readings, vital capacity, electrocardiograms of specific leads, blood pressures, periodic screening including routine chemistry screen, CPK with isoenzymes, lactic acid, etc. Douglas bag collections of the inspired and expired air were taken at various intervals. Several of the volunteers were requested to push themselves up with their feet and pull up with their hands in order to observe the angle of the wrist in the lower and raised positions as proposed by Barbet in his asphyxiation hypothesis.

In order to determine if the feet support had any effect on breathing, ten volunteers were suspended without strapping their feet to the cross with the seat belt device and all of the above procedures effected.

Results

1. The volunteers were suspended for periods ranging from 5 to 45 minutes determined by when they wished to come down. The major reason for this decision was almost always due to the pain or cramping in the shoulders and hands.

2. The angle of the arms with the upright varied between individuals with a wide range from 60 to 70 degrees.

3. There was no visual evidence of breathing difficulties throughout the suspension.

4. Subjectively, every volunteer affirmed that they had absolutely no trouble breathing either during inspiration or expiration. A common complaint was a feeling of chest rigidity and leg cramps between 10 and 20 minutes into suspension. When this occurred, they were allowed to straighten their legs or come down.

5. The oxygen content of the blood either increased or remained constant. Both visual observations and Douglas bag studies determined this to be the result of hyperventillation with abdominal breathing beginning after 4 minutes at a rate about 4-5 times normal.

6. Sweating varying in amount from mild to marked occurred at about 6 minutes in most volunteers.

7. The heart rate increased up to 120 but there were no arrhythmias. It went down after the volunteer got over the initial anxiety. The blood pressure increased to varying degrees but never above 160 mm. There were occasional rapid rates as high as 175 but this went systolic in everyone depending on their state of conditioning, and the electrocardiogram only showed muscle tremors and no cardiac abnormalities.

8. The backs of the volunteers never touched the cross except in the shoulder region where it was slight. Pain in the shoulders caused many of them to arch their bodies back so that the top of the head touched the stipes thereby relieving some of the pain.

9. None of the volunteers attempted to push up to facilitate breathing as was alleged by Tribbe and others except when they were requested to do so.

10. At no time did the wrists change their angle when the volunteers were requested to push themselves up instead the arms naturally flexed at the elbows.

11. The volunteers that were suspended without securing their feet had no difficulty breathing and afforded identical clinical values as those who had their feet secured. The only difference was that some had difficulty getting relief of their shoulder pains because of the

difficulty in arching their backs as was done by those who had their feet secured. As a result their times of suspension varied from 8 to 18 minutes.

Cause of Death

Determination of the most probable cause of death in this type of case is complicated and requires a complete forensic reconstruction. In this regard, it is essential to examine the sequence of all the events beginning with the severe mental anguish in the Garden of Gethsemani and ending at Golgotha. Every feature is considered. The loss in fluid volume both from sweating and hematidrosis coupled with the release of catecholamines with the severe mental suffering begins the symphony. The barbaric scourging utilizing a flagrum composed of leather tails containing metal weights or bone at the tip would cause penetration of the skin with trauma to the nerves, muscles and skin reducing the victim to an exhausted, wretched condition with shivering, severe sweating, frequent displays of seizures, and a craving for water. This degree of trauma to the chest would set the stage for fluid accumulation around the lungs called pleural effusion over the next few hours. The beginning results would cause a degree of traumatic shock and hypovolemia, the latter resulting from the sweating and the early stage of pleural effusion from the effects of the scourging. Animal experimentation by Daniels and Cate showed that blows to the chest in animals resulted in rupture of the air spaces in the lung called alveoli and spasms of the bronchi. Moreover the term "traumatic wet lung" refers to the accumulation of blood, fluid and mucous from severe trauma to the chest. The irritation of the trigeminal and greater occipital nerves of the scalp by the cap of thorns from the Syrian Christ Thorn plant, *Zizziphus spina christi* especially after he was struck several times with reeds would also contribute to traumatic shock. The bumpy, uphill road to Golgotha in the hot sun, carrying the patibulum for a time, with falling some of the time due to weakness and instability, and being struck other times also add to the hypovolemia and traumatic shock. The progession of the pleural effusion would lead to increasing hypovolemia with some dyspnea (shortness of breath), cough and more instability. The large, square iron nails driven through both hands into the cross would damage the sensory branches of the median nerve resulting in one of the most exquisite pains ever experienced by people like lighning bolts traversing the arms and known medically as causalgia. The nails through the feet would also elicit a great deal of pain. Both of these would cause additional traumatic shock and hypovolemia.

The hours on the cross, with pressure of the weight of the body on the nails present through the hands and feet would cause episodes of excruciating agony every time the *cruciarius* moved. Constant shifting because of muscle spasms would cause additional pain. These episodes and the unrelenting pains of the chest wall from the scourging would greatly worsen the state of traumatic shock and the excessive sweating—induced by the ongoing trauma and by the hot sun, would cause a greater degree of hypovolemic shock.

The pathophysiological events that occur as a result of these events leading to death are those of traumatic and hypovolemic shock. Shock, regardless of its cause is defined " ...as a constellation of syndromes all characterized by low perfusion and circulatory insufficiency, leading to an imbalance between the metabolic needs of vital organs and the available blood flow." It is "...a state of inadequate perfusion of all cells and tissues, which at first leads to reversible hypoxic injury, but if sufficiently protracted or grave, to irreversible cell and organ injury and sometimes to the death of the patient." This presents a very complex array of initiating factors, compensatory reactions and several interrelationships much too complex to include here.

Conclusions:

1. The asphyxiation theory is completely untenable.

2. The cause of death in crucifixion is a consequence of shock, traumatic and hypovolemic.

THE HAND WOUND ON THE SHROUD

It may be of interest that Monsignor Alfonso Paleotto Archbishop of Bologna, who accompanied St. Charles Borromeo to Turin in 1598, and who wrote the first description of the Shroud, postulated that the nail in the hand region would have entered the upper part of the palm obliquely, and pointing toward the arm, it would have emerged where the Shroud depicts it but Barbet severely criticized Paleotto's hypothesis as "anatomically impossible." Barbet did not believe that the palms of the hand could support the weight of the body and when he noted the image on the back of the hand which appeared to be the wrist area, he proceeded to perform a series of experiments to test his hypothesis. When he passed nails through the middle of the palms of freshly amputated hands, he found that they tore through the skin between the fingers at a pull of about 88 pounds. He then collated this with mathematical calculations that revealed that if the body is suspended with the arms at an angle of about 68 degrees with the upright there is a pull on each hand greater than the entire weight of the body. He then looked for a stronger area and noted that the hand wound appeared to be in the wrist area. After performing some dissections, he concluded that the nails passed through the area of the wrist called Destot's Space, a free space bounded by the capitate, the semilunar, the triquetral and the hamate bones and not through the palms of the hand. These studies have pervaded the Shroud and crucifixion literature to such a degree that they are interpreted as unqualified, proven facts instead of theories that require confirmation by scientific studies that might challenge the validity of his studies. In this regard, many medical articles have been written utilizing Barbet's work as confirmation of their own armchair speculations, but no one has attempted to confirm the results of Barbet's hypotheses.

Unfortunately, Barbet's anatomy was way off base because the space bounded by the capitate, semilunar, triqueteral and hamate bones was on the ulnar or little finger side of the wrist while the hand wound emanated from the radial or thumb side of the wrist. It was apparent that Dr. Barbet was confused because his 1937 book, *Le cinq plaie du Christ* that was written 13 years prior to his *Doctor at Calvary* book contained a diagram showing Destot's space on the ulnar side of the wrist. Moreover, there was a photo of a cadaver nailed to a cross with the nails in the ulnar side of the wrist and a photo of the Villandre Crucifix made to Dr. Barbet's specifications with the nails in the ulnar side of the wrist. The following shows the equivalent names for the metacarpal bones that comprise Destot's Space.

BOOK	BONE 1	BONE 2	BONE 3	BONE 4
Doctor at Calvary	Hamate	Semilunar	Capitate	Triqueteral
Le cinq plaies Du Christ	Os crochu	Semilunaire	Grand os	Pyramidal
Ciba Symposia	Hamate	Lunate	Capitate	Triqueteral
Gray's Anatomy	Hamate	Lunate	Capitate	Triangular
Sobotta	Os Hamatum	Os Lunatum	Os Capitatum	Os Triquetrum

Barbet compounded his anatomical error regarding Destot's space with another serious anatomical error when he said that when he drove the nail through Destot's Space, anywhere from 1/2 to 2/3 of the trunk of the median nerve was severed. This IS ALSO NOT anatomically possible because the median nerve is not present in the area of Destot's Space but instead runs along the wrist on the thumb (radial) side of the wrist and along the thenar furrow into the palm of the hand. An easy way to locate the median nerve on your own wrist is to bend your wrist forward. You will see a firm, rope-like structure jutting outward. This is the palmaris longus tendon, which tells us that the median nerve runs along the thumb side of this tendon. Barbet was obviously damaging the ulnar nerve, which runs in the area of Destot's space, when he drove the nail through Destot's space.

It must be remembered that the hand wound image is located on the back of the hand and only depicts the exit of the nail not its entrance. We don't specifically know where the nail entered!

We can immediately eliminate Destot's space because it's on the wrong side of the wrist, the center of the palm because it would not exit at the site of the wound image where the Shroud shows it nor could it support the weight of the body as determined by Barbet's experiments and by mathematical calculations and the space between the radius and ulna because it wouldn't exit where the Shroud shows it.

There are only two remaining possibilities. The nail could pass through the radial (thumb) side of the wrist through a space created by four other carpal bones: the navicular, lunate, greater multangular and capitate bones, emerging where the Shroud depicts it. This is a very strong area and the trunk of the median nerve would most likely be damaged by this path. The second possibility is through the thenar furrow in the upper part of the palm of the hand—not the middle of the palm. This area is equally as sturdy as either Destot's Space or the radial area indicated above and would emerge at the site depicted on the Shroud. This area is located as follows: if you bring your thumb and little finger together, a deep furrow called the thenar furrow is seen at the base of the bulky prominence extending from the base of the thumb. If a nail is driven into this furrow, a few centimeters from where the furrow begins at the wrist, with the point of the nail angled at ten to fifteen degrees toward the wrist and slightly toward the thumb, there is a natural inclination of the nail to an area created by the metacarpal bone of the index finger and the capitate and lesser multangular bones of the wrist which we have coined the "Z" area. I demonstrated this path over thirty-six years ago in the human anatomy dissection laboratory with the help of a noted hand surgeon where we were easily able to insert both a probe and a large nail (a duplicate of the nail in the Holy Chapel of Gerusalemma in Rome). Moreover, a few years ago, a major unrehearsed incident occurred in the medical examiner's office that fully confirms the existence of this path. A young lady had been brutally stabbed over her whole body. A defense wound was present on her hand where she had raised her hand in an attempt to protect her face from the vicious onslaught. Examination of this wound in her hand revealed that she had been stabbed in the thenar furrow in the palm of the hand; the knife had passed through the "Z" area and the point exited at the back of the wrist exactly where it is displayed on the Shroud. X-rays of the area showed no evidence of broken bones.

These findings are in total support of the observations made by Monsignor Alfonso Paleotto Archbishop of Bologna who postulated that the nail would have entered the upper part of the palm obliquely, and pointing toward the arm, it would have emerged where the Shroud depicts it. Although the radial side of the wrist cannot be excluded as a possible pathway, the upper part of the palm is the most plausible location for the following reasons:

1. The palm region is where most Christians across the centuries perceived the wound to be.

2. The path through the upper palm is very strong and anatomically sound.

3. The path ends exactly where the shroud shows the wound image.

4. In the ancient literature, Lipsius and other authors and painters and sculptors related and depicted the hands that were transfixed in crucifixion.

5. It assures that no bones are broken in accord with Exodus 12:46 and Numbers 9:12.

6. It explains the apparent lengthening of the fingers of the Turin Shroud because of nail compression at this area.

7. Lastly, it is where most of the stigmatists prior to Dr. Barbet like St. Francis of Assisi, Padre Pio, Theresa of Konnersruth, St. Catherine of Sienna, Catherine of Ricci, Louise Lateau etc. throughout the centuries have displayed their wounds.

When Barbet noted that only four fingers of each hand was present and the thumbs were missing, he immediately postulated that the missing thumb on the Shroud was due to injury to the median nerve by the passage of the nail. He indicated that each time the nail was driven through Destot's space, the median nerve was severed either halfway or two-thirds of the way causing the thumb to be drawn into the palm. The famous phrase by Barbet, "Could a forger have imagined this" has been propagated *ad infinitim* by the "shroud crowd" in numerous articles as a major point in proving authenticity of the Shroud. This, of course, is untenable by Barbet's hypothesis because as we demonstrated above, the median nerve does not pass through Destot's space but runs along the opposite side (thumb or radial side) of the wrist. But even if the median nerve did pass through Destot's space and was injured and did cause mechanical stimulation as Barbet claimed, this would still not cause the thumb to be drawn into the palm of the hand. Dr. Ernest Lampe, one of world's leading hand surgeons who in discussing injuries to the median nerve, relates in his book, *Surgical Anatomy of the Hand*, that in severance of the median nerve "there is inability to flex the thumb, index and middle fingers." This was also confirmed to me by several hand reconstruction surgeons. It is also of importance that dissection of the hand of the young lady who was stabbed through the thenar furrow of the palm as indicated above had damage to the median nerve but the thumb was not drawn into the palm.

The question that emerges then would be, "What, then, would account for the missing thumbs?" There is a very simple explanation as to why the thumbs are not visible on the Shroud. The thumbs are missing from the Shroud image because their natural position of the thumbs both in death and in life is in the front of and slightly to the side of the index finger. Therefore, it would be next to impossible to have impressions of the thumbs because the Shroud would not be in contact with them. You can demonstrate this by placing your arms and hands to your sides or extended in front of you and noting that the thumbs normally reside in front of the index finger. Deceased individuals are brought into the Medical Examiners Office every day, many of whom are transferred to our office from the local hospitals with their wrists crossed and tied together. In every case, the thumbs are in a position in front of the index fingers.

Legal Aspects of the
Trial and Death of Christ

Excerpt from "The Legal and Medical Aspects of the Trial and Death of Christ," originally published in *Medicine, Science and the Law*, January 1970.

In an approach to a topic of this type, one is immediately faced with a dearth of factual material with which to work. Very little, if any, data concerning the subject matter appears in secular writings, and it becomes obvious that the main and probably the only source of data is in the writings of the Evangelists. This poses a problem from the beginning, and if the facts as revealed by the Gospels are to be given credence it becomes necessary to make certain that these facts will fit into recognized rules of evidence as we understand them in the present day. The field of evidence is concerned with those rules of law which determine what testimony is to be accepted and what is to be rejected in a civil or criminal trial, as well as what weight is to be given to the testimony admitted. The rules upon which the admission of evidence is based must be governed by their adaptation to the development of the truth of the facts under consideration (60 A.L.R. 376; 66 A.L.R. 360). The usual rule is that questions of evidence are governed by the law of the forum, and this applies to all types of litigation as well as to the matter of the competency, admissibility, weight and sufficiency of the evidence and the degree of proof (89 A.L.R. 1278). In the realm of presumptions and burden of proof, the rules of evidence are determined by the *lex loci* (78 A.L.R. 889). In order to apply these propositions to the results of the trial of Christ, we must first examine the facts as they were presented, and the forum in which they were presented. In attempting to do this, the objective approach will be made, considering the qualifications and attitudes of the Evangelists upon whose descriptions we must rely in interpreting the incidents of the trial, as well as the makeup and functions of the legal bodies, both Hebrew and Roman, before whom the trial was conducted.

First of all, can we consider the factual descriptions of the Gospel writers to be accurate and unbiased? It is desirable, for the purposes of a legal approach at least, to divorce any concept of a Divine guide to the words of the Gospels, and to treat the Gospel reports as pure human efforts, even though there are satisfying grounds for a belief that there was an inspiring force behind them. Our knowledge of the lives of the Evangelists leads us to the consideration that they were honest men. Certainly they did not receive an earthly reward for their adherence to the truths which they preached, for they all were persecuted and treated shamefully. Their sincerity in attempting to report the facts would appear to be unquestionable. So also would their ability, as shown by the style of their writings, particularly the writings of Luke and John. Literacy must be assumed, since the Gospels were written either in Greek or Hebrew. One might logically assume that the backgrounds of the Evangelists would be helpful in their being able to reproduce in writing the events that they had observed. We know that Luke was a physician (Col. IV:14), and Matthew was a revenue collector (Matt. IX: 9), both of which occupations would tend to indicate more than minimal powers of observation as well as suggesting some degree of analytical ability. The dignity in which the writings are conducted seems to remove them from the realm of the fanatic, the biased or the prejudiced. The relationships of the Gospel writers to Christ is important in evaluating their truth, and it is well known that some of them, and John in particular, were very close to Christ and were actual eye witnesses of many of the facts about which they wrote. That the writings were made a number of years after the events took place should not detract from their accuracy, since in very many instances there is an amazing correlation of facts in accounts written far apart and with no chance of collaboration. Often, the Gospels interlock in their descriptions, so that it is necessary to read them together in order to get a full story, and in so doing, the reader is not dismayed but rather is brought to a more complete appreciation of the accuracy of the accounts. This is shown even more clearly in the instances where the accounts of an event are presented in almost identical language in each of the Gospels. Taken together, then, it may be accurately stated that the accounts of the events of the trial and death of Christ as related by the Evangelists are correct since the competency of the authors cannot be seriously questioned, and the accounts therefore fulfill the requirements of admissible evidence of the facts which they portray. For information about the legal bodies in charge of administering justice at the time of Christ, we must look to Hebrew law as it is contained in the Talmud. The latter is a collection of many volumes which may be conveniently divided into the Mishna or oral law, and the Gemara or commentary. Much of the Hebrew law was, of course, handed down by word of mouth, and the Mishna became a sort of Code that was the basis of conduct for the Jewish people. The Great Sanhedrin or Grand Council, was the major Hebrew tribunal, and as a court it was convened in Jerusalem and consisted of seventy-one members. There is much doubt about the date of origin of the Sanhedrin, but it probably can be traced back to the time of Moses (Numbers X:16, 17). The name comes from the Greek synedrion, meaning "a sitting together," and the earliest undisputed mention of the council dates from the time of Antiochus the Great (223-187 B.C.). Most likely it developed from a council of nobles, ancients and chiefs who carried out the administration of laws. There were three chambers in the Sanhedrin, each composed of twenty-three persons, and representing priests, scribes and elders. These, plus two presiding officers, made up the court of seventy-one members. Members were appointed for life, and a quorum of twenty-three members was necessary in criminal cases. The court sat in a semicircle with two clerks before them to record votes. By the usual rules, a majority of one vote was needed for acquittal, but a majority of two votes was required for a conviction. One of the more unusual policies of the court was the legal fiction that a unanimous vote for conviction served to free the defendant, the concept being that such a situation proved the court to be incompetent. Requirements for membership in the Sanhedrin included the following: Hebrew descent, knowledge of the law including the Mosaic Code, previous judicial experience in lower courts, proficiency in scientific knowledge and languages. In addition to these qualifications the member must be modest, popular, of good appearance, pious, strong and courageous. There were a number of disqualifications and among them were lack of a previous trade or occupation by which the member had made his living, advanced years, gambling and moneylending. No man who was concerned or interested in a matter under adjudication nor a relative of the accused could sit on the court, nor could any person who would be benefited by the death or condemnation of the accused. The king was not eligible to be a member of the Sanhedrin. The two court officers were the president and the vice-president.

Under the Hebrew law there were no advocates and the accused was not represented by an attorney. The witnesses were the only accusers and the suspect was considered innocent until accused.

The Sanhedrin sat in the Liscat Haggazith, a hall of polished stone which dated from the time of King Jannaeus. The ordinary days for holding court were Mondays and Thursdays and the court never sat on the Sabbath or on a feast day. The law was strict in holding that there be no trials during Passover, during the night or on the eve of the Sabbath. If it is remembered that there was poor artificial light at the best during those times, the reasons for not having a trial at night will be more obvious. In addition, tradition held that the examination of a criminal charge was like the diagnosing of a wound, and in both cases a more thorough and searching examination can be made in daylight. A capital case could not be tried in one sitting, but had to carry over to a second day in order to best accomplish the rules of justice. Also, a case could not be adjourned for more than one day, hence the reason for not allowing a trial to start on the eve of a Sabbath, since the trial could not be postponed, and no trial could be conducted on the Sabbath.

In addition to the policy of there being no defence attorney, there was also no prosecutor or States Attorney. The witnesses acted as informants and prosecutors alike. The Sanhedrin was not allowed, under rules of the Romans, to impose the death penalty, and all such penalties were required to be reviewed by the Roman Governor in Jerusalem.

At this point it might be well to briefly mention and comment upon the individuals and groups who took part in the trial and the crucifixion of Christ, and to try an place them in the proper perspective as far as the events which took place were concerned. There was, of course, the High Priest, Caiaphas, who served as presiding officer of the Sanhedrin during the trial of Christ. He was the son-in-law of Annas, also a High Priest and the political leader of Judea. Annas was in his eighties and had held power for over half a century. He was a Sadducee and he considered Christ a false prophet and was therefore ready to co-operate in the plot to arrest and try Christ. It was Annas who was in charge of those in the Temple who bargained and sold, and who were so drastically criticized by Christ, hence Annas resented Christ deeply. Caiaphas had held his position for eleven years and was entirely devoid of honor and decency. He was a close friend of Pontius Pilate, the Roman governor, and both these men hated Christ. Pilate, as Governor, had full jurisdiction over civil and criminal matters and was answerable only to the Emperor Tiberius Caesar in Rome. He had a violent record and was known to have executed hundreds of persons. He had great fear that the Jews might put him in the disfavour of the Emperor and try to remove him from office, so he co-operated with the Jews and at the same time acted as their Governor under orders from Rome. Pilate was a native of Spain. Actually the record shows that he declared Christ innocent no less than four times and tried to release Him, but finally gave in to the wishes of the crowd. Another party who played a role in the trial was Herod Antipas, the Tetrarch of Galilee, who was the son of Herod the Great. He was noted for his cruelty and for his lack of conscience. His part in the trial was small, and it is to be noted that Christ showed His contempt for Herod Antipas by keeping silence while before him. The two political and religious groups involved in the action against Christ were the Sadducees and the Pharisees. The former were arrogant and aristocratic and were the wealthiest members of Jewish society. They controlled the government as well as the Sanhedrin, and they believed nothing that Christ was teaching. They were ordinarily not close to the Pharisees but joined with them in the plan to destroy Christ. The Pharisees were haughty and boasted of their knowledge of the law and tradition. They demanded very strict compliance with the laws of fasting and all other regulations and they found fault with Christ because He brushed aside many of their habits.

The details of procedure in Hebrew criminal law are outlined in the Mishna and it was necessary that the rules be adhered to rigidly for the trial to be valid. As has been indicated, the witnesses were the mainstay of the legal process and they served as judges and accusers. They had to agree in all details for their evidence to be admissible, and each witness was required to give a complete account of the entire series of events constituting the crime in question. It was not permissible for one witness to present one facet and another witness to supplement this with facts which took place before or after those previously described. Two witnesses who were in full agreement were required, and both must tell the complete account of the crime, or else the accused would be released. No oath was ever administered, either to the witnesses or to the accused, should he testify in his own behalf. The Jews relied on the precepts of the Ninth Commandment, which forbade false testimony, and this took the place of the oath. In the examination of the witness, there was an arbitrary division into two parts, the first of which consisted of a series of questions related to the time and place of the offence, in the manner of a direct examination. This was followed by a more detailed series of questions designed to serve as both a direct and a cross-examination.

Hearsay evidence was not allowed, nor was pure circumstantial evidence. The accused was not required to testify in his own behalf, but could do so if he wished. He was not put under oath when he gave his evidence. It was the policy of the courts not to allow documentary evidence of any kind, since the Mishna was explicit in permitting oral testimony only. It is to be particularly noted that through the whole regime of Jewish law there runs a strong religious theme, and the judges were endowed with the concept that they were, in a way, acting under the direct influence of God. For that reason, caution in actions and sincere attempts to reach the truth of a situation were paramount in the functions of the courts. The innocence of the accused was presumed, and during the debate among the judges which followed the giving of testimony by the witnesses and preceded the balloting, the tendency was toward trying to find a reason for acquittal. Only after exhaustive debate on the merits of all the evidence presented did the judges cast their ballots in favour of or against the accused. As was mentioned before, it was necessary that there be a majority vote of at least two in order to convict. If this majority was not reached, the prisoner was immediately released and the trial was considered to be at an end. On the other hand, if the vote was for conviction, the court adjourned without passing sentence, and reconvened the following day. At that time, the evidence was again reviewed and another vote was taken. Those who had voted the day before for acquittal were not permitted to change their vote, but those who had voted to convict on the previous day were allowed, with valid reason, to change their vote in favor of acquittal. Here again, the scrupulosity and tendency to favor the accused is apparent, but once the vote was definitely for conviction, the court wasted no time in passing sentence and putting it into effect. There was no appeal as we know it, from that point on, and the very time that the judgment was passed became the moment of beginning of execution of the sentence.

One cannot help but be impressed at the thoughtfulness and attitude of fairness that permeates the Hebrew criminal code. But as this was applied to Christ during His trial, there is little resemblance to justice or fair play. The events leading up to the arrest, the arrest itself and the subsequent trial and punishment, as reported by the Evangelists, followed none of the rigid rules set out above.

In considering the numerous breaches, it is perhaps best to review them in chronological order, beginning with the arrest of Christ by the servants of the High Priest as He left the Garden of Gethsemane. It has been stated that the Hebrew code forbade any arrest or trial at night, yet it is clearly recorded that the arrest took place at night (Acts IV:3), probably sometime between midnight and three o'clock in the morning. The arrest was also illegal in that it was brought about through the medium of a traitor, Judas, who was hired by the Sanhedrin, the court which was to try Christ. Judas had broken the commandment of the old law in acting as he did (Leviticus XIX:17), and this was sufficient to add another factor of illegality to the arrest. The time and date of the trial was illegal, not only because it took place at night, but also because it took place on the eve of the Sabbath, thereby precluding any chance for the required adjournment to the next day in the event of a conviction. The date of the trial was on the fourteenth Nisan, which began at sunset of April 6, 30 A.D. and lasted until sunset Friday, April 7. The trial was conducted during the period of one day in addition to being held on a day when the court could not legally convene.

The Sanhedrin was without authority to instigate charges and was only supposed to investigate charges brought before it, yet in the case of Christ the court itself formulated the charges. Caiaphas, the High Priest presented the charge, and he was one of the judges (Matt. XXVI:6).

Perhaps one of the most striking errors in the procedure was the fact that the charges against Christ were changed during the trial. He was first accused of blasphemy on the basis of statements quoted by witnesses to the effect that He would be able to destroy the Temple of God and rebuild it within three days. These statements were made by witnesses coached by Caiaphas, while the actual words of Christ were: "Destroy this temple, and in three days I will raise it up" (John II:19). The reference to the "temple" was to His own body, not to the Jewish temple (John II:22) but the words were deliberately distorted. The blasphemy portion of the charge was brought out by Caiaphas when he asked, "Art thou the Christ, the son of God?," and when Christ answered, "Thou has said it," Caiaphas tore his garments in the traditional manner and declared that Christ had blasphemed. At the same time Caiaphas declared that there was no further need for more witnesses (Mark XIV:63). This was an illegal procedure since there had not been the required two witnesses who agreed on their stories. Later, in the appearance of Christ before the Roman Governor, Pilate, it was realized that the charge of blasphemy would not hold up, since such a charge was of no concern to the Romans. For that reason the charge was changed to treason and sedition and Pilate was told that Christ was undermining his authority before the Emperor.

Some question has been raised as to the actual site where the Sanhedrin met to conduct the trial. There is nothing which would indicate that the court met in its usual place, and, in fact, John implies that the proceedings took place at the palace of Caiaphas and from there Christ was taken directly to Pilate at the Praetorium (John XVIII:28).

It must be obvious that the members of the Sanhedrin were so prejudiced against Christ that they could not possibly judge Him fairly. This stems from both political and personal enmity against Him. Christ had upset the High Priests by His actions in clearing the money lenders and the salesmen from the Temple, and this served as a financial blow to those men who had built up a lucrative trade in selling of animals and birds for sacrificial purposes in the temple. This feeling was carried to other members of the court through the influence of Caiaphas, and certainly made the Sanhedrin a biased group. In addition to this, and probably much more important, is the fact that Christ had been prejudged by the court that tried Him. There are three separate references in the Gospels to events in which members of the Sanhedrin took part in a plan to entrap Christ. The first (John VII: 37-53) took place about six months before the arrest, when, at the Feast of the Tabernacles, Christ by his teachings and by the number of His converts caused much concern among the Pharisees. Similar consternation among the Pharisees took place at the resurrection of Lazarus (John XI: 41-53), and at that time the decision that Christ must die seems to have been made. The third event took place shortly before the Passover when the chief priests and scribes sought means whereby they could kill Christ (Luke XXII: 1-3; Matt XXVI: 3-5). Under these circumstances, it is impossible that there could have been an impartial trial. The one illegality in the proceedings which outshines all others is the fact that Christ was permitted no defense. It was strictly held under Jewish law that there be an exhaustive search into the facts presented by the witnesses in order to prove their accuracy. This was not done because the witnesses were false and were hirelings of the Sanhedrin and their testimony would not stand investigation. If the procedure had been followed, even if there had been a prima facie case against Christ, the court would have been obliged to make a searching study of the evidence and undoubtedly would have taken judicial notice of the many facts about the life of Christ which had been brought forth in the prophesies and had been fulfilled. The birth of Christ as the Messiah had been predicted, and the birthplace and heredity had been prophesied, as well as the little to be expected statement that Christ would be born to a virgin. Even the matter of the betrayal for thirty pieces of silver by Judas was spelled out, and these matters were well known to the judges. That they chose to overlook them speaks strongly in favor of the total illegality of the trial.

The final item in the list of illegal procedures was the pronouncing of the death sentence by the Sanhedrin. This power was removed from them by the Romans, and while the Sanhedrin could try a capital case and could enter a verdict of not guilty without interference by the Romans, the Sanhedrin was not allowed to convict and put the death sentence into effect (John XVIII: 31). This authority was reserved to the Romans who could either retry the accused or review the evidence before issuing its verdict. This policy resulted in there being actually two trials, the second of which was conducted in the presence of Pontius Pilate. Since the trial by the Jews was for a religious offense, which was of no interest to the Romans and would probably not have even been reviewed by them, it became necessary to add another charge which would serve to bring the prisoner under the jurisdiction of the Roman court. The second trial, then, had to be a trial de novo, since the charge was entirely different. The charge was vague at best, but included three items specifically: perverting the nation, forbidding the giving of tribute to Caesar, and claiming to be a king (Luke XXIII: 2).

The relationship between the Romans and the Jews at that time requires some explanation. The Jews had become subject to Roman control from the year 63 B.C. when Pompey took over Palestine. Judea became a Roman province in A.D. 6 and was governed by procurators sent from Rome. There was a mixture of independence on the part of the Jewish nation, but for the most part the Romans were in charge of the political scene. There was no treaty between the two, and there was no outline of duties and responsibilities, since the Romans preferred to permit whatever freedom seemed appropriate without jeopardising the relationship between master and subject. As has been seen, the Sanhedrin was still allowed judicial power, subject only to the Roman veto, and this actually amounted to a high degree of independence, not only in civil but also in criminal matters. It could dispose of most cases which did not involve sentence of death (Acts IV: 5-23, V: 21-40). That the Procurator had the right to impose the death sentence is proven by the words of Pilate to Christ when he threatened Christ with death (John: XIX: 10). Pilate exercised unlimited jurisdiction in military matters and was not required to follow particular rules and forms of law. He was in the position of being able to apply the law of the forum, that is, Roman law, or the law of the community, Jewish law. Most authorities feel that he should have strictly followed the criminal procedure in vogue in a capital case tried in Rome instead of handling the case against Christ as he did. The procedure before the permanent tribunal was involved and complicated, and was designed to insure justice. Criminal charges against any person were brought by a private citizen with permission of the presiding magistrate. An initial hearing was held to determine which prosecutor might present the case, in the event that there was more than one. A private hearing was often held before the president of the court in order to get more definite information about the charge. If it was thereby determined that there was a prima facie case to take before the tribunal, an indictment was issued. This procedure is not unlike the Grand Jury investigation of our day. The indictment was presented to the tribunal and a date was set for the trial, usually from ten to thirty days from that time. During this period the accused was free to go and come as he pleased and was under no bond. On the day of the trial the accused was expected to appear and was only excused if he were absent from the city on public service, or if he was in another court on the same day or if he was ill. Cases could be tried in the absence of the defendant but had to be postponed if the prosecutor failed to appear. If all was in order, the trial began with the impaneling of the judges by means of selecting names from a number of prospective judges whose names were placed in an urn and drawn out one by one. In the presentation of the case against the defendant, the argument and reasoning of the counsel was brought out first and was followed by evidence which was used to support the contentions made. This is the reverse of the modern courtroom procedure. The evidence having been presented, the judges voted and a majority determined the verdict. The type of punishment which could be administered by the tribunal included a great variety of sentences which ranged from scourging to being hurled from a high place and from beheading or being cast into the sea in a bag containing a number of voracious animals. Of all the punishments, crucifixion was the one most widely used, but it was ordinarily limited to those found guilty of the vilest of crimes. The civil law of the Romans protected Roman citizens against this form of punishment.

There is no question that the usual trial before a tribunal as practised in Rome was not accorded to Christ by Pilate. He was brought before the Roman only because the Sanhedrin was obliged to do so in order to put the death penalty into effect. This was done early in the morning, about sun up. The court of Pilate was held at the Antonia, a wing of his palace set up as a tribunal. There is no mention as to who was the accuser or prosecutor but it may be logically be assumed that Caiaphas played this role. When Pilate asked what Christ was accused of doing, the priests tried to avoid the answer and to persuade Pilate to merely accept their judgment and waive his rights to retry the case (John XVIII: 30). However, Pilate did not elect to do this but instead tried to refer the case back to the Sanhedrin for disposal. It was only then that the priests had to take a position and declare their reasons for seeking a trial before Pilate, and it was then that they accepted the jurisdiction of Pilate as far as the death penalty was concerned and gave this as their reason for bringing Christ before the tribunal (John XVIII: 31). Also at that point the Jews had to present a charge which would be of concern to Pilate and which would allow him to try the case. The charge of perverting the nation was very vague and was a form of sedition. More serious were the allegations that Christ had forbidden tribute to Caesar and that He had declared Himself king. The charge concerning the tribute was based upon Christ's advice to the Jews that they render to Caesar those things which are Caesar's, and to God the things which are God's (Matt, XXII: 21). It was another example of misinterpretation of words, and this was also true of the accusation that Christ claimed to be a king. Pilate decided to ignore the first two charges and proceeded to question Christ on the matter of His kingdom (John XVII: 34-38). The interrogation satisfied Pilate that Christ was not a king in the earthly manner and that He posed no threat to the Emperor. For that reason, Pilate then issued a verdict of not guilty and acquitted Him. This angered the Jews, and in spite of the verdict having been given and judgment rendered, they attempted to present new accusations and to reopen the trial. Pilate, breaking all procedural rules, and seeking to share the responsibility of the case with another, ordered that Christ be taken before Herod Antipas, the Tetrarch, at the Palace of the Maccabees in Jerusalem, only a short distance from the Antonia. The reaction of Herod to having Christ appear before him was favourable, although highly illegal as a judicial measure. He hoped to see a miracle performed (Luke XXIII: 8), but in this he was disappointed. He questioned Christ extensively, but received no answers but silence, in spite of the fact that the priests and scribes also stood by and made further accusations (Luke XXIII: 9-10). Herod tried mockery and carried this to an extreme by placing a gorgeous robe on Christ and returning Him to Pilate (Luke XXIII: 11). This must have upset Pilate, for he then strayed a bit further from the path of legality and justice and after declaring again that Christ was innocent, proceeded to punish Him by the scourge. The description by John of these proceedings is complete and reflects the mood and actions of Pilate (John XIX: 7-15). After offering Barabbas to the Jews and being refused, Pilate finally gave in to the wishes of the group and released Christ to them to be crucified. He had defied all the precepts of Roman law and had conducted a wholly illegal trial, and his final gesture in washing his hands before the multitude was only a theatrical act with no meaning, legal or otherwise. Thus ended the trials of Christ, first by the Jews and then by the Romans. The numerous illegalities of both are manifest and serve to justify the conclusion that these must have been the most infamous trials in history. Certainly the consequences of them have affected the world in the past and will undoubtedly continue to do so. The guilt of the parties, particularly the Jews, has been debated for centuries, and has been one reason for antipathy between religious groups and others who have felt that the guilt of a small group of persons should be transferred to a nation and all its progeny. The movement of the Second Vatican Council to formally exonerate subsequent generations of Jews from responsibility for the murder of Christ seems to be a step in the right direction, but, more important, this action served to formally document a fact previously left unsaid.

Bibliography

- Babylonian Talmud (1952) London: Socino Press.
- Barbet (1953) A Doctor At Calvary. N.Y. P.J. Kenedy.
- Bishop (1957) The day Christ Died. Harper Bros.
- Brandon (1968) The Trial of Jesus of Nazareth. London: Batsford.
- Bulst (1954) Das Grabtuch von Turin. Frankfurt: Verlag Josef Knecht.
- Bulst (1957) McKenna and Galvin, The Shroud of Turin. Bruce.
- Chandler (1925) The Trial of Jesus. Harrison Co.
- Hynek (1951) The True Likeness. Sheed and Ward.
- Jewish Encyclopedia (1903) Funk and Wagnall.
- McEvoy (1945) Death Image of Christ. Melbourne: St. Dominic Priory.
- New Catholic Encyclopedia.
- Otterbein, Adam J. Personal Communications.
- Rinaldi (1940) I saw the Holy Shroud. Mary Help of Christians School.
- Universal Jewish Encyclopedia (1943).
- Wingo (1954) A Lawyer Reviews the Illegal Trial of Christ. Wingo Publications.
- Wuenschel (1954) Self Portrait of Christ. Holy Shroud Guild.

The Shroud of Turin:
A Pathologist's Viewpoint

For many centuries, a piece of linen cloth, 4.3x1.1 meters in size and bearing the frontal and dorsal images of a human body, has been kept in Turin, Italy. Individual and group scientific studies have been performed on this cloth, known as the Shroud of Turin, the most exhaustive of which was done in 1978.[1]

Prior to 1978, nearly all studies of the Shroud of Turin were based on examination of photographs, the best of which were those prepared by G. Enrie in 1931. As a result of those studies, there has been general agreement among medical investigators that there are blood deposits on the cloth. These opinions were based on the physical appearance of the stains considered to be blood. The general configuration of the areas in question very strongly suggests that transfer of blood from the skin of the deceased to the burial cloth took place. The characteristics of bloodstains are quite clear and these blood deposits are in sharp contrast to the body imprint, while in other places on the cloth, they appear outside the body image. It is quite obvious that there is no relationship between the origin of the body imprint on the cloth and the bloodstains.

With color photos prepared by the Shroud of Turin Research Project in 1978, the evaluation of the bloodstains becomes more precise. The photographic material, particularly those pictures which accentuate the red color of the bloodstains, brings out detains of the stains very clearly. There is a distinct difference in the color of the body image and the stains representing blood deposits, with a definite carmine-red color in the latter. Enhancement photos made by the Digital Image Analysis and Display System show considerable internal structures of the blood prints. The stains have a central hollowness that probably results from the physical separation of red blood cells from serum and localization of the cells toward the periphery of the blood deposits.

In 1980, Heller and Adler reported the finding of blood on fibers taken from the shroud, based on spectroscopic and chemical tests that identify a porphyrin.[2] Later testing by the same authors has confirmed the presence of hemochromogen, protein, and serum albumin.

The imprint on the buril cloth outlines the body of an adult male, 71 inches in height and weighing an estimated 160 to 170 pounds. The general appearance of the body indicates stiffness, suggesting that rigor mortis is present. There is much physical evidence to show that the individual whose image appears on the shroud has been crucified and that his wrists, feet, chest, head, and large parts of his skin have been injured by a variety of objects. To a pathologist, the blood deposits and stains, which reflect injuries to the body, are of great interest.[3,4] A number of these are characteristic enough to permit an interpretation of their probable cause. There are some markings which reflect abrasions and contusions and others which indicate punctures and outflow of blood from cavities. Some markings on the image are good examples of patterned injuries.

The injuries on the body can best be divided into five groups: The marks of the skin, piercing lesions in the wrists, similar injuries in the feet, wounds on the head, and the wound in the chest. Each of these groups will be analyzed in some detail.

The marks on the skin appear on the anterior chest as well as the back of the body where they extend from the shoulders to the calves. On the back, the imprints appear in a sheaf-like fashion directed toward and medially from the shoulders. Each of the marks consists of two portions, indicating that the instrument used was bifid. There are indented bleeding points at each of these sites. Ultraviolet fluorescence photos of these wounds reveal no fluorescence. Some of the other blood deposits on the shroud show a pale aura around the area suggesting a separation of serum from other blood components. While these injuries involve the lower extremities, none are present on the arms or forearms. The appearance of these wounds is consistent with the application of a whip-like device having sharp or rounded ends which tore the skin in a characteristic fashion. The marks are difficult to count but they number at least 100.

Two large discolored areas over the shoulder blades are consistent with bleeding from surface abrasions as if a heavy, rough object had been in contact with the skin at these points. From what little is known about crucifixions, it was the custom for the crossbar of the cross to have been carried by the victim, supported across the upper back and shoulders. It is quite likely that it was this sort of structure which produced abrasions over the scapulae.

The imprints of the hands show that they are crossed, with the left hand covering the right wrist. The outlines of four fingers are clear but there are no imprints left by the thumbs. In the left wrist area, there is a bloodstain which is composed of two projecting rivulets from a central source and separated by about a 10 degree angle. That this bloodstain is not in the palm of the hand can be determined by simple measurement taken from a site of the mark to the tips of the fingers. It is too far from the fingertips to be in the palm. A nail can be easily driven through the bones of the wrist, separating these bones but not producing fractures. This was done experimentally by Barbet[5] and has been repeated by others. Since the right wrist is covered by the left hand, no puncture mark is visible on the right wrist. The fact that on the imprint of the hands no thumbs are clearly visible is explained by the penetrating pointing objects passing through the wrists having damaged the median nerve. The motor function of the median nerve is to produce flexion of the thumb. The thumb may either be adjacent to the hand or flexed over the palm.

From the angulation of the stain on the wrist as well as the direction flows of blood on the forearms, it is possible to approximate the position of the victim at the time of the injury and subsequent blood flow. Blood follows the laws of gravity and if one were to extend the arms laterally until the bloodstains appear vertical, it would show that the arm position was approximately 65 degrees above the horizontal at the time of the blood flow. The divergence of the streams suggests that two positions were maintained by the victim during the period of blood flow. The difference in angulation is about 10 degrees and can be explained by the victim elevating his body by directing his weight toward the feet and then changing position to permit the full body weight to be supported by the wrists.

A study of the imprints of the feet is somewhat less complicated. On the shroud, there are two prints representing the marks left by bloodcovered feet. The imprint of the right foot is a nearly complete one in which the outline of the heel and toes can be seen. In the area corresponding to the metatarsal zone is a square image surrounded by a pale halo and this represents the place where the foot has been pierced. The imprint of the left foot is less clear. Examination of the calves of the legs on the dorsal view shows that the right calf has left a well-defined outline in which the marks of the whip can be seen. The imprint of the left calf is much less distinct. This, coupled with the fact that the left heel is elevated above the right heel, leads to the conclusion that there is some degree of flexion of the left leg at the knee. It appears that the right foot was directly against the surface of the cross and the left leg was flexed at the knee and the foot rotated so that the left foot rested on the instep of the right foot. The right foot became completely covered with blood while the left foot did not. A single, impaling sharp object, like a nail, was used to fix both feet in position, passing between the metatarsal bones. One medical investigator has presented evidence that both feet may have been impaled separately rather than together.[7]

The fourth group of injuries consists of those about the head. On the front portion of the forehead are several bloodprints. These was formed by the blood flow following the normal skin creases of the forehead. Circling the scalp posteriorly is a row of blood prints and high on the scalp at the vertex are similar prints. Any puncture of the scalp ordinarily produces excessive bleeding because of retraction of torn vessels. To account for all the bloodstains on the head, one must assume that more than a simple circlet of sharp pointed objects was used. A cap-like structure with thorns at the center and periphery would account for the bloodstains on these portions of the head.

On the face over the right cheek, there is a swelling and there is partial closure of the right eye. There is a very slight deviation of the nose and at the tip of the nose is an area of discoloration consistent with a bruise. Detailed photographs and microscopic studies of the cloth in the nose image area show scratches and dirt. These are consistent with the nose having made contact with the ground, most likely as the result of a fall. The deviation of the nose may reflect injury to the nasal cartilage, although this is less clear.

The largest bloodstain on the burial cloth is on the right side of the chest. It covers the area of the fifth and sixth ribs. This stain very clearly shows separation of blood from a clear, watery material. Some of the latter may be serum, but there seems to be much more of it than can be explained by a simple process of serum release from a blood clot. Early investigations, including Barbet[5] and Judica-Cordiglia[6], believed that the blood came from the right side of the heart and that the water was fluid from the pericardial sac. It is well-known that the pericardial sac contains a very small quantity of fluid, rarely more than 30 to 50 ml. This would hardly seem to be an adequate source to account for the amount of watery fluid on the shroud. One of the theories of the origin of blood and water was presented by Sava.[8] He quotes the experience of physicians who treat severe chest injuries and the frequency of nonpenetrating injuries to the chest producing accumulation of bloody fluid in the pleural spaces around the lungs. Since red blood cells gravitate to the bottom of the cavity, the lighter serum accumulates at the upper part of the chest cavity. Sava's concept was that the piercing of the chest resulted first in an outflow of the settled bloody portion of the effusion followed by release of a clear fluid as the level of fluid in the chest cavity was lowered.

While this is a very plausible explanation of the sequence of events, there is one which is more realistic. With the exception of the whip-like injuries in the area of the upper back and chest, there is little evidence of direct trauma applied to the thoracic area. This would seem to refute one of the requirements put forth by Sava that there be severe chest injury. Accumulation of clear serous fluid in the pleural space is very frequent and occurs under a variety of situations. It may be caused by a simple irritation of the pleura and, much more likely, by congestion related to failure of the cardiovascular system. Because of the posture of the suspended crucifixion victim, it is likely that some degree of congestive heart failure occurred. One of the earliest signs of this is the accumulation of clear fluid in the pleural spaces as well as in other body cavities, including the pericardial sac. In such a situation, if there were perforation by a sharp, pointed object to the rib cage into the pleural space, there would be an outflow of clear fluid. If the piercing object were then to be pushed further into the chest, it would penetrate the pericardium and the right side of the heart and release a quantity of blood. This combination of blood and water would account for the stain on the front of the chest as well as the heavy stains which appear over the lower back.

The most logical mechanism for death by crucifixion is development of respiratory asphyxia related to failure of the cardiovascular system from shock and pain. The posture of the victim, the duration of the suspension, and the lack of adequate support for the body weight all serve to promote a condition of diminished respiratory capacity, resulting in cardiac failure and subsequent fluid accumulation in body cavities.

SUMMARY

This has been an analysis of the medically significant imprints on the Shroud of Turin by a forensic pathologist with suggestions as to their probable cause. It is a scientific and objective presentation with no direct attempt at correlation between the Shroud imprints and

New Testament accounts of the crucifixion of Christ. However, the author cannot help but comment that a remarkable consistency exists between the Gospel accounts and the forensic pathologic findings depicted on the Shroud of Turin.

References

1. Weaver, K., "The Shroud of Turin," 157 *National Geographic* (June 1980).
2. Heller, J., and Adler, A., "Blood on the Shroud of Turin," 19 *Applied Optics* (August 15, 1980).
3. Bucklin, R., "The Legal and Medical Aspects of the Trial and Death of Christ," 10 *Medicine, Science and the Law* (1970).
4. Willis, D., *Did He Die on the Cross?* 74 Ampleforth J. *(1969)*.
5. Barbet, P., *The Passion of Our Lord Jesus Christ*, Paris, Dillon et Cie, 1950.
6. Judica-Cordiglia, G., "La Sepoltura Di Gesu a La Sacra Sindone," 16 *Salesianum* (1954).
7. Gambescia, J., Personal correspondence.
8. Sava, A., "The Wound in the Side of Christ," 19(3) *Catholic Biblical Quart.* (1957).

DOROTHY CRISPINO

FORMER EDITOR AND PUBLISHER OF
SHROUD SPECTRUM INTERNATIONAL MAGAZINE

Two dates and two places can be given as the beginning of Dorothy Crispino's life; one would be November 1972 when, on the cover of a book, for the first time she saw a picture of the Holy Face. The existence of the Shroud so captured her that in the spring of 1973 she made her first extended visit to the author of the book, the Jesuit sindonologist Pere Paul de Gail, near Paris. Soon after, a visit to the Centro Internazionale at Turin was followed by visits to Don Pietro Rinaldi wherever he might be, and to many others whose work remains a living legacy.

The second date and place is perhaps a more likely starting point: Turin, covering the historic Exposition of 1978 and the II International Congress. For when these two great events had come to a close and Turin had subsided into quietude, the unforgettable Don Piero Coero Borga, in a commanding tone of voice, gently suggested that the subject of this sketch publish an international journal of sindonology in the English language. *Shroud Spectrum International* appeared in December 1981 and survived for twelve years.

Of course, for Dorothy Crispino there were other beginnings, notably her conversion to the Catholic Chruch shortly before the revelation of the Holy Face on Pere de Gail's book; nor was her first trip to France in 1939-1940, without significance in this context.

It was, in any case, inevitable that at last she would settle permanently in the countryside near the city where the Shroud resides. And who knows if it is the end, or another beginning.

A Chronological Survey of Obeservations on the Shroud Textile

Originally presented at the "Scientific Roundtable on the Holy Tunic" held in Argenteuil, 14 November 1998.

Notes from various authors concerning the physical properties of the Shroud fabric: knowledge basic to conservation studies. This is by no means a complete bibliography but a culling of technical details from primary sources at hand.

1. At eight o'clock in the morning of 16 April 1534, the Shroud, having escaped destruction in the fire of 1532, was solemnly carried in procession to the convent of the Poor Clare Nuns of Chambéry, France. To them had been entrusted the task of mending and patching the damage from the fire.

The text of the Reverend Mother Abbess was presented in *Spectrum* #2, March 1982. On page 23 we read: "After dinner, the embroiderer brought the wooden frame to stretch the Holland cloth on which the Holy Shroud was to be placed; after two hours, the cloth was fixed on the loom and we laid out the precious Holy Shroud upon it, and basted all around." And page 25, describing the wounds: "The blood drops appear as large as marjoram leaves...on looking through the underside of the Shroud, when it was stretched on the Holland Cloth or on the loom, we saw the wounds as if we had looked through a glass."

2. Alfonso Paleotto: *Esplicatione del Sacro Lenzuolo ove fu involto il Signore,* first published in 1598. Anastatic copy by Bottega d'Erasmo, Turin, 1975.

Mons. Paleotto's description is based on his close observation during the Exposition of 13-14 June 1582. "It is worth considering the fact that the sacrosanct Shroud is of linen; one notices that the material of origin is quite coarse. Length 12 feet, width 3 feet."

3. Paul Vignon: *Le Saint Suaire de Turin*, Masson, Paris 1939. Anastatic copy by Bottega d'Erasmo, Turin 1978.

In pages 78-83, Vignon initiates textile analysis; he identifies the 3:1 twill weave; describes the method of weaving a twill and compates the Shroud fabric to various ancient examples.

Vignon was one of the few privately admitted to study the Shroud previous to Giuseppe Enrie's photographic session. With Enrie, the group had passed the night of Friday, 22 May 1931, in vigil before the Shroud.

4. Virginio Timossi: "Analisi del tessuto della S. Sindone," *La Santa Sindone nelle ricerche moderne*. Acts of the congress of Studies, Turin 1939 and Rome/Turin 1950. Marietti reprint, 1980, pp. 105-111. First pub. by Beruti, Turin, 1941.

This analysis of the Shroud fabric by a textile expert was awarded a gold medal at the National Meeting of Textile Experts in Rome, 1938. The study is based on observations and data that Timossi collected during a direct examination. "In 1933, I was able to observe the Shroud intensely in every detail, close to it with eyes and heart...."

The fabric is opaque, closely woven with raw fiber. The cloth used has the necessary consistency for the practical considerations for which it was intended, i.e. for a bedsheet. A bedsheet must be robust and compact, able also to absorb perspiration, "a consideration observed up to recent times...for high quality bed linen." In fact (p. 108) one of the outstanding characteristics of linen is its excellent absorbency.

Timossi suggests that the species is *Linum usitatissimum*, which has a marvelous brilliance and fineness.

Pliny tells that cotton was widely used in Egypt; from early times, Egyptians had made use of this plant growing so commonly in their land. But linen was preferred for bed linen and undergarments because in a warm climate it remains fresh while cotton, more porous, clings to the body.

The structure is a 45° diagonal, an uneven herringbone in irregular longitudinal bands about 11 mm wide. The thread count is approximately 50 for the warp (English title for flax), a reduction of 40 threads/cm; and a thread count of 30 for the weft, 27 insertions/cm. On this basis, the weight of the cloth comes to 296 grams for every square meter. The Shroud measure being 436 cm X 110 cm, ergo 4.80 square meters, the probable weight would be 1.420 kgs.

The Holy Sheet no longer has the fresh clear color it originally had; candle fumes, the 1532 fire, etc., have darkened it to light ochre. The image is light brown.

The Shroud (p. 109) has the form of those that the Hebrews and Egyptians folded longitudinally for their narrow beds. In Turin's Egyptian Museum, there is a sheet from the XIIth dynasty (1996-1784 B.C.) in perfect condition, 7 m long and narrow like the Holy Shroud.

The cloth is solid and compact but soft, supple and easily folded; it does not tend to ravel. Although it has been folded and refolded thousands of times, it *presents no splitting in the folds* [Timossi's italics]. A fabric of this quality was woven on a vertical loom. Each warp thread was kept in tension by a separate weight, instead of all being attached to a beam as in most looms.

In the section of the Rome Acts (1950), Mons. Pietro Scotti presents a summary of the 1939-1949 research. He reports (p. 226) that Timossi had constructed a loom on which an exact replica of the Shroud was woven as a gift for Cardinal Maurilio Fossati, "The Cardinal of the Holy Shroud." In May 1965, the replica was given to the Centro in memory of Card. Fossati (*Sindon* 9:36). It was on display in the temporarily constructed Museum on occasion of the 1978 Exposition.

5. Giovanni Judica-Cordiglia: "La S. Sindone documento autentico della Passione di Cristo," Acts of the First Regional Congress of the Centro Internazionale di Sindonologia, Vercelli 1960.

Ordinary linen was grown and woven in Palestine; fine linen was imported from Egypt for temple paraments, clothing, and burials for the nobility, and other special uses. Funeral cloths even longer and more ample than the Shroud have been found at Antinoë. Prof. Marmowski, expert in textile history at the University of Magonza (Germany) asserts that it would be practically impossible to paint on such an uneven weave.

6. Vittorio Marchis: "Interrogativi e risposte sul tessuto della Sindone," *Sindon* #4 1960, pp. 15-17.

Remarking that information about the linen industry in ancient times is scarce, Marchis poses three questions: 1) Looking at the fabric, what does one see, what is its structure? 2) Could such a weave exist in the time of Christ? 3) Could the fabric have been manufactured in the 14th century?

Marchis had no answer for opponents who objected that ancient Egyptian cloth was plain weave, and that there was no documentation that in ancient times there existed looms, however rudimentary, capable of weaving a herringbone, that is, with at least four heddles.

By now the doubts have all been discussed and for the most part resolved. But in 1960, Marchis' ponderings were a challenge to a widowed weaver in Germany, Frau Lindermüller. At the end of this survey you will find a few words about her.

7. *La S. Sindone* #10 1967; Newsletter of the Cappella S. Sindone. 1868, Shroud measured 4.10 m x 1.40 m (incorrectly measured). 1898, Shroud measured 4.36 m x 1.10 m.

The measure in the middle (widthwise) was 1.105; at one end, 1.104; at the other end, 1.10. (Measure was taken before the 1898 Exposition.) 1898, measured 4.34 m x 1.095 m in a double-check measuring after the Exposition. 1978, Shroud measures 4.36 m x 1.10 m.

8. Pietro Savio: *Ricerche sul Tessuto della Santa Sindone*, Grottaferrata, 1973.

In Mons. Savio's compilation of ancient texts, he discusses Egyptian weaving techniques, linen merchants, *othonia* and *sindone*, linen garments. What interests us here is in the Preface, written by Mons. Giulio Ricci. According to Roman law, the clothes of a condemned criminal became the property of the executioners. The criminal was buried naked, as we see on the Shroud. Joseph of Arimathea therefore purchased "an excessive length" of material to cover the entire Body, back and front. An abundant measure would have been cut from a bolt, on which 30 m of material would have been rolled at the time of weaving. Persons deceased in normal circumstances would be washed, the hair cut and nails trimmed; the deceased dressed and wrapped in a shroud, leaving the face exposed. A *sudaruim* was then laid over the face, completing the burial dress.

9. From *La S. Sindone: Ricerche e studi della Commisione di Esperti nominata dall' Arcivescovo di Torino, Card. Michele Pellegrino, nel 1969*. Published by Rivista Diocesana, Turin, 1976.

Silvio Curto: "Osservazioni archeologiche circa il tessuto e l'immagine," p. 59.

The cloth measures ca. 4.36 m x 1.203 m. Ancient Egyptian cloths of the same remarkable dimensions have been found. All the Egyptian cloths were of linen up to the third century; but all of plain weave. For a technical analysis, we contacted a specialist in the field, Prof. Raes, whose report is Appendix B.

Cotton originated in India and spread in the Mediterranean area during the Roman Empire.

During our investigation (p. 65), a small area of the Holland cloth was unstitched and it was seen that the image lay on only one surface of the original cloth, i.e. it did not penetrate the thickness of the fabric. Laboratory analyses of samples taken from places of the most intense coloration proved, with sufficient certainty, the absence of impregnation of the threads by any substance whatsoever, pointing to an infinite probability that the entire image is superficial overall.

Since the cloth is pure linen, it is practically impervious to parasites, microbes, humidity less than 90 percent; it is less resistant to smog. The image can suffer from sunlight, artificial light, radiation. It is unacceptable that the Shroud is kept rolled up in a silk sheet, closed in a double chest practically of lead. It would be well to conserve the Object, even permanently exposed, laid out flat under crystal...

10. Enzo Delorenzi: "Osservazioni sui Rappezzi e Rammendi della Sindone," (ibid.).

The sidestrip (p. 108) is sewn to the main piece by a stitch used to join fabrics that lack selvages. This results in a "little cord seam," in this case a seam 4-5 mm wide. At the extreme right [above dorsal figure], the cloth is worn away leaving nothing except about 2 cm of the cord seam.

11. Riccardo Gervasio: "Bruciatore, Macchie ed Aloni che si riscontrono sul tessuto della Sindone," *Sindon* #24, 1976.

Prof. Gervasio, an assiduous and deeply devoted student of the Shroud, was one of those invited to attend an all-night prayer vigil preceding the Shroud's first television appearance on 23 November 1973. His research is thus imbued by direct observation.

The sidestrip is attached by an overcast seam or an almost invisible cord seam, perhaps formed by a rolled hem. The outer ends of the sidestrip were completely consumed from the habit of grasping the corners at times of exhibiting [notice the manner on the Duch illumination, *Spectrum* #37]. Therefore, "before 1532" the frayed ends were replaced by two rectangles of smooth white cloth. One addition is 35 cm long, the other 15 cm; attached with close stitching with frequent back-stitches. The sewing of the longer piece was later mended with an irregular whip-stitch in brown thread.

12. John Tyrer: "Looking at the Turin Shroud as a Textile," *Spectrum* #6, March 1983; based on the Author's paper published in *Textile Horizons*, 1981.

The study was made from photographs.

Tyrer quotes Pausinius: "The flax of Palestine is a beautiful yellow color. Galilee is the center of production, in a city called Arbeel."

The Gerumsbrerg cloak, Bronze Age, from Northern Europe, in wool, was woven in a 2:2 herringbone twill with a Z-twist warp. The cloak is shaped (by dropping warp threads) and without seam.

Flax fibers are not attacked by moth grubs; under certain conditions of warmth, dampness and contamination, micro-organisms may attack cellulose, notably cotton, but flax fibers resist damage well if kept dry. The fire at Chambéry would have sterilized the Shroud and helped with its preservation.

There are numerous dark warp threads that run for some distance and cross from image to non-image areas. The color difference indicates that the yarns were bleached in hanks before weaving.

"In a reversing twill the opposing lines of twill are mirror images; in a herringbone weave the two opposing lines of twill drop out of strict correspondence by two or three weft threads." It would appear that the Shroud twill is not always a true mirror image, but "drops out" to give a herringbone effect. "These changes may be faults in the weave because of incorrect drawing-in through the healds [heddles].... Only one warp thread in four would need to be lifted...by handloom, a 3:1 fabric was easier to weave than a plain-weave."

The structure of the Shroud linen is closely sett; so may not be immediately absorbent of water, let alone the more viscous liquids draining from a corpse. Concerning its draping qualities, the cloth would be stiffer warpways than weftways. Mr. Tyrer suggests that the "cord" in the seam that joins the sidestrip to the main piece could have aided in the weaving; but could also have caused difficulties when the cloth was wound onto a roller at the front of the loom.

"...the shroud is probably the most remarkable 'Standard Sample' for the interpretation of the history of textiles that has come down to us."

13. P.L. Baima Bollone: "Indagini identificative su fili della Sindone." Reprinted from *Giornale dell' Accademia di Medicina di Torino*, 1981.

Doctor Abima reports on his direct examination of the Shroud in 1978.

The thickness of the fabric, depending on the area and the traction, measure 300-350 microns. Threads are not homogeneous: some are knotted, some double. Warp and weft seem to show structural differences. Each thread is composed of about 70 fibers. Diameter of threads is variable between 10-20 microns. The overwhelming majority of fibers are of linen, with occasional cotton fibers.

14. Nicola Scarpelli: "Analisi delle deformazioni del tessuto della S. Sindone," *La Sindone, Scienza e Fede,* Acts of the II National Congress of Sindonology, Bologna, CLUEB, Bologna 1983.

Scarpelli's study offers an explanation of the observation, often noticed but never explained, of why the weft threads appear thicker than the warp. In seven pages, with diagrams, Prof. Scarpelli demonstrates that hanging and rolling have altered the original dimensions of the Shroud: the chevrons have stretched lengthwise, narrowing their angle; consequently widthwise the chevrons contracted.

Robert de Clary's description comes immediately to mind: every Friday (for how many years?) the *sydoine* stood up straight.... (See P. Dembowski's analysis in *Spectrum* #2). Hanging vertically, probably doubled over between the heads, as many treasured "true copies" are today.

To experiment, Scarpelli split longitudinally part way up the center of a swatch of Timossi's exact replica; he applied traction to one half. After six hours the angle of the chevron on the weighted portion had diminished from 58° to 47°; the overall length increased from 11.6 cm to 12.7 cm while the width lost 1 cm. The weft threads bunch up as the warp threads draw closer to each other by the traction.

Photos of some areas of the Shroud confirm the distortions. The angles resulting from a 3:4 proportion (40 warp threads/30 weft) are calculated by trigonometry; but the actual proportion on some parts of the Shroud are found to be only 2.7:4—an absurd choice for any weaver.

The most important consequence of the lengthwise stretching of the fabric is that the Holy Face appears longer and narrower by 20 percent, a fact that obliterates the effects of the curvature of the cloth over the Face. The effect is illustrated by comparing a photo of the Holy Face as we see it with a photo of the Face dilated 20 percent, giving a fuller, more natural appearance.

15. L.A. Schwalbe and R.N. Rogers: "Physics and Chemistry of the Shroud of Turin; A Summary of the 1978 Investigation," *Analytica Chimica Acta,* 135 (1982) pp. 41ff.

The Shroud appears to consist of two panels of visually identical linen joined by a seam 4-5 mm wide. The sidestrip varies between 7.8-8.4 cm. A radiograph suggests that the sidestrip is, or was at one time, an integral portion of the main cloth. The radiogram [illustrated on p. 42] shows "alternating high- and low-material-density 'bands' that evidently correspond to weft lots of different weight used in the weaving." The weft structure is continuous across the seam.

Frau Anna Lippoldt-Lindermüller

One of the pilgrims to the 1978 Exposition was a middle-aged weaver from Dachau vor München, Frau Anna Lippoldt-Lindermüller. Having read the textile article by Vittorio Marchis in *Sindon* #4, 1960, Frau Lindermüller determined to fabricate a replica of the Shroud. She studied Timossi's book *La Santa Sindone nella sua constituzione tessile; analisi e ricostruzione tecnica del Sacro Lenzuolo* (Turin 1942) concerning the structure, attentively noting the faults and imperfections of the ancient weave, so clearly shown on Enrie's photographs. Believing that there must have been a technique now lost, she studied Egyptian papiri and hieroglyphs seeking the key to a technique different from what is generally known to have been in use in Egypt. In the end, she constructed a vertical loom on which she wove an exact replica. Her first results were examined by Turin's textile experts, who found them scrupulously scientific.

Lindermüller's loom is conserved in the Museum of the Centro.

Ancient Loom.   (Vatican Vergil.)

Why Did Geoffroy de Charny Change His Mind?

Crusaders, Templars, knights, and knaves have been stalked by sleuths intent on identifying the man who carried the Holy Shroud away from Constantiople in 1204 and —presumably but not necessarily—took it to France. Some investigators have even alleged that the deed was done by Geoffroy de Charney, forgetting that he was not born until the next century. But no crusader, Templar, knight, or knave, left fingerprints on Exhibit A; so in default of evidence the case, for the moment, hangs suspended. We can confidently eliminate those who took part in the Fourth Cursade: the Shroud is still listed in Constantinople's inventory of treasures as late as 1247.

In his monumental opus, "Ricerche Storiche sulla Santa Sindone,"[1] Mons. Pietro Savio examines documents that almost certainly point to that crucially important moment in which Geoffroy de Charny receives the Holy Shroud. Other sindonologists—notably Luigi Fossati, S.D.B.,[2]—have added evidence from the same period, and the search goes on.

Andre Perret[3] remarks that the military career of Geoffroy carried him to too many places for us to determine, in the present state of our knowledge, where the relic came into his possession. From 1337, when he first distinguished himself in a battle in Guyenne, until his death at Poitiers in 1356, Geoffroy was constantly crisscrossing France from Flanders to Vannes on the Atlantic, from Picardy and Normandy to Anjou. Twice he was outside France: in 1345 he joined the Dauphin Humbert II on the Smyrna crusade and some authors have suggested that it was there the Shroud came into his hands. Undoubtedly, he sailed; only first-hand experience could have dictated his descriptions, in his long poem, of the perils of the sea. But the problem of his participation in the Smyrna campaign has not yet been fully investigated; and since the documents we are about to consider in this essay pertain to a later period, the Smyrna question is chronologically not relevant.

The gallant soldier decidedly did not volunteer for his second departure from France. In 1350, villainously betrayed and after a furious battle at Calais, he was taken to London as Edward III's prisoner-of-war.

Not until 20 December 1350 did the English king give safe-conduct to a servant and two valets of Geoffroy to go to France to raise money for his release. In the meantime, Philip VI had died (1350) and on 31 July 1351, his son and successor, John II, paid the enormous ransom—a resounding 12,000 gold scudis. Geoffroy, however, had been allowed to return to France beforehand, for on 28 June 1351, John II appointed him Bearer of the sacred Oriflamme of St. Denis. In that same month, Geoffroy renewed his efforts to take Calais, attacking at Ardres.

In October of 1351, there were other combats in the Calais area. On 6 January 1352, at the ceremony inaugurating King John's new Order, Geoffroy was one of the first to be created Knight of the Star. Then, in February, he went to St. Omer as captain-general of the army, invested with all the authority of the king himself. At this time, he was counsellor to John II, as he had been to Philip VI from 1348 until Philip's death. The seigneur of three modest domains had risen to be one of the foremost figures in France.

Fighting the English again in June and September of 1352; in 1353, Picardy; 1354, Normandy; and after the battle of Breteuil in July of 1356, John II rewarded him with two houses in Paris.

He had precious little time to enjoy them; on 19 September 1356, at the disaster of Poitiers, Geoffroy de Charny was killed, holding aloft the Oriflamme until he fell. John II gave him a hero's funeral at the church of the Celestins in Paris.

That the *preux chevalier* did receive the Shroud in connection with a battle seems implied in the statement of his granddaughter, Marguerite de Charny, who claimed that the Shroud was "conquered" by the late messire de Charny.[4] A slightly different account was recorded in a Bull of Clement VII (1390) in which Geoffroy II attests that the Shroud was given to his father *sibi liberaliter oblatam;* freely or generously presented to him.

The statements given by Geoffroy II (1389 & 1390) and by his daughter Marguerite (1443) are not necessarily incompatible. They might both be correct, each one but a glimpse of the whole story. They do agree in this: the Shroud was personal property legitimately acquired, and legitimately held by Geoffroy's heirs. Neither Geoffroy II nor Marguerite makes any mention of the place, the donor, the circumstances; these are still totally unknown.

But Geoffroy himself, according to Mons. Savio's demonstration, may have circumscribed the time-frame in which the transfer took place.

Geoffroy de Charny was the second son and third child of Jean de Charny and great-grandson of Ponce de Mont-Saint-Jean, who founded the Charny branch in the thirteenth century. Geoffroy's elder brother Dreux became sire of Charny. Geoffroy inherited the property, which had been his mother's dowry consisting of the lands and tiny hamlet of Lirey,[5] nearly a hundred miles away.

Tucked in a joyous dip of undulating Champagne in the diocese of Troyes, parish of St. Jean Bonneval, the Lirey fief provided very little revenue. At the end of the thirteenth century, there were fifty hearths; today the total population is less than sixty souls. To take up residence there, Geoffroy had to build himself a castle; of which nothing now remains but the stump of a tower buried in brambles and weeds.

And the village had no church.

Early in 1343, Geoffroy appealed to King Philip VI for revenues, land or other, which would accrue to 140 livres annually; as it was his desire to found a chapel with five chaplains, so that he and his family might hear Mass and benefit from the good works of the clergy. In an Act of June 1343, Philip donates to his *amé et féal Geoffroy de Charny chevalier* 140 livres of land, tax exempt, for financing the project.

These documents, dated seven years before Geoffroy's captivity, refute the romantic legend that the "perfect knight" was miraculously freed from prison after making a vow to the Virgin to build a church in her honor.

A document in the Lirey archives, dated 3 January 1349, confirms Philip's donation. Geoffroy himself contributed his inheritance from an aunt (undated).

Three months later, in a petition to Clement VI dated 16 April 1349,[6] Geoffroy announced to the Pope that he has constructed a chapel dedicated to Blessed Virgin Mary of the Annunciation and therein established five canons, each to receive a stipend of 30 livres. He requests that the church be raised to a collegiate. In the petition dated 26 April 1349, he requests an indulgence of 100 days for all who, in devotion and penitence, visit the church on the feasts of the Virgin; that the church have its own cemetery beside it for the canons, chaplains, and whosoever desires. As for the disposition of his own remains, he desires that, after the dissolution of his body, his bones be divided and buried in divers places.

> *Item eidem supplicanti concedere dignemini, ut post dissolutionem corporis sui, quod idem corpus possit dividi et diversis locis sepeliri, prout duxerit ordinandam, et alias ut in forma.*

All these requests were granted; but Item 1, concerning the collegiate status, was not accomplished because Geoffroy left again for Calais where in the night between 31 December 1349 and 1 January 1350, he was taken prisoner.

There is some perplexity about Geoffroy's statemnet of 16 April 1349 that a church had been built:

> *Significat Sanctitati vestre devotus filius vester Joffridus de Charny miles dominus de Lirey Trecensis diocesis, quod ipse in villa de Lirey infra limites parrocchie Sancti Johannis de Bonnevauls eiusdem diocesis de bonis sibi a Deo collatis quandam ecclesiam in honore beate Virginis Marie et precipue Annunciationis Jhesu Christi fecit construi...*

It is inconceivable that Geoffroy would have announced to the Pope (in 1349) that he had built a church if he had in fact not done so. Yet, according to the extant Act of Foundations,[2] construction was begun on 20 February 1353 and completed on 20 June 1353. Remarkably short time to build a church.[7]

And further surprises follow: on 30 January 1354, addressing himself to Innocent VI, who had succeeded Clement, Geoffroy renews his request to raise the church to a collegiate. This time, he asks that an indulgence of 1 year 40 days be granted to those who visit the church on the four principal feasts of the Virgin. Geoffroy request that *ius patronatus* be accorded to him and his successors. He repeats his petition for a cemetery, but with an arresting modification: he begs permission for himself and his successors to be buried in the cemetery beside the church.[8] Geoffroy has changed his mind.

> *Item quod eisdem...decano et capitulo concedere dignemini, ut cymiterium iuxta ipsam eccleseam habere valeant consecratum et in quod in eodem cimiterio ipsum dominum et successors suos dominos de Lireyo...sepeliri possint.*

This petition is followed on 3 August of the same year by another that repeats Geoffroy's request to be buried in the cemetery beside the church, and asks the indulgence of 1 year 40 days for all who visit on Christmas, Easter, Ascension, and Pentecost.

Furthermore, according to the Act of Foundation, the church is erected in honor of the Holy Trinity, dedicated to the Virgin of the Annunciation. It has six canons, one of whom is to be elected dean, and three clerics. Every day at Matins there was to be a Low Mass of the Virgin and, at 9 o'clock, a High Mass to invoke God's protection on the founder. And the Chapter's income was increased, as we learn from an Act dated 1 October 1353, in which John II concedes another 62 livres of revenue.[9]

Thus, the rural chapel dedicated to the Virgin—typical of countless thousands that dotted medieval Europe—appears to have grown to major dimensions. In fact, Geoffroy's foundation in a country village of fifty hearths became a center of pilgrimage for people "from all over the world,"[10] where indulgences were to be gained—not only on the feasts of the Virgin, but also on those holy days commemorating the great events of Redemption.

Is this the interval in which Geoffroy obtained the Shroud? Comparing the two petitions:

1349

1. 100 days indulgence on feasts of the Virgin
2. Geoffroy wants his bones to be distributed and buried in diverse places.
3. A church is built
4. Five canons established there
5. Stipends of 30 lvrs.

1353

1. 1 year 40 days indulgence on feasts of Virgin, and 1 year 40 days indulgence on feasts of Christ
2. Geoffroy and his heirs to be buried in the cemetery beside the church
3. Act of Foundation
4. There are six chaplains, three clerics
5. Their income is increased by 60 lvrs.

Several documents leave no doubt that the Shroud was publicly exposed for veneration in the Lirey church before Geoffroy died. The above-mentioned Bull of Clement VII dated 6 January 1390 (almost identical to another from that pontiff in 1389) records that Geoffroy de Charny placed the Shroud of Our Lord Jesus Christ in the church of

Lirey. A document of 6 February 1464 states that Geoffroy de Charny placed in the church, along with other relics, "the Holy Shroud bearing the effigy of Our Saviour and Redeemer Jesus Christ."

And two mute survivors from Geoffroy's own time signify the same:

1. Henry of Poitiers, Bishop of Troyes, on 28 May 1356, sent Geoffroy a letter of praise and approval.

2. In 1855—the year Secondo Pia was born—a souvenir medallion representing the Shroud and the arms of Charny and Vergy (Geoffroy's wife) was found in the Seine at the Pont-au-Change.

The relic could not have been publicly exposed without papal permission. Geoffroy would had to have sent a report and a petition to the Pope. This document has not yet been found; but as Prof. Francesco Cognasso observed in his address to the Turin Congress of Shroud Studies in 1939,[11] the "documents pertaining to the installation of the Shroud in St. Mary of the Annunciation certainly exist."

At this Congress, Prof. Cognasso expressed his opinion that there were two possible periods in which the Shroud was placed in the church: either in 1349, or between 1351 and 1356, year of Geoffroy's death. At the 1950 Congress in Rome, Mons. Joseph Rosérat de Melin, vicar-general, diocese of Troyes, was more definite: "Between 20 June 1353 and 19 September 1356, the collegiate church of Lirey receives a Shroud which is presented to the faithful as that which covered the Body of Our Lord..."

It seems reasonably certain that the evidence so far accumulated applies to the time-frame in which the Shroud was placed in the Lirey church. Knowing Geoffroy's religious character,[12] we can be morally certain that he would have provided a "decent and venerable"[13] setting for it as soon as possible after it came into his hands. It would seem to me that he obtained the Shroud surely after 1349, and not long before February 1353; that the Act of Foundation refers to an enlargement or embellishment of a church already existing since 1349; and that Geoffroy was exposing the relic prior to the congratulatory letter from Henry of Poitiers.

NOTES:

1. Mons. Pietro Savio: "Ricerche Storiche sulla Santa Sindone," *Societá Editrice Internazionale*, Italy, 1957.

2. Luigi Fossati, S.D.B.: "La Santa Sindone; Nuove Luce su Antichi Documenti," Borla, Turin, 1961.

3. Andre Perret: "Essai sur l'histoire du Saint Suaire du XIVe au XVIe siècle." in *Mémoirs de l'Académie des Sciences Belles-Lettres et Arts de Savoie*, 1960.

4. Fossati's amputated quotation, "Conquis par feu" gives the impression that the Shroud had been taken in the fire of battle. The complete phrase, given by Perret, reads that the Shroud "Fut conqûis par feu messire Geoffroy de Charny;" 'feu' in French has the two meanings of "fire" and "late, lately deceased."

5. Charny is located in the Côte-d'Or; Lirey is in the Aube.

6. Savio explains that Vatican records affixed the date of the Pope's *Fiat* to the documents they copied, without mentioning the date of the petition which preceded.

7. Is it possible that the 1353 records refer to an addition or enlargement of a building of 1349? Whatever happened, the church, erected inside the castle moat, was built of wood—a fact which would have serious repercussions a century later. The chapel that stands today is the third erected on the same site. Built in 1897 of stone and brick, it serves only for weddings and baptisms. Otherwise parishioners go 1¼ miles to St. Jean Bonneval, as they did before Geoffroy built St. Mary in the 14th century.

8. Savio adds, "ai piedi della Sindone," at the feet of the Shroud.

9. This information was found by Fossati in the Archives of the Department of the Aube. Savio, relying on Père Anselme, gives the date as July 1356, and the amount as 60 livres.

10. Memo of Pierre d'Arcis, Bishop of Troyes; undated but shortly after 6 January 1390.

11. La Santa Sindone nelle Ricerche Moderne; Atti dei Convegni' di Studio: Torino 1939; Roma e Torino, 1950. Riedizione anastatica per cura di Pietro Scotti, S.D.B., Marietti ,Alessandria, Italy.

12. Abundantly attested by documents, chronicles, and Geoffroy's own poetry.

13. Bull of Clement VII, 1390.

Also Consulted:

· Auguste et Emile Molinier: Paris 1968, "Chronique Normande du XIVe siècle."

· Froissart: "Chroniques."

· Auguste Longnon: "Documents Relatifs au Comté de Champagne et de Brie 1172-1361."

· Courtepee: "Description du Duché de Bourgone" Editions F.E.R.M., Paris 1968.

· Notes taken by Author *sur place* at Lirey Charny, Mt. St. Jean, etc.

JOHN J. "JACK" MARKWARDT

LITIGATION SPECIALIST

Jack Markwardt was born in Philadelphia, Pennsylvania and raised in Blackwood, New Jersey. He attended Rutgers University where he majored in history and, in 1974, graduated with honors from Albany Law School where he edited the Law Review and authored several legal articles. A litigation specialist and the managing partner of a general practice law firm, he resides in Deptford, NJ, with his wife Joann.

Since 1986, Jack has researched, lectured on, and written about the Shroud of Turin. In a paper presented in 1997 to the CIELT International Scientific Symposium held in Nice, France, "Was the Shroud in Languedoc During the Missing Years?" he suggested that heretical Cathars had possessed the Shroud during the thirteenth and fourteenth centruries. In a paper presented in 1998 to the Third International Congress on the Shroud held in Turin, Italy, "The Fire and the Portrait," he postulated that the Shroud had been fire-damaged and portraitized in sixth-century Edessa. In a paper presented in 1999 to the Shroud of Turin International Research Conference held in Richmond, VA, "Antioch and the Shroud," he theorized that the Shroud had been taken from first-century Jerusalem to Antioch and was moved from there to Edessa in the sixth century.

Mr. Markwardt's papers have been published in the official Acts of Shroud conferences and symposia, in the Newsletter of the British Society for the Turin Shroud, and on the Internet.

ANTIOCH AND THE SHROUD

The Early Centuries

If the Shroud of Turin is truly that holy icon employed to save the city of Edessa from the Persian army in the sixth century,[1] just how and when did it make its way there from first-century Jerusalem?

In 1978, Ian Wilson, cognizant that the cloth would never be accepted as authentic in the absence of a complete and credible biography, boldly and convincingly postulated its history from 544, when it mysteriously appeared in Edessa, to 1204, when it suddenly disappeared from Constantinople.[2] In an attempt to reach even further back into time, however, Wilson's "Mandylion theory" also suggested that, shortly after the Crucifixion, an otherwise-unknown disciple named Thaddeus had carried Christ's image-bearing burial shroud[3] to Edessa[4] where it was soon portraitized and concealed in the city walls for almost five centuries.[5] This particular portion of the theory was not grounded in history but, instead, was based upon the so-called Abgar legend, a fourth-century Syrian tale[6] significantly permutated by tenth-century Byzantines in order to bestow an Apostolic history upon the Mandylion cloth that had been brought from Edessa to Constantinople in 944.[7] Yet, that very Abgar legend has been called "one of the most successful pious frauds of antiquity"[8] by J.B. Segal, whom Wilson rightly regards the best modern authority on Edessa,[9] and its earliest Syrian versions do not relate the existence of any miraculous image of Jesus.[10] Segal concluded that Christianity did not arrive in Edessa until late in the second century[11] and Wilson himself has recently acknowledged that the factual underpinnings of the Abgar legend may well be attributable to that latter era.[12]

The mere existence of such unresolved questions challenge sindonology to seek out and provide some alternative route for the Shroud's likely first-century escape from Jerusalem and the author believes it is to be found on the road which leads to the Syrian capital of Antioch on the Orontes.

ANTIOCH

Now lying substantially buried beneath the rubble of numerous earthquakes and wars near the modern city of Antakya, Turkey, ancient Antioch was, at the time of Christ, the third most important city of the Roman Empire.[13] Founded in 300 BC, it served as capital of the Seleucid Empire until, in 64 BC, it was annexed to the Roman Republic by Pompey.[14] When Rome's puppet ruler, Herod Archelaus, was banished to Gaul by Augustus Caesar in 6 BC, his territories of Judea, Samaria, and Idumea were incorporated into the imperial Roman province of Syria with Antioch as its capital.[15] A favorite city of Julius Caesar and a number of Roman emperors,[16] Antioch featured immense aqueducts, an imperial palace, a Circus, an Amphitheater, a Forum, and a grand Colonnade connecting it with the Temple of Apollo in the Vale of Daphne, an ancient center of pagan worship.[17] At the time of Christ's death, the city bustled with commerce, diplomacy, and news of religious movements throughout the Roman world.[18]

Although relatively little is known about the Apostolic Church of Jerusalem,[19] it is believed that the disciples of Jesus saved and maintained certain relics of his Passion.[20] In the decades following the Crucifixion, Jewish authorities expelled, arrested, and executed the leaders of the new Church[21] and, at some time during this period of persecution, martyrdom, and war, these relics were surely transported out of Judea for their protection and preservation.[22]

There can be little argument that, for the better part of the period that encompassed the persecution of the Jerusalem Church, Antioch provided the most logical and likely repository for the relics of the Passion.[23] Nicolaus of Antioch served as one of the first seven deacons of the Jerusalem Church[24] and, upon the execution of Stephen, a number of Christians fled to Antioch where they preached to the Jews.[25] In approximately 40, under the leadership of Barnabas and Paul,[26] Christian missionaries shifted their attention to the Gentiles[27] and, within a year, Antioch was hosting the world's first Gentile Christian community[28] whose members were being referred to as "Christians."[29] By the middle of the first century, two distinct and official Christian churches existed side-by-side: The mother church of Jewish Christians in Jerusalem and the mother church of Gentile Christians in Antioch.[30]

While some believe that Barnabas and Paul may have conveyed the relics of Christ's Passion to Antioch,[31] it is also possible that they arrived there during the Roman war against the Jews when many Christians fled from Judea to Antioch and Asia Minor.[32] Eminent historian Glanville Downey has noted that such refugees "may have taken with them their books and their collections of the sayings of Jesus, by means of which the spiritual life of the community of Antioch would have been enriched."[33]

The author suggests that it was Peter who brought the Shroud, together with certain other relics of the Passion,[34] to Antioch. Ordained chief of the Apostles by Jesus himself,[35] Peter was undoubtedly entrusted with the most sacred possessions of the nascent Church. Peter was the first to enter the empty tomb where the Shroud was discovered[36] and he seems to be identified as a sindonic custodian in two of the earliest reports concerning Christ's burial cloth. Although the lost second-century Gospel of the Hebrews related that Jesus gave his Shroud to "the servant of the priest," scholars have suggested that, before falling victim to a copyist's error, this text had actually stated that the Shroud was given to Peter.[37] In the fourth century, St. Nino, who had visited Jerusalem, recounted that the Shroud had been preserved by Pilate's wife, given to St. Luke, and hidden until it was found and kept by Peter.[38] Not only did Peter assuredly live in Antioch, argue there with Paul over the circumcision of Gentiles, and use the city as the base for his missionary activities between 47 and 54,[39] but also, according to ancient tradition, he established the Church of Antioch and served as its first bishop.[40]

ANTIOCH'S PASSION RELICS

Unlike Edessa, Antioch has laid claim to Passion relics other than the Shroud and it is logical to conclude that all such preserved relics would probably have been transported together to the same safe haven.

In 1098, the Crusaders captured Antioch only to become surrounded by a Moslem force. Discovering there the hiding place of the Holy Lance of Longinus that had pierced the side of the crucified Christ, the Crusaders, with this relic placed at the head of their army, routed the enemy and set off for Jerusalem.[41]

In 1910, local Arabs unearthed, at the traditional site of Antioch's ancient cathedral,[42] a silver chalice comprised of an unfinished inner cup and a finished outer holder, akin to a reliquary, exquisitely decorated with ten human figures, in two groups of five.[43] Professor William Newbold has noted that only in the middle of the first century did two groups of five men each govern the respective Churches of Jerusalem and Antioch and only at such time would a Christian religious object have displayed such a depiction.[44] Dated to the first century and considered genuine by many archeological and scientific authorities,[45] the Great Chalice of Antioch has been called "a most sacred Cup, in all probability the one which once served the Lord and his disciples at the Last Supper, the most precious object in Christian history, legend and tradition."[46]

THE PRE-CONSTANTINIAN ERA (30-324)

During the first three centuries of its existence, the Christian Church was continually threatened with extinction and Roman imperial persecutions, first instituted by Nero, persisted, almost unremittingly, for two and a half centuries.[47] These persecutions fell particularly hard upon the Church of Antioch and, in 115, the city produced several martyrs, including Bishop Ignatius who was taken to Rome and killed by wild beasts.[48] By 180, the appellation "Christian" was still considered an evil name in Antioch and during the reign of Decius (249-251), the Bishop of Antioch was arrested and died in prison.[49] The Emperor Valerian (253-260), responsible for particularly severe persecutions, used Antioch as the base for his military campaigns against Persia[50] and, from 303 to 305, while Diocletian destroyed churches and scriptures and banned Christian worship,[51] many Antiochenes were martyred and their bishop was condemned to the marble quarries of Pannonia.[52] Galerius prosecuted this so-called "Great Persecution" in the eastern portion of the Empire until 311, and at Antioch, the site of his imperial residence, he had martyrs slowly roasted over open fires.[53]

During this rather extended period of persecution, all of the Passion relics would have been kept concealed due to the danger of their being confiscated and destroyed by imperial agents. Were the Shroud then known to be image bearing,[54] it would have been kept hidden from radically iconoclastic Jews[55] and Christians[56] who insisted that God be worshipped in a purely spiritual manner.[57]

THE CONSTANTINIAN ERA (324-337)

When, in 323, Constantine defeated Licinius,[58] enforcement of the Edict of Milan in Antioch was assured. Nevertheless, even after official imperial persecution had ended, there were still several compelling reasons why the relics of the Passion, particularly if hidden in Antioch, would not have been extracted from three centuries of concealment.

A. ICONOCLASM IN THE EAST

Although Constantine's triumph precipitated a gradual shift toward the arts within the Church, the iconoclastic views of many ecclesiastics were never altered.[59] Thus, were the Shroud then known to bear an image,[60] its very existence remained threatened by radical iconoclasts, particularly in the Eastern Church. Bishop Eusebius of Caesaria, nearly appointed Bishop of Antioch in 326,[61] confiscated images of Peter and Paul,[62] and as late as 393, St. Epiphanius of Salamis tore down an image-bearing veil in Palestine.[63]

B. IMPERIAL RELIC APPROPRIATION

By 324, Christian relics were in vogue, a tradition of venerating saintly remains had become established, and magnificent sanctuaries were being erected over the graves of martyrs.[64] By century's end, St. Augustine could recount miracles wrought by Holy Land soil, flowers which had touched a reliquary, oil from church lamps, and items connected with saints.[65]

In 326, the pagan-bred Constantine, enthralled by his new religion's relics, sent his elderly mother, Helena, to Jerusalem to search for momentos of Christ's Passion.[66] Having located the Holy Sepulchre, Helena promptly demonstrated that, once found, such relics would be appropriated and conveyed to the imperial capital,[67] to Rome, or to some other city closely connected with the imperial family. Dividing both the True Cross and the Title into three pieces, Helena left one part of each relic in Jerusalem and sent the remaining portions to the Emperor and to Rome.[68] Similarly, of the three Holy Nails found in the tomb, Helena sent two to Constantine and the other to Rome.[69] The Empress also reportedly conveyed the Holy Stairs from Pilate's palace to Rome[70] and took the Holy Coat to her own administrative capital in Trier, Germany.[71]

Once these sacred objects were in the hands of Constantine, he reportedly employed them as lucky charms or military paraphernalia. Believing that it would make his new capital city impregnable, the Emperor placed a portion of the True Cross in his statue set high above the Forum of Constantinople.[72] He also attached one of the Holy Nails to his helmet and made a bridle for his horse from the other.[73] Under such circumstances, no truly devout Eastern clergyman would dare disclose the existence of any of

Christ's Passion relics and thereby risk both their transmittal to the West and the possibility of their desecratory employment by the Emperor.

C. ARIANISM AND THE ANTIOCH SCHISM

In the third century, Paul of Samosata had preached that there was only one God, the creator, and, extending this heretical doctrine, Lucian, an Antiochene priest, taught that Christ could not have existed for all eternity since he was, by definition, the Son of the Father.[74] When Arius, one of Lucian's students and an Alexandrian priest, espoused such teachings in the time of Constantine, they became popularly known as Arianism.[75] Although Arians dominated the religious affairs of Antioch itself, a regional synod of orthodox bishops met in 324, elected an orthodox bishop, and condemned Arius.[76] The Arians of Antioch, who would have likely maintained possession of the city's most precious ecclesiastical treasures, were now in conflict with their orthodox bishop.

From the inception of his association with Christianity, Constantine had demonstrated a proclivity to interfere in ecclesiastical affairs.[77] In 325, he presided over the Council of Nicaea which duly adopted his own compromise definition of the substantive nature of God, anathematized Arianism, sent Arius into exile, and decreed that Easter would no longer be celebrated according to Eastern church tradition.[78] The Arians of Antioch were now also in conflict with their orthodox Emperor.

In 330, the orthodox bishop of Antioch was removed from office and sent into exile.[79] When Constantine attempted to interfere in the appointment of his successor, two bishops, one Arian and the other orthodox, were elected and the Church of Antioch was divided by a schism that was to last for the next eighty years.[80] Under such circumstances, the Arian faction could not but continue to conceal any Passion relic in their possession if they were to prevent its appropriation by Constantine and his orthodox allies.

THE POST-CONSTANTINIAN ERA (337-540)
A. THE REIGN OF CONSTANTIUS

When Constantine died in 337, he left his Empire in the hands of his three surviving sons.[81] Both the eldest, Constantine II who ruled in the West, and the youngest, Constans who ruled in the South, were closely aligned with the orthodox Church;[82] however, the third son, Constantius, assumed control of the Eastern Empire and became an avowed Arian.[83]

Notwithstanding the support of Constantius and their desire to establish an Arian Church dominated by the Emperor,[84] the Antiochene Arians were confronted with the distinct possibility that one of his two orthodox brothers might take control of the Eastern Empire and, like their father before them, send Arians into exile.

As fate would have it, however, Constantine II was killed in 340,[85] and when Constans died ten years later, Constantius was left in absolute control of the entire Roman Empire.[86] In Antioch, the orthodox faction split, an Arian was elected bishop in 357, and the city was thereby turned into "a stronghold of Arianism."[87] The Arians immediately took control of the official Church and assumed sole occupancy of the Golden Basilica of Constantine,[88] a magnificent domed cathedral with marble walls and a gold exterior[89] that had been dedicated in 341.[90]

With Arians now in control of both the imperial government and the official Church of Antioch, it became propitious to extract the relics of the Passion from hiding and to exhibit them to Arian believers within the confines of the city's magnificent cathedral. Had the sindonic image developed only gradually and over a period of decades or centuries,[91] this may have been the first occasion on which anyone noticed that the Shroud bore an incredible representation of the crucified body of Jesus Christ.

B. THE REFLECTED KNOWLEDGE OF PASSION RELICS

In Syria itself, archeologists have discovered, in fourth-century tombs, amulets and molded figures connected with the life and passion of Christ, including a zigzag lance, the Cup of the Last Supper, and so-called "objects from the resurrection of Lazarus."[92] Were such resurrection objects actually intended to represent the burial linens of Christ and not those of Lazarus, it could indicate that the lance, the cup, and the Shroud were all copied in Syria during the fourth century. After exhaustively studying the evidence for many years, Professor Gustavus Eisen concluded that these artifacts had, in fact, been modeled upon actual sacred objects that were once kept in seclusion for their safety and were later lost when concealed upon the approach of persecution or war.[93]

To the East, the Abgar legend was suddenly modified by the *Doctrine of Addai* to include, for the very first time, mention of a non-miraculous and painted portrait of Jesus.[94] Since the sindonic image itself has always been described as not being made by human hands[95] or as a moist secretion of sweat,[96] it would appear that an artistic copy of the Shroud face, perhaps painted in Antioch, was taken to Edessa by the close of the fourth century.

To the West, there suddenly appeared, during the Theodosian era (370-410), distinctly Shroudlike depictions of Christ with a long, narrow, and majestic face, a moustache and medium-length beard, and long hair falling upon his shoulders, sometimes parted in the center. A sarcophagus located at the University of Perugia, dated to about 350-360, shows Jesus with a lengthened face and long unparted hair and, beginning in approximately 370, the classic Shroudlike Christ began to be depicted in sarcophagi now to be found in Rome, Arles, Milan, and the Vatican.[97]

The foregoing and other circumstantial evidence[98] demonstrates that, shortly after the middle of the fourth century, artists and artisans began to make copies of the lance and the chalice, both later discovered in Antioch, and the now-familiar face of the sindonic image. This would have occurred only had such relics been placed on exhibit and could not have taken place if, during this period, they had continued to remain out of sight, anonymous to the artistic community.

C. THE CONCEALMENT OF ANTIOCH'S CHURCH TREASURES

In 361, Constantius died at the age of forty-four and was succeeded by his cousin, Julian, a confirmed pagan who promptly proclaimed universal religious tolerance.[99] Although he undoubtedly desired to restore pagan worship, Julian wanted to project himself as the sponsor a new era of genial polytheism and, consequently, he opposed both illegal means and open persecution to eliminate Christianity and, instead, urged his fellow pagans to imitate Christianity's best virtues.[100]

On October 22, 362, while Julian visited Antioch, a fire struck the Temple of Apollo, damaging both its roof and a statue of the god.[101] Although the fire was likely caused by a pagan worshipper having left candles burning before a statue, blame was laid upon the Christians[102] and Julian ordered the Great Cathedral to be closed[103] and its liturgical vessels and other treasures confiscated.[104] When the Count of the East, Julian's uncle, closed the Basilica and attempted to confiscate its sacred objects, the treasurer of the cathedral resisted.[105] In the words of Professor Eisen:

> *Theodoretus, for this was his name, refused to deliver some objects which he had hidden and, it is said, suffered torture and final execution rather than reveal some important secret. What that secret was is not known, but we may conclude that it referred to the treasure which he had hidden and whose hiding place he refused to divulge.*[106]

Julian's punitive measures represented the only occasion of his short imperial tenure (361-363) when he closed a religious house of worship, executed a churchman, or appropriated religious objects of veneration.[107] The author believes that this logical and tolerant emperor, aware that the fire's cause was uncertain[108] and that his order would alienate the Antiochenes,[109] would not have taken such uncharacteristic action unless he believed it necessary to obtain, and destroy, three of the most precious relics of Christianity. The author also suggests that the Arian Presbyter, Theodoretus, at the cost of his head,[110] successfully concealed Antioch's Passion relics in places located throughout the Golden Basilica of Constantine.

D. The Rise Of Monophysitism

In 380, the Emperor Theodosius established orthodoxy as the official religion of the Empire, condemned all heretics to serious penalties, expelled the Arians from Antioch, and restored custody of the Golden Basilica to the orthodox.[111] Yet, even with Arianism outlawed, basic differences between Syrian and Greek concepts of Christ's divinity remained. In 451, the Council of Chalcedon dogmatized the Greek view that Christ had two natures, human and divine, rather than the single divine nature ascribed to him by the majority of the Eastern clergy.[112] In 471, dissenting Monophysites seized control of the Church at Antioch[113] and the city became the "rallying point of the Syrian people who now felt...that the government in Constantinople was their enemy."[114]

By the late fifth century, the Patriarch of Antioch had become the acknowledged leader of the Monophysite movement, his patriarchate was no longer in communion with Rome or Constantinople,[115] and the Greek-speaking clergy became known in the East as "the Emperor's men."[116] In 518, Emperor Justin exiled Severus, the Patriarch of Antioch,[117] and the orthodox instituted a purge of the Monophysites.[118]

E. The Discovery Of The Shroud

In October of 525, a great fire ravaged a considerable part of Antioch[119] and, seven months later, a major earthquake destroyed almost the entire city, including the Great Cathedral, and killed the Patriarch and more than 250,000 other people.[120] The new orthodox Patriarch, Ephraemius, described as a worse persecutor than Paul, promptly initiated a vigorous campaign to eradicate Monophysitism.[121] In November of 528, a second earthquake destroyed all of Antioch's buildings and the Emperor Justinian sent financial assistance for reconstruction.[122] The city was rebuilt throughout the period of 528-540 and the Golden Basilica of Constantine was rededicated in 537-538.[123]

The author suggests that, in the process of clearing away the debris of the earthquake-ravaged cathedral, Monophysites discovered the Shroud in the place where it had been hidden in 362. Intensely persecuted by both Patriarch Ephraemius and Emperor Justinian,[124] they could not publicly acknowledge discovery of the sacred relic, but their possession of the cloth may have become rumored. In approximately 529-530, Justinian sent one of his robes to Antioch where, most strangely, it was displayed in an orthodox church and in a manner suggesting that it had healing powers.[125] There being no plague then ravaging the city,[126] this may have been an orthodox attempt to counter a reported Monophysite possession of some miraculous cloth. Curious too is the fact that, at about this very same time, Justinian changed the name of Antioch to Theupolis, the City of God.[127]

F. The Destruction Of Ancient Antioch

The kingdom of Persia threatened to attack Antioch in 529 and 531[128] and its truce with the Roman Empire, reached in 532,[129] ended in 540 when King Chosroes I invaded Syria and marched his army to Antioch.[130] Just prior to the initial assault, many fled the city, including the Emperor's representative and the orthodox Patriarch.[131] In the bloody assault that followed, the Persians captured Antioch and took many of its survivors as hostages and slaves and, after personally supervising the looting of the Golden Basilica, Chosroes had the ancient city burned to the ground.[132] The resultant destruction was so complete that "those few who had not been killed or carried away as slaves, could not find the site where once had stood their homes."[133]

THE APPEARANCE OF THE EDESSA ICON

The author proposes that, shortly before the Persian attack, the Monophysites of Antioch fled with the Shroud to a nearby safe haven where the local Christian Church had maintained a long tradition of ecclesiastical independence and where Monophysites constituted the religious majority and had their own bishop.[134] In 540, the city of Edessa, lying only about 145 miles to the northeast,[135] was clearly the most logical and attractive destination for the Monophysite refugees of Antioch.[136]

In 544, a holy icon "not made by human hands" was present in Edessa during its siege by King Chosroes.[137] Ernst Von Dobschutz concluded that this date indicates, more or less, the arrival of the icon in the city[138] and his opinion finds support in the fact that, prior thereto, no icon is mentioned in Edessan literature,[139] particularly the *Edessan Chronicle*, an orthodox Syriac text composed between 541 and 544.[140]

When Chosroes constructed a huge timber tower from which missiles could be fired down upon the city,[141] the Edessans devised a plan to dig a tunnel and to set fire to the siegeworks from below ground. The scheme having failed,[142] Edessa remained encircled by an enemy that, only four years before, had destroyed Antioch, and the Monophysite refugees were forced to produce the Shroud and allow it to be thrown "into the breach"[143] in the hope that it might, somehow, miraculously save them and the city.

Evagrius reports that, with the aid of the icon, the tunnel wood immediately caught fire and ignited the Persian siegeworks above ground.[144] Soon thereafter, the Persians abandoned their siege[145] and the icon became recognized as a holy relic and mighty palladium.[146] The author has previously proposed that, in the course of these events, the Shroud incurred the fire damage generally referred to as its "poker holes" and that, in order to conceal this damage, the Edessan church hierarchy doubled the cloth in four to create the portrait known as the holy Image of Edessa.[147]

THE SYRIAN GRAIL

Hints of a lost Syrian sindonic history are to be found in the legends of the Holy Grail, an object which, in recent years, has been increasingly linked to the Shroud.[148] Some seventy-five years ago, Professor Eisen concluded that the earliest Grail legends attempted to account for the loss of real sacred objects known in fourth-century Syria and that these stories reflected a passionate desire to locate and recover such objects from concealment.[149]

A mere seventy years after Crusaders had discovered the Holy Lance in Antioch, Chretien de Troyes wrote the first of Western Europe's Grail romances[150] and coupled the mysterious Grail with a bleeding white lance.[151] Soon thereafter, Robert de Boron mentioned an image of Christ on a shroud,[152] identified the chalice as the Grail, and related that Joseph of Arimathea, the Shroud's first owner, had died in Syria,[153] in stark contrast to later tales which, integrated with the Arthurian legend,[154] placed him in Britain.[155] Seraphe, one of Boron's characters, is the name of a young man taken captive by Julian the Apostate during his siege of Strassburg and later reportedly placed in charge of the Teutonic legions in fourth-century Syria.[156] As previously noted, it was Julian who orchestrated the very persecution that caused Antioch's church treasures to be concealed in 362.

The author perceives a direct linkage between the fourth-century disappearance of Antioch's Church treasures, the eleventh-century discovery of the Holy Lance in Antioch, and the twelfth-century birth of European Grail romances having Syrian roots and emphatic references to the lance, the chalice, and the Shroud. He identifies the mysterious Grail as symbolic of the Passion relics that Crusaders reported as having disappeared from Antioch's Great Cathedral during the persecution of Julian the Apostate and suggests that memories of these lost Syrian relics inspired the earliest of the Christian Grail romances.[157]

THE HISTORICAL VACUUM

A well-founded criticism of the Shroud's claim to ancient provenance is the undeniable fact that, after the victory of Constantine, its existence should surely have been reported, and those who seek to promote the relic's authenticity must provide an adequate explanation for its historical anonymity. While Wilson attempted to resolve this problem for the period prior to 544 by claiming that the Shroud remained hidden in the city walls of Edessa, one must also seriously consider the distinct possibility that, over the centuries, certain sindonic custodians may have been religious heretics. Most such heretics were, in fact, devout Christians who cherished Jesus either as God's Son or as his holy and anointed prophet and who would have assuredly protected his image-imprinted burial cloth as zealously as any orthodox believer—the Arian Presbyter Theodoretus may provide a perfect example of such uncompromising devotion. Upon the demise of their respective religious movements, however, heretics were invariably exiled or executed, their teachings suppressed, and their writings destroyed. Thus, for any period when the Shroud may have been in the possession of Christian heretics, its history was undoubtedly expunged with that of the banished sect. Tragically, both for history and sindonology, the records of fourth-century Arians, sixth-century Monophysites, and thirteenth-century Cathars[158] have been forever lost.

In addition, and unlike Edessa, ancient Antioch has bequeathed to posterity very little ecclesiastical or historical information.[159] Antiochene writings do not become plentiful until the pagan Libanius details the city's administrative, social and intellectual life in the late fourth century and great gaps of knowledge occur in the fifth and sixth centuries.[160] This tragic historical vacuum is attributable, in part, to the numerous fires, earthquakes,[161] and wars which ravaged Antioch throughout the early Christian centuries and to that extraordinary series of sixth-century calamities which virtually erased whatever might have then remained of the ancient city.[162] While some hold hope that buried objects might yet provide testimony to Antioch's Christian history,[163] archaeological excavations conducted between 1932 and 1939 did not produce many texts and it is rather unlikely that any new excavations would add much to that which is presently known.[164]

A PROPOSED CHRONOLOGY

Blending the central core of Ian Wilson's Mandylion theory[165] with the trilogy of proposals that the author has advanced in papers presented to the Nice International Scientific Symposium in 1997,[166] the Turin Third International Congress in 1998,[167] and the Richmond International Conference in 1999[168] produces the following chronology:

30-47	Peter conceals the Passion relics in Jerusalem.
47	Peter brings the Passion relics to Antioch.
47-357	The Church of Antioch conceals the Passion relics.
357-362	Arians exhibit the Passion relics in Antioch's Golden Basilica.
362	Theodoretus conceals the Passion relics in the Golden Basilica.
362-528	The Passion relics remain hidden in the Golden Basilica.
528-540	Monophysites discover the Shroud in the Golden Basilica.
540	Monophysite refugees bring the Shroud to Edessa.
544	The Shroud is fire damaged as Edessa defeats the Persian army.
544-549	The Shroud is portraitized to become the Image of Edessa.
549-944	The Edessans venerate the holy icon "not made by human hands."
944-1204	The Byzantines venerate the Mandylion and sindon in Constantinople.
1098	Crusaders discover the Holy Lance in Antioch.
1170	Grail romances, with lance, cup, shroud, and Syrian roots, appear in the West.
1204	The Shroud disappears during the Crusader sack of Constantinople.
1204-1349	Cathars conceal the Shroud in Languedoc.
1349	Geoffrey de Charny acquires the Shroud pursuant to the terms of a royal grant.
1355	Geoffrey de Charny exhibits the Shroud in Lirey.
1910	Arabs discover the Great Chalice at the site of Antioch's ancient cathedral.

CONCLUSION

The author suggests that the proposed early sojourn of the Shroud in Antioch provides both a plausible biography for the relic prior to its appearance in Edessa and a credible explanation of why its existence during that period was not historically documented. He believes that the first Christian Grail romances were inspired by the disappearance of Antioch's church treasures in the fourth century.[169] He considers it more than mere coincidence that the chronicled history of the Shroud begins[170] almost immediately after the glorious history of ancient Antioch concludes.[171]

Bibliography

Boron, Robert de, *Joseph of Arimathea* (Trans. Jean Rogers), Rudolph Steiner Press (London 1990).

Bowersock, G. W., *Julian the Apostate*, Harvard University Press (Cambridge 1978).

Carrington, Philip, *The Early Christian Church*, Cambridge University Press (London 1957).

Chadwick, Henry, *The Early Church*, Wm. B. Eerdmans Pub. Co. (Grand Rapids 1968).

Cruz, Joan Carroll, *Relics*, Our Sunday Visitor, Inc. (Huntington 1984).

Currer-Briggs, Noel, *The Shroud and the Grail*, Weidenfeld and Nicolson (London 1987).

Dowley, Tim, *Eerdmans' Handbook to the History of Christianity*, Guideposts (Carmel 1977).

Downey, Glanville, *A History of Antioch in Syria*, Princeton University Press (Princeton 1961).

Downey, Glanville, *Ancient Antioch*, Princeton University Press (Princeton 1963).

Downey, Glanville, *Antioch in the Age of Theodosius the Great*, University of Oklahoma Press (Norman 1963).

Drews, Robert, *In Search of the Shroud of Turin*, Rowman & Allanheld (Totowa 1984).

Eisen, Gustavus A., *The Great Chalice of Antioch*, Kouchakji Freres (New York 1923).

Franzen, August and Dolan, John P., *A History of the Church*, Herder and Herder (New York 1969).

Frend, W.H.C., *The Rise of the Monophysite Movement*, Cambridge University Press (London 1972).

Garza-Valdes, Leoncia A., *The DNA of God?*, Doubleday (New York 1999).

Harvey, Susan Ashbrook, *Asceticism and Society in Crisis*, University of California Press (London 1990).

Kousoulas, D.G., *The Life and Times of Constantine the Great*, Rutledge Books, Inc. (Danbury1997).

Palmer, Andrew, *The Seventh Century in the West-Syrian Chronicles*, Liverpool University Press (Liverpool 1993).

Parker, Samuel, *The Ecclesiastical Histories of Socrates, Sozomen, and Theodorit* (London 1707).

Procopius of Caesarea, *History of the Wars* (Trans. H. B. Dewing), Harvard University Press (Cambridge 1996).

Scavone, Daniel C., *The Shroud of Turin*, Greenhaven Press (San Diego1989).

Segal, J.B., Edessa, *The Blessed City*, Oxford University Press (London 1970).

Troyes, Chretien de, "The Story of the Grail," published in *Arthurian Romances*, (Trans. William W. Kibler), Penguin Books (London 1991).

Wigram, W.A., The Separation of the Monophysites, The Faith Press (London 1923).

Wilson, Ian, *The Blood and the Shroud*, The Free Press (New York 1998).

Wilson, Ian, *Jesus: The Evidence*, HarperCollins (San Francisco 1996).

Wilson, Ian, *The Shroud of Turin, The Burial Cloth of Jesus Christ?*, Image Books (Garden City 1979).

Notes

1. See Wilson, *The Shroud of Turin*, pp. 136-137. Drews, p. 66.
2. Wilson, *The Shroud of Turin*, pp. 136-172.
3. Wilson believed the sindonic image was produced by a force rather than a substance, that it resulted from the cloth having been scorched during the Resurrection, and that it was readily observable on the first Easter morning. See Wilson, *The Shroud of Turin*, pp. 248-251.
4. Wilson, *The Shroud of Turin*, pp. 126-130.
5. Wilson proposed that the Shroud was rediscovered in the aftermath of a devastating flood that struck Edessa in 525. See Wilson, *The Shroud of Turin*, pp. 134; 138-139.
6. See note 10 and Wilson, *The Shroud of Turin*, pp. 129-130.
7. This account is referred to both as "The Story of the Image of Edessa"

and as the Festival Sermon. See Wilson, *The Shroud of Turin*, pp. 272-290. Drews, pp. 55-58.

8. Segal, p. 64.

9. See Wilson, *The Shroud of Turin*, p. 308, n. 1.

10. The first Syrian account, related by Eusebius, mentioned only a wonderful vision and the later *Doctrine of Addai* spoke only of a portrait made by human hands in choice paints. See Wilson, *The Shroud of Turin*, pp. 129-130.

11. Segal, p. 70.

12. See Wilson, *The Blood and the Shroud*, pp. 161-175.

13. Dowley, p. 62. Eisen, p. 4.

14. Downey, *A History of Antioch in Syria*, pp. 57; 117; 143-147.

15. Downey, *A History of Antioch in Syria*, pp. 167-168.

16. Downey, *A History of Antioch in Syria*, pp. 151-158; 169-188; 318-327.

17. Eisen, pp. 3-4.

18. Downey, *A History of Antioch in Syria*, pp. 188; 272.

19. Chadwick, p. 17.

20. Cruz, p. 4.

21. Between 30 and 62 AD, Hellenistic Christians were driven out of Jerusalem, Peter was arrested, and Stephen, the Apostle James, and James, the brother of Jesus, were executed. See Franzen, p. 14.

22. It is likely that the "relics of the saviour were sought for conveyance to safety and these included the Shroud, whose mysterious markings...would have ensured its preservation as an object of the greatest curiosity if nothing else." Currer-Briggs, p. xiv.

23. In 1989, Professor Daniel C. Scavone speculated that the Shroud was taken from Jerusalem to Edessa or Antioch, but felt that "the evidence points to Edessa." Scavone, p. 80.

24. Acts 6:5.

25. Acts 11:19.

26. Acts 13:1. Downey, *A History of Antioch in Syria*, pp. 273-275.

27. Downey, *A History of Antioch in Syria*, pp. 192-195.

28. Franzen, pp. 15-16.

29. Acts 11:26. Dowley, p. 62. This appellation was probably used by the Romans to distinguish the new religious sect from Judaism. Downey, *A History of Antioch in Syria*, p. 198.

30. Cruz, p. 29.

31. Cruz, p. 29.

32. Franzen, p. 15. Dowley, p. 62. Chadwick, p. 17. Many of those who

fled Jerusalem at this time likely sought refuge to the south and east of the city. Downey, *A History of Antioch in Syria*, pp. 286-287. Some may have relocated to Pella on the east bank of the Jordan River. See Wilson, *Jesus: The Evidence*, pp. 165-166.

33. Downey, *A History of Antioch in Syria*, pp. 286-287.

34. As mentioned hereinafter, the lance and the chalice.

35. See Matthew 16:18-19.

36. John 20:3-8.

37. Wilson, *The Shroud of Turin*, pp. 92-93

38. Scavone, p. 75.

39. Gal. 2:11-12. Chadwick, p. 18. Downey, *A History of Antioch in Syria*, pp. 281-282.

40. Downey, *A History of Antioch in Syria*, pp. 281-282. A chronicle dated to 640 reports that "Simon Cephas laid the foundations of the church at Antioch." See Palmer, p. 19.

41. It was reported that the relic's hidden location was disclosed to a priest in a dream. See Eisen, pp.5-6. There are other so-called "holy lances" that also claim authenticity. See Cruz, pp. 44-45.

42. Eisen, p. 3.

43. Cruz, p. 28.

44. Cruz, p. 29.

45 Cruz, p. 28. Some art historians believe that, while the Great Chalice is not a modern forgery, it was made in the fourth or fifth century. See Downey, *Ancient Antioch*, pp. 214-215.

46. Eisen, p. 10.

47. In addition to the emperors specifically mentioned in the text, imperial persecutors included Domitian (81-96), Trajan (98-117), Marcus Aurelius (161-180), Septimius Severus (193-211), and Maximinus the Thracian (235-238).

48. Downey, *Ancient Antioch*, p. 132

49. Downey, *A History of Antioch in Syria*, pp. 292-293; 303.

50. Downey, *A History of Antioch in Syria*, pp. 308-310.

51. Segal, p. 83.

52. Downey, *A History of Antioch in Syria*, pp. 329-330.

53. Downey, *A History of Antioch in Syria*, p. 331.

54. See note 91.

55. The Shroud image violated the second commandment and a ritually unclean gravecloth constituted a blasphemy and an abomination to Jews. See Wilson, *The Shroud of Turin*, pp. 100; 133.

56. Some of the Christian clergy inherited the Jewish animosity toward

graven images and viewed art of all kinds as incompatible with religion. See Drews, pp. 76-77. Wilson, *The Shroud of Turin*, p. 100. Pfeiffer, Heinrich, "The Shroud of Turin and the Face of Christ in Paleochristian, Byzantine and Western Medieval Art," *Shroud Spectrum International*, No. 9, p. 7 (1983).

57. Both art and artists were disavowed by the Church. Drews, p. 77. This despite the faithful's yearning for religious images. See Wilson, *The Shroud of Turin*, p. 100.

58. Kousoulas, p. 340.

59. Drews, p. 77.

60. See note 91.

61. Downey, *A History of Antioch in Syria*, p. 352.

62. Lest they be the cause of scandal. Drews, p. 77.

63. Presumably because Scripture did not authorize such objects. Drews, p. 77. Pfeiffer, Heinrich, "The Shroud of Turin and the Face of Christ in Paleochristian, Byzantine and Western Medieval Art," *Shroud Spectrum International*, No. 9, pp. 7-9 (1983).

64. As early as 156, the inhabitants of Smyrna had venerated the remains of St. Polycarp. Cruz, pp. 2; 5.

65. Cruz, p. 3.

66. Cruz, p. 38.

67. Located, at that time, in Nicomedia. Constantinople was not officially dedicated until May, 330. Kousoulas, p. 393.

68. The Roman portion of the True Cross was placed in the city's Basilica of the Holy Cross in Jerusalem which now maintains three pieces of the True Cross, each about six inches long, in a cross-shaped reliquary. The Basilica also preserves a faded and illegible portion of the title, together with a replication of its text. Cruz, pp. 38-39; 43.

69. Rome's Holy Nail relic is still preserved at the Basilica of the Holy Cross in Jerusalem. Other so-called "Holy Nails" are preserved at the Cathedral of Monza, the Cathedral of Notre Dame, the Cathedral in Florence, and the Cathedral in Trier, Germany. Cruz, pp. 41-42.

70. They are now maintained at the Sancta Sanctorum. Cruz, p. 32.

71. The Trier Cathedral contains an ivory tablet, dating from the fifth or sixth century, which shows a translation of relics there with the cooperation of Helena. An eleventh-century biography of the Trier's first bishop reports that Helena donated the Holy Coat to the Cathedral. Cruz, pp. 25-26.

72. Cruz, pp. 38-39.

73. Cruz, pp. 41-42.

74. Kousoulas, pp. 345-346.

75. Kousoulas, p. 345.

76. Kousoulas, pp. 355-356.

77. Constantine had proclaimed: "There is no higher responsibility for me by virtue of my imperial office than to dispel errors and repress all rash thought so as to cause all to offer to the Almighty God true religion, honest concord, and proper worship." Kousoulas, p. 307.

78. Kousoulas, pp. 355-356; 363-370.

79. Downey, *Ancient Antioch*, pp.145-146. Kousoulas, p. 440.

80. Kousoulas, pp. 441-442.

81. Constantine II was then twenty-two, Constantius twenty, and Constans eighteen. Kousoulas, p. 470.

82. Kousoulas, p. 470.

83. Kousoulas, p. 470. Downey, *Ancient Antioch*, pp. 149-150. Downey, *Antioch in the Age of Theodosius the Great*, p. 48.

84. Downey, *Antioch in the Age of Theodosius the Great*, p. 48.

85. In an ambush arranged by his brother Constans. Kousoulas, p. 471.

86. Kousoulas, p. 472.

87. Downey, *Ancient Antioch*, p. 157.

88. Downey, *Ancient Antioch*, p. 176.

89. Eisen, p. 4.

90. Constantius himself had attended the official ceremony. Chadwick, pp. 137-138.

91. The cloth's early historical anonymity could be simply explained if, during that period, it was not known to exhibit an image. Although Wilson noted that botany specimens could develop, in seventy-plus years, into "strikingly precise images in a sepia color closely akin to that of the Shroud," he discounted all image formation processes that could not have been completed within the thirty-six hour entombment of Christ's body. Wilson, *The Shroud of Turin*, p. 247. In 1981, S.F. Pellicori produced an image on linen sensitized by contact with a body covered in myrrh, olive oil, and skin secretions and theorized that the sindonic image had developed over a period of decades or centuries. See Drews, p. 19, citing S.F. Pellicori and M.S. Evans, "The Shroud of Turin Through the Microscope," 34 *Archaeology*, pp. 34-43 (1981). In 1993, Dr. Leoncia Garza-Valdes suggested that bacteria had not only invalidated the results of the Shroud's carbon dating, but had also formed the sindonic image over the course of a century. Garza-Valdes, pp. 56-57. Were an image not readily observable after the Resurrection, the Shroud's earliest custodians

may well have believed it to be only a blood-stained burial cloth, folded it, and hidden it away with other Passion relics, the image thereby being permitted to develop unperceived until the cloth was extracted from concealment.

92. Eisen, pp. 161-162.

93. Eisen, pp. 164; 166.

94. The Doctrine of Addai. See Wilson, *The Shroud of Turin*, pp. 129-130.

95. Wilson, *The Shroud of Turin*, p. 137.

96. Wilson, *The Shroud of Turin*, p. 115.

97. Pfeiffer, Heinrich, "The Shroud of Turin and the Face of Christ in Paleochristian, Byzantine and Western Medieval Art," *Shroud Spectrum International*, No. 9, p. 13 (1984).

98. The *Cateches* of Theodore of Mopsuestia (ca. 350-428) reflected his knowledge of a post-passion image of Jesus inscribed upon his linens in the sepulchre. See Dreisbach, Albert R. Jr., *Liturgical Clues to the Shroud's History*, p. 3, Shroud of Turin Website Library, http:\\www.shroud.com (1995). Theodore of Mopsuestia was born in Antioch and attended classes given there by the pagan sophist Libanius.

99. Bowersock, pp. 61; 70.

100. Bowersock, pp. 31; 79; 83; 87.

101. Bowersock, p. 99.

102. Chadwick, p. 156. Downey, *A History of Antioch in Syria*, p. 388.

103. Chadwick, p. 156.

104. Downey, *A History of Antioch in Syria*, p. 388.

105. "He (the Count of the East) plundered, by order from his master, the great Church at Antioch, which was at that time in the hands of the Arians, and then shut up the doors of it; upon which the Clergy there thought it high time to shift for themselves. Only Theodorus, a Presbyter, who had the care of the church-plate, etc., kept his ground, was apprehended, and no tortures prevailing with him to make any sacrilegious discoveries, or any way to disgrace his holy profession, he lost his head." Parker, p. 256.

106. Eisen, p. 5.

107. In the only other remotely similar event of his reign, Julian had summarily confiscated property owned by the Edessan Christian community. Bowersock, p. 92.

108. Downey, *Ancient Antioch*, p. 169.

109. Bowersock, p. 99.

110. Parker, p. 256. Eisen, p. 169.
111. Downey, *Ancient Antioch*, p. 184.
112. Downey, *Ancient Antioch*, p. 227.
113. Downey, *Ancient Antioch*, pp. 226-227.
114. Downey, *A History of Antioch in Syria*, p. 12.
115. Frend, pp. 49; 186. Downey, *A History of Antioch in Syria*, p. 12.
116. Dowley, p. 176.
117. Downey, *A History of Antioch in Syria*, p. 513.
118. Frend, p. 241.
119. Downey, *A History of Antioch in Syria*, pp. 520-521.
120. Eisen, p. 6. Downey, *A History of Antioch in Syria*, pp. 521-522.
121. Downey, *A History of Antioch in Syria*, pp. 526-528; 533.
122. Downey, *A History of Antioch in Syria*, pp. 524-528.
123. Downey, *A History of Antioch in Syria*, p. 533.
124. One edict exiling Monophysites, issued in 532, provoked riots in Antioch. Downey, *A History of Antioch in Syria*, p. 527. Another, issued in 536, prohibited Monophysites, including Severus, from preaching, gathering assemblies, or celebrating the Eucharist. Wigram, pp. 118-119. Harvey, p. 194.
125. Downey, *A History of Antioch in Syria*, p. 531.
126. Some twelve years later, in 542, a plague struck both Antioch and a large part of the Eastern Empire. See Downey, *A History of Antioch in Syria*, pp. 553-557.
127. The Emperor's reason for doing so remains unknown, although some believe that this was a propitiatory gesture to God after the devastation of the fire and the two earthquakes. Downey, *A History of Antioch in Syria*, p. 529. Eisen p. 6.
128. Downey, *A History of Antioch in Syria*, pp. 530- 532.
129. Segal, pp. 112-113.
130. Downey, *A History of Antioch in Syria*, pp. 533-544.
131. Downey, *A History of Antioch in Syria*, p. 541.
132. Downey, *A History of Antioch in Syria*, p. 552.
133. See Eisen p. 6.
134. Segal, pp. 77; 81.
135. About 233 kilometers distant from Antioch. See Downey, *A History of Antioch in Syria*, Plate 4, "Roman Roads in Northern Syria."
136. Only two years later, Jacob Baradaeus, with the assistance of the Empress Theodora (a stalwart Monophysite supporter despite the official policies of her husband), was ordained a bishop and dispatched to Edessa where he initiated rather prodigious efforts to

reorganize the Monophysites into a church independent from the orthodoxy. Harvey, p. 105. Wigram, pp. 198; 136. Downey, *A History of Antioch in Syria*, p. 534.

137. This according to the Syrian church historian, Evagrius, who wrote late in the sixth century. See Wilson, *The Shroud of Turin*, p. 137.

138. Dobschutz, Ernst Von, *Christusbilder; Texte und Untersuchungen*, Leipzig 1899, as cited in Pfeiffer, Heinrich," The Shroud of Turin and the Face of Christ in Paleochristian, Byzantine and Western Medieval Art," *Shroud Spectrum International*, No. 10, p. 9 (1984).

139. For example, the diary of Egeria (who visited Edessa in approximately 383), the writings of the late-fourth century St. Ephraim, the works of the early-sixth century Jacob of Serug, and the *Chronicle of Joshua the Stylite*, written in Edessa in approximately 507. See Wilson, *The Shroud of Turin*, p. 131.

140. Professor Robert Drews feels that this omission constitutes "strong evidence" that the icon was not found in the aftermath of the flood which devastated the city in 525. Drews, pp. 60-61. See also Crispino, Dorothy, "A Unique Manuscript on the Image of Edessa," *Shroud Spectrum International*, No. 40, p. 25 (1991).

141. Drews, p. 64. The Persians may also have wanted to scale the city's high walls. See Wilson, *The Shroud of Turin*, p. 137.

142. A fire could not be started in the underground passage due to a lack of air. See Wilson, *The Shroud of Turin*, p. 137.

143. See Drews, p. 66.

144. Drews, p. 61. Wilson, *The Shroud of Turin*, p. 137.

145. Procopius of Caesaria, in his *History of the Wars* written in approximately 546, confirms that the Edessans dug a tunnel, experienced problems with starting a fire due to a lack of air in the underground chamber, and succeeded in setting a fire which spread to the Persian siege-works; however, he does not mention the intervention of any icon and he attributes the Edessans' victory to their own courage and resourcefulness. Procopius, pp. 503-515. Segal, p. 77. Drews, pp. 64-66.

146. Wilson, *The Shroud of Turin*, p. 140. Drews, p. 66.

147. Markwardt, Jack, "The Fire and the Portrait," *British Society for the Turin Shroud Newsletter*, No. 48, p. 18 (Dec. 1998). Shroud of Turin Website Library, http:\\www.shroud.com (1998).

148. See, e.g., Currer-Briggs, pp. 1-29; 72-73.

149. Eisen, pp. 164-166. Some ancient Syrian legends contain Grail

themes, usually in accounts of the Apostles Philip, James, and John. Eisen, p. 168.

150. The *Story of the Grail* was written ca. 1175. See also Currer-Briggs, pp. 6; 212.

151. Chretien, p. 420. In the later Welsh Grail romance, Peredur, two young men carry a spear of incalculable size with three streams of blood running to the floor. See Currer-Briggs, pp. 1; 12.

152. Boron, pp. 26-27.

153. See Eisen, p. 166.

154. Currer-Briggs, pp. 1-2.

155. Eisen, p. 166.

156. Eisen, pp. 5; 169.

157. Professor Daniel C. Scavone also believes that Western travelers or crusaders to the East were the source of the Christian Grail romances, but suggests that these tales resulted from their having heard whispers of something mysterious kept in Constantinople and intimately identified with the body and blood of Christ and Joseph of Arimathea (i.e., the Shroud). See Scavone, Daniel C., "Joseph of Arimathea, the Holy Grail and the Turin Shroud," Shroud of Turin Website Library, http:\\www.shroud.com (1996).

158. See Markwardt, Jack, "Was the Shroud in Languedoc During the Missing Years?," Acts of the Third International Scientific Symposium of CIELT-Nice 1997, p. 177 (Paris, 1998). Shroud of Turin Website Library, http:\\www.shroud.com (1997).

159. Particularly from its Apostolic and sub-Apostolic periods. "Any information about the Antiochene church is of value, since it is so scarce." Carrington, p. 438.

160. Downey, *A History of Antioch in Syria*, pp. 4-7.

161. In addition to the two serious earthquakes of 526 and 528, an earthquake crippled Antioch in 115, almost killing the visiting Emperor Trajan and, in 458, "nearly the whole city fell" and a fire followed the quake. Downey, *Ancient Antioch*, pp. 98; 221-233.

162. See Eisen, p. 5.

163. Eisen, p. 6.

164. Downey, *A History of Antioch in Syria*, p. 6.

165. Wilson, *The Shroud of Turin*, pp. 136-172.

166. Markwardt, Jack, "Was the Shroud in Languedoc During the Missing Years?," Acts of the Third International Scientific Symposium of CIELT-Nice 1997, p. 177 (Paris, 1998). Shroud of Turin Website Library, http:\\www.shroud.com (1997).

167. Markwardt, Jack, "The Fire and the Portrait," *British Society for the Turin Shroud Newsletter*, No. 48, p. 18 (Dec. 1998). Shroud of Turin Website Library, http:\\www.shroud.com (1998). "The Fire and the Portrait" is scheduled for publication in the official Acts of the Third International Congress of the Shroud.

168. "Antioch and the Shroud" is scheduled for publication in the official Acts of the Richmond International Conference.

169. In accordance with arguments initially advanced by Professor Eisen.

170. Evagrius' report of an icon "not made by human hands" and employed to defend Edessa during the Persian siege of the city in 544.

171. "The real greatness of the city must have come to an end in A.D. 540." Downey, *A History of Antioch in Syria*, p. 559.

THE FIRE AND THE PORTRAIT

A HISTORY OF MYSTERY

The Shroud of Turin has presented its students—believers and skeptics alike—with a seemingly unlimited number of unsolved scientific, historical, and religious mysteries. This paper proposes to resolve, and to reconcile, two of the Shroud's most tantalizing mysteries: (1) When and how did it incur the fire damage now generally referred to as the "poker holes;" and (2) When and why was it converted into the portrait known as the Image of Edessa.[1]

THE MYSTERY OF THE FIRE

Framing the thighs of the Shroud's ventral and dorsal body images[2] are four sets of holes and burn marks,[3] three of which appear in right-angle patterns.[4] If the Shroud is folded once lengthwise and once widthwise, all four sets of holes and burn marks superimpose upon one another in the dead center of the folded cloth.[5] The charred edges of all twelve holes appear much blacker than the fire damage of 1532[6] and present evidence of pitch.[7]

This damage appears on the Lierre Shroud copy of 1516[8] and, thus, clearly antedates the Chambery fire by at least sixteen years.[9] With each folded layer of the cloth having been penetrated to a decreasing degree, it has been suggested that a hot poker was thrust into the Shroud during some primitive ceremony[10] and that, since it had been a favorite medieval practice to use pitch-soaked pokers as "trial by fire" truth devices,[11] the cloth was subjected to a fire-based authenticity test in either the late-fifteenth or very early-sixteenth century;[12] however, in approximately 1986, this damage was found depicted in the Hungarian Pray Manuscript,[13] a document reliably dated to 1192-1195.[14] Not only did this discovery effectively undermine the notion that the Shroud had been tried by fire in medieval times,[15] but it also proved problematic to both the radiocarbon testing results[16] and a claim that the sindonic image was the creation of Leonardo da Vinci.[17]

While some believe this damage to be the product of "deliberate rather than accidental" action,[18] others have suggested that it derives from some inadvertent event, such as the discharge of hot coals from "a clumsy swinging of the thurible"[19] or the dripping of pitch from a torch.[20]

THE MYSTERY OF THE PORTRAIT

The Mandylion theory asserted that the Shroud was once made into a portrait by being folded, attached to a backing board, and overlaid by gold trelliswork in a manner which left visible only the face of its crucified image.[21] This hypothesis was based, in part, upon the following passage from the late sixth-century *Acts of Thaddeus*:

> And he (Christ)…asked to wash himself, and a "doubled-in-four" cloth was given to him; and when he had washed himself he wiped his face with it. And his image having been imprinted upon the linen…[22]

The Mandylion theory persuasively linked this literary reference to an icon which was then known and venerated as the Image of Edessa; however, there being no historical record of any portraitization of that cloth, it reconstructed the occasion by first embracing the so-called "Abgar legend"[23] and by then hypothesizing that, in the first century,[24] the disciple Thaddeus doubled the Shroud in four in order to make it presentable to King Abgar V of Edessa.[25] The Mandylion theory also proposed that the portraitized Shroud was hidden and forgotten in the city walls,[26] rediscovered there centuries later,[27] and deployed as a palladium to save Edessa from the Persian army in 544,[28] its true sindonic nature having never been detected by the people of Edessa during their nine-centuries-long possession of the cloth.[29]

Nevertheless, there are several reasons to doubt that the Shroud was taken to Edessa in the first century.[30] The historical evidence clearly establishes that Edessan Christianity was not born until late in the second century[31] and "the whole story of Edessa's evangelisation" can probably be traced to the reign of King Abgar VIII (177-212).[32] It is also rather difficult to accept the notion that the Shroud could have remained

completely unknown for almost five hundred years[33] when obvious
artistic familiarity with the sindonic image is evidenced in the Shroudlike
portrayals of Christ during the third[34] and fourth centuries.[35] It is the
author's personal view that the Shroud was taken from Judea, placed in
the care of the Antiochene Christian community, and remained in the
Syrian capital until it was brought to Edessa in 540.[36]

In addition, a relatively recent discovery has confirmed that the above-
cited passage from the *Acts of Thaddeus* actually evidences popular
knowledge that the Image of Edessa was a full-sized gravecloth:

> Ananias...looked carefully and intently at Christ and
> was unable to capture him. That knower of hearts asked
> to clean himself; he took a *tetradiplon*, and having
> washed, he wiped his face. Impressing his image on
> the...sindon he gave it to Ananias.[37]

Given that the *Acts of Thaddeus* specifically recites that Christ's image
had been left upon a shroud, whereas earlier versions of the Abgar legend
make no mention of a burial cloth,[38] it is rather clear that the Christians
of Edessa did view the cloth's full-body image sometime between the
beginning of the fourth century and the close of the sixth.[39] Therefore,
the cloth could simply not have been folded-in-four in the first century
and then have been maintained in such folded form throughout its entire
stay in Edessa, as the Mandylion theory suggests.[40]

So, if not penetrated by a pitch-soaked instrument during some
medieval trial by fire, how did the Shroud become scarred by poker holes,
and if not to permit its presentation to an Edessan king, why was the
Shroud portraitized? This paper proposes that each of these sindonic
mysteries is integrally related to the other.

SOLVING THE MYSTERY OF THE FIRE

In seeking to establish the time and cause of the fire damage, the
following conclusions may be logically and reasonably drawn from the
relevant evidence:

- Based upon the illustration contained in the Hungarian Pray Manuscript, the damage occurred prior to 1192-1195.
- Based upon the physical evidence, the damage occurred at a time
  when the Shroud was folded once lengthwise and once widthwise
  and, therefore, not at a time when the Shroud was "doubled-in-
  four" as a portrait.

- Based on the *Acts of Thaddeus*, the Shroud had already been converted into a portraitized *tetradiplon* by the close of the sixth century.[41]
- Based upon artistic portrayals and other evidence cited in the Mandylion theory,[42] the Shroud was maintained in portraitized form during its sojourn in Edessa from the sixth to the tenth century.[43]
- It is unlikely that the damage occurred after the Shroud had been portraitized[44] and, therefore, it is most probable that the damage occurred prior to the close of the sixth century.[45]
- The Shroud is known to have been exposed to fire only once prior to the close of the sixth century; i.e., during the Persian siege of Edessa in 544 and, therefore, it is likely that the damage occurred on that occasion.

The Syrian historian, Evagrius, writing late in the sixth century, reported that, in 544, the Christians of Edessa[46] were in possession of a holy icon not made of human hands.[47] This literary reference, the Shroud's first appearance in non-canonical history, did not specify whether the icon was a full-length gravecloth or a folded portrait.[48] In that year, the Persians, under King Chosroes I, laid siege to Edessa and constructed a huge timber tower from which missiles could be fired down upon the city.[49] The Edessans devised a plan to dig a tunnel and to set fire to the siegeworks from below ground; however, a fire could not be started in the underground passage due to a lack of air.[50] In this crisis, it is likely that a centuries-old Edessan palladium, the so-called Letter of Jesus,[51] was invoked to start the fire or to otherwise halt the Persian advance; however, when it failed to do so and the city remained encircled by an enemy that, only four years before, had killed and enslaved the people of Antioch and burnt that ancient city to the ground,[52] the Edessans were left with no alternative but to extract the Shroud from concealment in the hope that it might, somehow, miraculously save the day. Evagrius reports that the holy icon was brought into the tunnel:

> They sponged it with water and with the same water they sprinkled the stack and the timber. And immediately, with divine aid added to their faith, what before had been impossible was now accomplished. For the wood immediately caught fire, and more quickly than one can say it, was burned to ashes and ignited what lay above it.[53]

Shortly after this miracle had been performed,[54] the Persians abandoned their siege, the city was saved, and the image-bearing icon became the holy relic and mighty palladium of Edessa, replacing in this role the now-discredited Letter of Jesus.[55]

The sudden elevation of this cloth to such religious and civic prominence leaves no room for doubt that

> the Icon was brought to bear in the crisis of 544. We may suppose that in the emergency, when the Letter of Jesus, read aloud from the main gate, seemed to be offering the city insufficient protection, whatever icons were available were thrown into the breach. It is indeed very likely that, as Evagrius tells us, Abgar's cloth was carried through the tunnel to bless the efforts of those who were attempting to ignite the tower-stack.[56]

According to Evagrius, water sprinkled from the Edessan icon brought about an instantaneous conflagration; however, it is self-evident that had the tunnel timber really been doused with water, the chances of starting a fire would only have decreased and, consequently, the Evagrius account has been described as both "fanciful"[57] and "distorted."[58] Nevertheless, since the Shroud was unquestionably involved, in some manner, with starting the fire,[59] it seems very likely that the "poker holes" now observable on the cloth are the product of those events which actually did transpire in the tunnel. So, what actually happened?

The physical evidence indicates that the Shroud was laid out to full-length, its ventral image to the bottom, and then folded once lengthwise, from right to left, and once widthwise, from top to bottom, thereby concealing the image within and creating four separate linen layers.[60] The observable damage reflects four distinct fire penetrations of the folded cloth by a pitch-soaked instrument. The single unaligned hole evidences penetration of the two dorsal layers and the infliction of a burn mark upon the image side of the topmost ventral layer. Of the three holes in alignment, the two located closest to the center of the cloth evidence penetration of the two dorsal layers and the topmost ventral layer and the infliction of a burn mark upon the image side of the bottom ventral layer. Only the aligned hole located furthest from the center of the cloth evidences a complete penetration of all four layers.

In view of the physical evidence and the miraculous powers which were later attributed to the icon, this paper proposes that the utterly-perplexed Edessans,[61] having decided to deploy the Shroud as an intermediary fire-starting device, folded the cloth, placed it directly upon the timber stack, prayerfully invoked its presumed miraculous powers, and administered a pitch-soaked firebrand to its dead center, four times and in a right-angle pattern, their final effort penetrating all four layers and communicating fire to the woodpile beneath.[62] The three partial penetrations of the cloth may simply reflect previous unsuccessful attempts to push the firebrand through all of the linen folds or, consistent with Ian Wilson's "trial by fire" vision,[63] may evidence three intentionally-partial firebrand applications, each dedicated to a member of the Holy Trinity, followed by a final purposeful thrust through the entire folded cloth and a resounding "Amen."[64]

SOLVING THE MYSTERY OF THE PORTRAIT

Upon extracting the Shroud from the tunnel and unfolding it, the Christians of Edessa must have been shocked and horrified to discover the extent of the damage that had been occasioned by their actions, each quadrant of the image-bearing side of the cloth now grotesquely scarred by edge-charred holes and blackened burn marks. In their minds, the fiery miracle had proved that this desecrated icon was truly the authentic burial Shroud of Jesus Christ and the fire damage on the cloth served only to convict them of an unforgivable sacrilege.

This paper proposes that, confronted with the dilemma of how to accord the cloth appropriate credit for having saved their city and yet avoid the consequences of personal culpability, the leaders of the Edessan Church first concocted a tale that water, which they had respectfully sponged upon the cloth and then sprinkled on the timber, had started the fateful fire, and that they then concealed the damning evidence of the fire damage beneath the folds of a "doubled-in-four" portrait.[65] Almost immediately after the events of 544, the icon became the city's holy relic and mighty palladium[66] and, within a mere five years, there appeared the first-known artistic portrayal of the disembodied head of a Shroudlike Christ in a circle.[67] The Edessans soon began to refer to their portrait, now known as the holy Image of Edessa, as "*acheiropoietos*" (not made by human hands)[68] and to attribute its creation to Christ himself.[69]

Thus, at the close of the sixth century, it was really no secret that the portraitized icon known as the Image of Edessa was, in fact, a four-folded and full body image-bearing sindon and, for that simple reason, the cloth is specifically described as such in the *Acts of Thaddeus*.[70] What was kept hidden, however, was the fact that the portrait concealed, beneath its folds, the fire damage which the cloth had sustained in 544, a secret spawned when the Edessan Church hierarchy doubled the Shroud in four and permitted its veneration only in such folded and portraitized form. As this sixth-century practice became a hallowed Edessan tradition, one scrupulously honored for almost four hundred years, the true sindonic nature of the cloth was gradually forgotten[71] and it was not until 944, when the Byzantines disassembled the Edessan portrait in Constantinople, that the full-body image of Christ crucified was revealed once more.[72]

Bibliography

Drews, Robert, *In Search of the Shroud of Turin*, Rowman & Allanheld (Totowa, N.J. 1984).

Gove, Harry E., *Relic, Icon or Hoax*, Institute of Physics Publishing (Bristol 1996).

Hexter, Ralph J., *Equivocal Oaths and Ordeals in Medieval Literature*, Harvard University Press (Cambridge, Mass. 1975).

Kramer, Heinrich, and Sprenger, James, *The Malleus Maleficarum* (Trans. Montague Summers), Dover Publications (New York 1971).

Segal, J.B., *Edessa, The Blessed City*, Oxford University Press (London 1970).

Wilson, Ian, *The Blood and the Shroud*, The Free Press (New York 1998).

Wilson, Ian, *The Mysterious Shroud*, Doubleday & Company (Garden City, N.Y. 1986).

Wilson, Ian, *The Shroud of Turin, The Burial Cloth of Jesus Christ?*, Image Books (Garden City, N.Y. 1979).

Notes

1. As proposed by Ian Wilson in his remarkable Mandylion theory. See Wilson, *The Shroud of Turin*, pp. 118-124; 132-135.

2. The Shroud's dorsal image is flanked by two sets of four holes, three in alignment and a fourth located more toward the edge of the cloth, together forming a right-angle pattern. Lying nearby are several "irregular, ancillary burn marks as from stray sparks". Wilson, *The Shroud of Turin*, p. 25. To one side of the ventral image lies a set of three holes in alignment and a burn mark which, together, form a right-angle pattern. To the other side of the ventral image lies a single hole aligned with two burn marks. Editor's Note: See the article on this website titled The Red Stains on the Lier and Other Shroud Copies by Remi Van Haelst. The article includes four detailed color

photographic closeups of the burn holes as well as a transmitted light image of the Shroud.

3. This damage is very clearly shown in photographs of the Shroud which have been illuminated with transmitted light. See Wilson, *The Mysterious Shroud*, illus. inter pp. 46-47. Also, see above Editor's Note.

4. See Dreisbach, Albert R., Jr., "More Evidence for a Pre-Medieval Date," *Shroud News*, No. 61, pp. 7-8. These patterns have also been described as "L-shaped". See Paci, Stefano M., "All Those Carbon 14 Errors," *Shroud News*, No. 80, p. 6.

5. Van Haelst, Remi, "The Lier Shroud: A Problem in Attribution," *Shroud Spectrum International*, No. 20, p. 8 (originally reported in Sindon 8:26). Wilson, *The Shroud of Turin*, p. 25.

6. Wilson, *The Shroud of Turin*, p. 25.

7. This observation was made in 1978 by Dr. Ray Rogers, a member of STURP. See Wilson, *The Mysterious Shroud*, p. 78, citing L. Schwalbe and R. N. Rogers, *Physics and Chemistry of the Shroud of Turin*, p. 47, note 7.

8. On the Lierre copy, these holes are shown in red paint, apparently reflecting the artist's belief that they were bloodstains. The holes were not repaired when the Poor Clare nuns patched over the damage caused by the Chambery fire of 1532. See Van Haelst, Remi, "The Lier Shroud: A Problem in Attribution," *Shroud Spectrum International*, No. 20, pp. 6-11.

9. Wilson, *The Shroud of Turin*, p. 25.

10. Wilson, in imagining this ritual, could almost hear the incantation "in nomine patris et filii et spiritus sancti." Wilson, *The Shroud of Turin*, p. 25. In 1933, Don Antonio Tonelli examined the Shroud and expressed his belief that this damage was probably caused by the deliberate insertion of a hot poker into the folded cloth. Van Haelst, "Remi, The Lier Shroud: A Problem in Attribution," *Shroud Spectrum International*, No. 20, p. 8 (originally reported in *Sindon* 8:26).

11. "Trial by the ordeal of red-hot iron" may be equated with a *judicium Dei* whereby God is seen to verify or deny the validity of a formal oath and this practice may have developed from the so-called oriental "Act of Truth." Hexter, pp. 1-7. A hot iron was placed into a person's hand and the extent of healing was employed as a measure of determining veracity or innocence. Trial by fire was denied to witches because they knew how to protect the skin through the application of herbs. See Kramer and Sprenger, pp. 233-235.

12. While not providing an example of an ordeal having been employed to test the authenticity of a relic, Wilson speculated that the Shroud's "trial by fire" may have been a preliminary to the institution of the full Holy Shroud cult in 1506. Wilson, *The Mysterious Shroud*, pp. 78-81. However, there is no apparent reason for soaking a heated iron in pitch prior to conducting an ordeal. Wilson has recently reiterated his belief in the hot poker theory, humorously referring to "trial by fire" as "a Dark Ages equivalent of the carbon dating test." Wilson, *The Blood and the Shroud*, pp. 66-67.

13. This detail was apparently first observed by a correspondent of Fr. A. M. Dubarle. See Bonnet-Eymard, Bruno, "The Eastern Pre-History of the Relic," *Contre-Reforme Catholique*, No. 217, p. 9 (March 1989). In 1993, Professor Jerome Lejeune examined this manuscript and found that the physical characteristics of the illustrated cloth, in its portrayal of superimposable hole patterns, coincided "perfectly with the Shroud." Paci, Stefano M., "All Those Carbon 14 Errors," *Shroud News*, No. 80, pp. 6-7.

14. Wilson, *The Mysterious Shroud*, p. 114 (this illustration appears on p. 115). Professor Lejeune proclaimed this dating to be "without doubt" because the manuscript was bound in 1192 and contains historical facts and musical passages which clearly pre-date the thirteenth century, thereby establishing, in his opinion, that the Shroud's existence before 1192 is "a definitive historic certainty." Paci, Stefano M., "All Those Carbon 14 Errors," *Shroud News*, No. 80, pp. 6-7.

15. Wilson has recently acknowledged that he did not notice these holes, and certain other sindonic markings, in the Hungarian Pray Manuscript when he performed the research upon which the Mandylion theory was based. Wilson, *The Blood and the Shroud*, pp. 145-147. Trial by fire was employed in medieval Western Europe until first criticized by the Pope in the late twelfth century and then banned altogether in 1215 by the Fourth Lateran Council. Hexter, p. 26, n. 96; p. 27, n. 97. However, there is no evidence that, prior to 1192-1195, the Shroud had been in the hands of Western Europeans and, indeed, the Mandylion theory places the Shroud, at that time, in the possession of devout Edessan and Byzantine Christians who venerated it as both a holy relic and a mighty palladium.

16. Carbon-14 testing of Shroud samples conducted by Oxford University, the University of Arizona, and the Zurich Polytechnic resulted in a finding, with a 95% statistical certainty, that the linen cloth dated

from 1260-1390. P.E. Damon, et al., "Radiocarbon Dating of the Shroud of Turin," *Nature*, Vol. 337, No. 6028, pp. 611-615 (Feb. 16, 1989). Dr. Leoncio A. Garza-Valdes and Dr. Faustino Cervantes Ibarola thereafter discovered that the linen fibers were blanketed by a bioplastic bacterial coating. See Morgan, Rex, "The Rome Symposium, Part 2," *Shroud News*, No. 78, p. 11 (August 1993). In subsequent experiments, radiocarbon testing misdated, by at least 500 years, a Mayan carving and the outer wrappings of an Egyptian mummified ibis, both covered by a bioplastic bacterial coating. Wilson, *The Blood and the Shroud*, pp. 225-231. Professor Harry Gove, who developed the accelerator mass spectrometry (AMS) testing method which was used to carbon date the Shroud, has stated that claims of the cloth being covered by a bioplastic bacterial coating "should be taken seriously" and has conceded that Dr. Garza-Valdes' theory that this caused the Shroud to be substantially misdated "needs further detailed investigation." Gove, p. 308.

17. Leonardo was born in 1452 and died in 1519. See Scavone, Daniel C., Review of Lynn Picknett and Clive Prince. "The Turin Shroud: In Whose Image?," *Shroud News*, No. 87, pp. 3-5 (February 1995).

18. This solution was proposed by Wilson who astutely noted that the damage lies dead center in a specific folding arrangement, forms right-angle patterns, and displays evidence of pitch. See Wilson, *The Shroud of Turin*, pp. 24-25.

19. This solution was proposed by Fr. A.M. Dubarle. See Bonnet-Eymard, Bruno, "The Eastern Pre-History of the Relic," *Contre-Reforme Catholique*, No. 217, Eng. ed., p. 9 (March 1989). Bonnet-Eymard, Bruno, "The Physics and Chemistry of the Holy Shroud," *Contre-Reforme Catholique*, No. 218, Eng. ed., p. 17 (April 1989).

20. This solution was proposed by Brother Bruno Bonnet-Eymard. See Bonnet-Eymard, Bruno, "The Physics and Chemistry of the Holy Shroud," *Contre-Reforme Catholique*, No. 218, Eng. ed., p. 17 (April 1989).

21. Wilson, *The Shroud of Turin*, pp. 118-124; 132-135.

22. This version is derived from Alexander Roberts and James Donaldson, eds., *The Ante-Nicene Fathers* (Grand Rapids, Mich.; Eerdmans, 1951), vol. VIII, pp. 558-59, and includes Wilson's well-justified substitution of "doubled-in-four cloth" for "towel" in translation of "*tetradiplon*" in the original Greek text. Wilson, *The Shroud of Turin*, p. 120.

23. In the earliest version of this Syrian legend (early third century), the disciple brings with him a wonderful vision, in a later version (late third century), a portrait, and in a final version (mid-tenth century), the Mandylion itself. See Wilson, *The Shroud of Turin*, pp. 127-130.

24. Sometime between the Crucifixion and the end of Abgar's reign in approximately 50.

25. The Mandylion theory asserts that it would have been unseemly to present a reigning monarch with an object as repellant as "the gravecloth of man who had been executed as a convicted criminal, in the most degrading circumstances possible." Wilson, *The Shroud of Turin*, p. 134. This rationale (1) presumes that it would have been inappropriate to present a burial cloth to Abgar, but entirely appropriate to do so upon having disguised it in order to deceive the king; and (2) further assumes that Abgar could have remained oblivious to the underlying bulk of the cloth and never once sought to unfold it, thereby discovering the deceit which had been practiced upon him.

26. From approximately 57 to 525. See Wilson, *The Shroud of Turin*, p. 135; pp. 138-139.

27. As the result of a devastating flood which occurred in 525. Wilson, *The Shroud of Turin*, pp. 138-139. "The trellis-covered work, unrecognizable as the Shroud...seems to be the form it had at the time of its rediscovery in Edessa in the sixth-century A.D." Wilson, *The Shroud of Turin*, p. 126.

28. Wilson, *The Shroud of Turin*, pp. 137-138.

29. "The air of hallowed mystery ensured that the image of the body would lie unsuspected in the folds to await another era and men of a different city." Wilson, *The Shroud of Turin*, p. 147.

30. No other putative relic of the Passion has ever surfaced in Edessa and even those historians who agree that the Shroud did ultimately reach Edessa have nevertheless concluded that this event did not take place as early as the first century. Drews, pp. 52-75. Bonnet-Eymard, Bruno, "Superabundant Historical Testimony," *Contre-Reforme Catholique*, No. 237, Eng. ed., pp. 4-5 (March, 1991).

31. Segal, p. 70.

32. See Wilson, *The Blood and the Shroud*, pp. 161-175. To his own question of whether it is actually the latterday monarch who lies behind the Abgar legend, Wilson now responds: "Not necessarily." Wilson, *The Blood and the Shroud*, pp. 169; 172. Professor Robert Drews believes that it was during or after the reign of Abgar VIII that the Shroud was brought to Edessa. Drews, pp. 52-75.

33. Wilson, *The Shroud of Turin*, p. 135; pp. 138-139.

34. In an early third-century fresco found in the Hypogeum of the Aurelians, Christ is realistically depicted as a shepherd with a bipartite beard, long hair falling to the shoulders, and an oval face. Drews, p. 78. Pfeiffer, Heirich, "The Shroud of Turin and the Face of Christ in Paleochristian, Byzantine and Western Medieval Art," *Shroud Spectrum International*, No. 9, p. 15 (1984). Wilson, *The Shroud of Turin*, pp. 100-101. Roman art of the fourth century provides several examples of a long-haired and bearded Jesus and, in the Catacomb of Commodilla, Christ has undulating hair, a long beard, large eyes, and a large nose. Drews, p. 79. Wilson, *The Shroud of Turin*, pp. 100-101.

35. During the Theodosian era (370-410), there suddenly appeared distinctly Shroudlike depictions of Christ; i.e., unprecedented portrayals of Jesus with a long, narrow, and majestic face, a moustache and medium-length beard, and long hair falling upon his shoulders, sometimes parted in the center. Pfeiffer, Heirich, "The Shroud of Turin and the Face of Christ in Paleochristian, Byzantine and Western Medieval Art," *Shroud Spectrum International*, No. 9, p. 13 (1984). If the Shroud is authentic, such artistic representations were clearly intended to be realistic portrayals of Christ. Drews, p. 79.

36. Markwardt, Jack, "Antioch and the Shroud." Paper presented at the Third International Congress on the Shroud, Turin, 1998. (copyright 1998)

37. Scavone, Daniel C., personal correspondence. This translation was derived from the Greek text contained in the *Acta Thaddaei*, ed. R.A. Lipsius, *Acta Apostolorum Apocrypha I*, p. 274 (1891). See Scavone, Daniel C., "Joseph of Arimathea, the Holy Grail and the Turin Shroud" (1996), Shroud of Turin Website Library, http://www.shroud.com.

38. Eusebius (ca. 325) mentioned no image whatsoever and the *Doctrine of Addai* (ca. 400) spoke only of a "portrait of Jesus in choice paints." See Wilson, *The Shroud of Turin*, pp. 127-130.

39. The respective appearances of the *Doctrine of Addai* and the *Acts of Thaddeus*.

40. See Note 29.

41. In fact, the first-known artistic portrayal of the disembodied head of Christ in a halo-type circle had already appeared "at the center of the huge jewelled cross in the apse of Sant'Apollinare in Classe, Ravenna, completed shortly before 549." Wilson, *The Shroud of Turin*, pp.

141-142. This circumstance strongly suggests that the Shroud had already been "doubled-in-four."

42. See Wilson, *The Shroud of Turin*, pp. 101-102; 144-147.

43. A deportraitization of the Shroud would have involved "a great deal of dismantling." Wilson, *The Shroud of Turin*, p. 122. However, although the Mandylion theory asserted that the Shroud was doubled-in-four in the first century and was never unfolded again until the eleventh or twelfth century, it was discovered in 1987 that the Shroud must have been unfolded upon its arrival in Constantinople in August of 944. See Wilson, *The Blood and the Shroud*, pp. 153-154. Bonnet-Eymard, Bruno, "The Eastern Pre-History of the Relic," *Contre-Reforme Catholique*, No. 217, Eng. ed., p. 9 (March 1989).

44. While it is possible that, at some point during its centuries-long portraitization, the Shroud was dismantled, refolded, and subjected to fire damage, this particular era in sindonic history was one of great reverence for the holy and palladian virtues of the cloth and extreme care would have been exercised to protect it from harm. There is evidence of the cloth being unfolded only once during this period, upon its arrival in Constantinople (see Note 43), and there is absolutely no hint of a Shroud-related fire occurring in either Edessa or Constantinople between 544 and 1192.

45. In fact, probably prior to 549 (see Notes 41 and 67).

46. It has been speculated that the orthodox Melkites were in possession of the icon and the Monophysites (known in Edessa as Jacobites) held the so-called Letter of Jesus. See Note 116. Segal, p. 77. Drews, p. 68. Wilson, *The Shroud of Turin*, pp. 139-140. However, the author believes that the Shroud was actually in the possession of Antiochene Monophysite refugees. Markwardt, Jack, "Antioch and the Shroud," paper presented at the Third International Congress on the Shroud, Turin, 1998 (copyright 1998).

47. Wilson, *The Shroud of Turin*, p. 137. If the Shroud had been reposing in Edessa prior to 544, the residents of the city may have regarded it as a painted icon rather than as a holy relic. See Drews, pp. 62-63.

48. Evagrius describes the icon only as a "divinely made image" and a "sacred likeness." See Wilson, *The Shroud of Turin*, p. 137.

49. Drews, p. 64. The Persians may also have constructed this tower to permit them to scale the city's high walls. See Wilson, *The Shroud of Turin*, p. 137.

50. Wilson, *The Shroud of Turin*, p. 137.

51. For centuries, the people of Edessa had venerated a writing in which Christ had supposedly promised his protection to the city and the palladian powers of this letter had been invoked to thwart prior Persian threats. Segal, pp. 74-76. Wilson, *The Shroud of Turin*, pp. 136-137. Although declared apocryphal in a decree issued by Pope Gelasius in 494, this letter continued to remain popular and widely credited. Segal, p. 73; p. 75.

52. Markwardt, Jack, "Antioch and the Shroud," paper presented at the Third International Congress on the Shroud, Turin, 1998 (copyright 1998).

53. Translation from Drews, p. 61. See also Wilson, *The Shroud of Turin*, p. 137.

54. Procopius of Caesarea, in his *History of the Wars* written in approximately 546, confirms that the Edessans dug a tunnel, experienced problems with starting a fire due to a lack of air in the underground chamber, and succeeded in setting a fire which spread to the Persian siege-works; however, he did not mention the intervention of any icon and he attributed the Edessans' victory to their own courage and resourcefulness. Segal, p. 77. Drews, pp. 64-66.

55. Wilson, *The Shroud of Turin*, p. 140. "From 544 onward, the prestige of the letter (of Jesus) began to decline in Edessa, and the icon's began to rise." Drews, p. 66.

56. Drews, p. 66.

57. Wilson, *The Shroud of Turin*, p. 137.

58. Drews, p. 63.

59. According to the so-called "Festival Sermon," composed shortly after the Shroud was taken to Constantinople in 944, "...the sacred image helped to light the fire that destroyed the wall." See Drews, p. 58.

60. Such folding would result in the following top-to-bottom layered sequence: (1) dorsal image underside and dorsal image side; (2) dorsal image side and dorsal image underside; (3) ventral image underside and ventral image side; and (4) ventral image side and ventral image underside. See the theorized folding graphic which is depicted in Bonnet-Eymard, Bruno, "The Eastern Pre-History of the Relic," *Contre-Reforme Catholique*, No. 217, Eng. ed., p. 8 (March 1989). Dr. P. L. Baima Bollone examined the Shroud in 1978 and reported that the thickness of the fabric, depending upon the area and the traction, measured from 300 to 350 microns. Crispino, Dorothy, "A Chronological Survey of Observations on the Shroud Textile," *Shroud Spectrum International*, No. 38/39, p. 26. Thus, the four-layered thickness of

the Shroud, as folded at the time when it incurred this fire damage, would have measured from 1200 to 1400 microns.

61. See Wilson, *The Shroud of Turin*, p. 137.

62. In accordance with Wilson's theory that the damage was caused by "deliberate rather than accidental" action (see Note 18).

63. See Note 10.

64. Far less likely, but nevertheless in accordance with Brother Bruno's theory (see Note 20), would be a scenario wherein the folded Shroud, while being carried through the subterranean passageway to the timber stack, was accidently damaged by pitch which dripped from an illumination torch, with the locations and degrees of the fire penetrations being merely a matter of circumstance.

65. According to the so-called "Festival Sermon," written immediately after the Image of Edessa's 944 arrival in Constantinople, the Evagrius account of the tunnel episode was attested to by three patriarchs. Drews, p. 58.

66. Wilson, *The Shroud of Turin*, p. 140. Drews, p. 66.

67. As previously noted (see Note 41), this "at the center of the huge jewelled cross in the apse of Sant'Apollinare in Classe, Ravenna, completed shortly before 549." Wilson, *The Shroud of Turin*, pp. 141-142. In Emesa (Homs), Syria, there appeared, by about 570, a medallion portrait of a Shroudlike Christ on a silver vase. Wilson, *The Shroud of Turin*, p. 102. Wilson, *The Blood and the Shroud*, p. 141.

68. This terminology seems to have first been used in 569. Segal, p. 77. Wilson claims that it appears in no account earlier than that of Evagrius. Wilson, *The Shroud of Turin*, p. 140.

69. Segal, pp. 76-77. Drews, pp. 66-67.

70. See discussion hereinbefore and Note 37.

71. "The air of hallowed mystery ensured that the image of the body would lie unsuspected in the folds to await another era and men of a different city." Wilson, *The Shroud of Turin*, p. 147.

72. See Note 43. As to evidence of subsequent unfoldings of the cloth in Constantinople, see Wilson, *The Shroud of Turin*, pp. 155-172.

The Role of the Internet in the Future of Shroud Research

Communications and Shroud Research

My personal observations of Shroud research began in late 1976, when I became the Official Documenting Photographer for the Shroud of Turin Research Project (STURP). As a member of the team, I was directly involved in the two years of planning and meetings that culminated in STURP's participation in the 120-hour examination of the Shroud in October 1978.

The STURP team spent over two years planning their experiments. This period was often frustrating because the team was comprised of small groups of researchers located in many different cities across the United States. The only available means of communications between the various groups was either telephone or written correspondence. This limited our efficiency and added considerable time to the planning process. The first time the entire team actually met was not until thirty days before their departure for Turin.

In the years following the testing, while the collected data was being reduced and evaluated, the intensity of Shroud research increased worldwide. During this period, as I worked closely with the STURP scientists and provided them with the Shroud photographs that they required for their work, the need for increased interaction and communications in Shroud research became even more apparent. I attended every team meeting, documenting each, and in 1981, I completed the photo-documentation paper for which I was responsible.[1]

One of the more obvious problems I observed during this period was the lack of communication that existed, not only within the project, but between our team and researchers from other groups. In part, it was due to the limits of 1970s communications technology. There were no fax machines or e-mail and the researchers were truly scattered around the world. But other times it appeared strictly personal. I observed apparent friction between some of the scientists as early as the first hour of the first day of our 120-hour examination. I was beginning to see a pattern develop that eventually resulted in each scientific group working within itself, with little or no sharing of information with other groups. Although new Shroud groups were being formed in the United States and in Europe, few were in active cooperation with each other. Lack of funding, nationalism, individual egos and the very nature of the subject matter all seemed to contribute to a rather uncooperative and even adversarial attitude. At a time when *increased* cooperation and communication was an obvious and important necessity, it seemed that just the opposite was occurring.

In all fairness, the STURP team was bound, not only by a written agreement amongst themselves, but also by an agreement with the Turin authorities. They were legally obligated to maintain silence about their conclusions until they published their final report, in order to prevent incomplete data from being released piecemeal and consequently, being misinterpreted.[2] On the other hand, the Shroud of Turin is a very public object, and no one was completely immune from the pressures being encountered due to increased worldwide interest. At times, it seemed as though the world of Shroud research was acting like children on a playground, arguing over a ball that didn't even belong to them.

Throughout this same period, researchers around the world frequently discussed the establishment of an International Center for Shroud study. Although several groups incorporated the word "international" into their names, there was very little actual international activity. It was clear to everyone that there was a need for a truly global organization or center, but concerns over costs, location, language and administration made it nothing more than a distant dream.

Like many others, my continued involvement in Shroud research was cut short in 1988 when the results of the radiocarbon 14 dating were made public. In the following years, I noticed items still appearing in the commercial press and media, but most of these were just attempts to explain how the so-called "forgery" of the Shroud was perpetrated. Many claimed to have "solved the mystery" of the image, although often these were written by people with apparently little first-hand knowledge of the subject matter. Yet the media attention they garnered made them seem credible to the public.

In effect, after the release of the carbon dating results, many serious scientists disengaged from Shroud research, leaving a vacuum that was quickly filled with theorists driven by what appeared to be other than scientific motives. This had the unfortunate side effect of clouding the waters even more and blending Shroud fact with fiction. After all the hours of serious, scientific research that had been performed on the Shroud of Turin, the science wound up hidden away in journals available only from research libraries while the public continued to be misinformed by the popular and tabloid press. It seemed as if no progress had been made at all and that so much effort by so many people had been wasted.

A Solution Is Found

In the early 1990s, new information about the Shroud started to filter out to the public. My own interest was renewed at this time and I began to consider the best means possible to make my 1978 materials available to a larger segment of the public. I started thinking about the Internet as a possibility and found myself online for the first time in October 1995.

It was immediately obvious that the Internet provided something that no other medium before it could offer: universal access to instant global communications. I decided this was a great way to make Shroud information available and began designing the Shroud of Turin Website.[3] On January 21, 1996, the website went online.

The response was almost immediate. E-mails began arriving from many veteran Shroud researchers and from others who were new to sindonology. All were excited at the prospect of a dedicated Shroud website and several offered to allow their work to be reprinted online. Soon I was corresponding with hundreds of people and everyone agreed that the website could become the perfect international center for Shroud studies. In addition to dedicated Shroud researchers, many other scientists were viewing the site and writing me with ideas or comments. And the lay public was visiting as well. Many wrote just to tell me how happy they were to find Shroud science finally available to everyone. It quickly became clear that my original idea of a small website to share some of my Shroud materials was growing into something much larger and more important than I ever imagined. It appeared that this new technology could finally provide the mechanism to make Shroud research a truly international effort.

Now, little more than two years later, with over 200,000 visitors from 117 countries, my little experiment has grown into the largest Shroud website on the Internet. It has succeeded only because of the cooperation I have received from many in the world involved directly or indirectly with the Shroud. More than that, it has shown that the Internet can in fact be used to enhance and further the goals of sindonologists everywhere.

A Blueprint For The Future

One of the most important requirements for Shroud researchers is the need for peer review of their work. Unfortunately, at times it has been difficult to find a scientific journal willing to accept work on the subject due to its highly controversial nature. Sindonologists often find themselves submitting their work to smaller, more obscure journals, or not submitting it for peer review at all. Sadly, this also limits the credibility of any conclusions drawn by the researchers and provides substantial grist for the skeptics' mill.

Over the years, a number of peer reviewed journals were published that were dedicated to sindonology. Most notable are *Sindon*, published in Italy by the Centro Internazionale Di Sindonologia and *Shroud Spectrum International*, published in the United States from 1981 to 1993 by Dorothy Crispino.[4] These excellent journals gave sindonologists a proper forum for presenting their work, but brought with them their own set of limitations. *Sindon* is published only in Italian, limiting international access to those who speak the language. *Shroud Spectrum* provided an excellent solution to the problem by reprinting English translations of papers that originally appeared in *Sindon*, as well as new papers, but sadly, it ceased publication in 1993.

The Internet can provide an ideal solution by presenting articles in multiple languages and permitting the viewer to select the language of his choice. With closer cooperation between major Shroud organizations worldwide, the Shroud of Turin Website, currently published only in English, could easily be expanded to include articles in any number of languages. The only requirement would be the delivery of qualified translations in digital form. And the elimination of printing and postage costs makes publishing such an electronic journal far more economically practical. Another advantage of the Internet is the simplicity of making corrections or additions to an article when necessary, a virtual impossibility with conventional printed journals. In addition, with such increased international cooperation, a multidisciplinary panel of experts could eventually be established to serve as a peer review board for any new papers submitted for publication without the typical physical restrictions of a printed journal.

Over the past two years, with the cooperation of the Collegamento pro Sindone, a number of articles previously available only in Italian have already been translated into English and reprinted on the Shroud of Turin Website.[5] In addition, through the cooperation of the Centro Mexicano de Sindonologia, a Spanish language version of the "1997 Fire" article has also been included.[6]

Non-reviewed articles can also be reprinted for the benefit of researchers and the lay public alike. The "Scientific Papers & Articles" page of the website already includes many of these.[7]

One of the greatest challenges to modern Shroud research is finding and accessing previously published work. Even with access to a sophisticated research library, many references are very hard to find. Through the cooperation of all of the world's largest Shroud collections, a massive bibliography of books and articles is currently being compiled and a substantial list is already found on the "Shroud Booklist" page of the website, with many more soon to be included.[8] Finally, an easily accessible, centrally located bibliography is available to everyone.

Along these same lines, even when a reference is determined, it is often impossible to find the actual paper or journal. Many important references are out of print and more than twenty years old. Over the last two years, rights have been obtained to reprint a number of these on the website and more are being added constantly.[9] This will be continued and in time, the website could become the central repository and primary resource of Shroud data for sindonologists worldwide.

Without question, the Shroud of Turin stimulates heated debates. These often take the form of personal correspondence between individual researchers. The website has already been host to a number of such debates through the good graces of the researchers who have made their correspondence available for publication.[10] This feature could easily be expanded and provide a true open international forum for continued discussion and would allow other interested parties to enter the debate.

Also available via the Internet is a written forum known as a newsgroup, where viewers read posted comments and then add their own comments to the page. Such a newsgroup already exists on the subject of the Shroud, created by William Meacham of Hong Kong.[11]

In addition to such published debates, live discussion forums are now very practical on the Internet. With advanced planning, the technology allows live forums to become a regular feature on the website. Such live "net meetings" or conferences would certainly enhance the interchange of ideas. Not only verbal exchange, but video and audio teleconferences could be scheduled from time to time to allow researchers to share their ideas and discuss the details of their work.

Symposiums such as this one would also greatly benefit from using the Internet. A "call for papers" could be posted on the Internet to inform sindonologists of upcoming conferences, including deadline dates, fees and schedules. Abstracts could be easily submitted via e-mail, as could acceptance notices to prospective speakers from the conference organizers. Conference schedules could be posted and modified quickly if necessary. And of course, the final papers could eventually be published on the Internet to supplement the production of the written acts or proceedings.

In recent years, one of the greatest difficulties for many researchers has been gaining access to certain materials necessary for their work. This includes the need for photographs, copies of out of print or hard-to-find references and other types of data. Already in place on the Shroud of Turin Website is the "Research Registry" page, where many researchers have already "advertised" for materials they needed.[12] These have included blood and linen samples, access to special facilities and even some seeking new colleagues in specific disciplines to assist them in their research. And in some cases, organizations or individuals with resources to offer for Shroud research have posted them on the site to make them available to those who might need them.

With the continued worldwide interest in the Shroud, many researchers are often called upon by lay and professional groups to make presentations and give lectures. A new service planned for the website is an international Shroud Speakers Bureau. This will give organizations looking for such speakers a central source of qualified experts to select from. Participating researchers will be listed by discipline, physical location and availability. Along these same lines, an e-mail Directory of Shroud Researchers will also be included. This will make it even easier for sindonologists to contact each other.

Another useful function of the website is the gathering of statistical information and data. Researchers can design a questionnaire that will be converted to a form that website viewers fill out and send directly over the Internet. The researchers will receive the information immediately via e-mail and can integrate the responses directly into their analyses.

Finally, a search capability will be added in the near future that will allow website viewers to enter key words and quickly search through all of the website materials to find information specific to their needs. This will be particularly useful as the quantity of materials on the website increases.

Conclusions

Interaction and communication between Shroud researchers world-wide has historically been limited by the state of existing communication technologies and the inability or unwillingness of some researchers to cooperate with each other and openly share their data. Although the value of a globally accessible international center for Shroud studies has long been accepted, little if any progress has been made in realizing this goal.

Recent developments in communication technology have provided us with powerful new methods for instant global communications. With the advent of these new technologies, one of the major obstacles to creating an international Shroud center has been eliminated. The value of these advances has been clearly demonstrated by the Shroud of Turin Website, which has gained the confidence and cooperation of many researchers simply by creating an unbiased and fair atmosphere for presenting ideas of every point of view.

Only one major obstacle remains in taking Shroud research into the 21st century with renewed vigor and success, and that is a willingness on the part of sindonologists worldwide to share their information and cooperate with each other. As Archbishop Saldarini pointed out in his opening remarks, this will require us to *forget* our national boundaries, the languages we speak, the groups we belong to or the positions we take on authenticity and *remember* the common thread that binds us all together. We have an obligation to do the best science possible. That can only happen if we all work together so that true progress can be made. The tools are now available. The rest is up to us.

(Note: I have chosen to include my references as Internet addresses rather than in the conventional form since they all can be found on or via the Shroud of Turin Website. If you are reading this in a printed proceedings, just open your Internet browser, select the File Menu, Open Location, type in the address and hit the Enter key.)

References

1. http://www.shroud.com/mapping.htm - "Mapping of Research Test Points on the Shroud of Turin"
2. http://www.shroud.com/78conclu.htm - "A Summary of STURP's Conclusions"
3. http://www.shroud.com - The Shroud of Turin website's home Page
4. http://www.shroud.com/spectrum.htm - "Index to Shroud Spectrum International"

5. http://www.shroud.com/collegam.htm - "Collegamento pro Sindone" – Gateway Page
6. http://www.shroud.com/firespan.htm - Abril 12, 1997 - "Reporte Especial sobre el Incendio de 1997" - EN ESPANOL
7. http://www.shroud.com/papers.htm - "Scientific Papers & Articles" Page
8. http://www.shroud.com/booklist.htm - "Shroud Booklist" Page
9. http://www.shroud.com/nature.htm - "Radiocarbon Dating the Shroud of Turin" - This is the most recent paper added to the website (as of June 5, 1998). Reprinted from *Nature*, Vol. 337, No. 6208, pp. 611-615, 16th February, 1989
10. http://www.shroud.com/lombatti.htm - "Doubts Concerning the Coins Over the Eyes" A debate between Antonio Lombatti and Dr. Alan Whanger
11. alt.turin-shroud - The address of the Shroud of Turin Newsgroup founded by William Meacham
12. http://www.shroud.com/registry.htm - "Research Registry"

The Sanctuary of the Shroud: A Security Challenge

In today's society, security represents an industry that is so broad, complex and sophisticated, that a simple definition is not adequate. However, for the purpose of this paper, *security* can be basically defined as the *protection of an asset*, or anything of value. This includes people, property, and information. Security management is the professional application of current technology and the appropriate, combined use of hardware, personnel, electronics and procedures in order to secure something of value. Security should be a vital concern regarding the Shroud.

The history of the Shroud has been peppered with numerous security breaches and "close calls." The cloth has been subjected to several fires and a flood; it has been stolen, hidden, ransomed, and not to mention, contaminated by industrial pollutants and even by man's own hands. With the recent media coverage, the risks have dramatically increased, whether visible or not. History has shown us that important relics or historical artifacts are prime targets of attack from other opposing groups. Media coverage increases interest and draws attention to a specific arena. I do not think current times are any different, unfortunately.

A master security plan can offer the most comprehensive, integrated, and supportive protection available. It basically covers all foreseeable contingencies and relies on a redundant circle of defense. Sometimes, affairs of urgency must be boldly stated, even at the risk of sounding presumptuous. Having said that, I feel that I am the *most qualified* international security management consultant for the task of developing such a comprehensive protection program for this most Holy Relic and other Relics of the Passion.

I say that for the following reasons: With over fifteen years experience in former federal law enforcement and security management, coupled with 4 years of working on Shroud-related matters, I am uniquely qualified for such an undertaking. The experiences learned from service as a Physical Science Technician and Special Agent with the FBI would be advantageous for scientific testing, forensic evidence controls, investigations, the criminal mindset and behavior, threat assessment and prevention, liaison, and training. I also served as the Corporate Security Manager for an international manufacturing company which provided the organizational aspects necessary in Security Management. Since 1994, I have served as the Executive Director of the Council for Study of the Shroud of Turin, CSST, where part of my duties include security management of the premises, the Frei Collection and fire safety. This experience has also provided me with the intricacies involved with Shroud studies.

Numerous contacts made with other related groups would be immensely helpful in an overall program. As a member of both the International Association of Professional Security Consultants, IAPSC, and the American Society for Industrial Security, ASIS, knowledge of current technology and association with some of the industry's leaders and worldwide contacts is readily available. I earned the prestigious Certified Protection Professional, CPP, designation in 1996. Also, in 1997, I started **SECURITY INSIGHT**, a security management consulting company. As a fan of the Shroud since first seeing the televised exhibition in 1973, and an active "Shroudie" since 1994, I fully understand the complexities involved with securing such a Relic of veneration.

All too often, security is approached on an ad-hoc basis, usually after something went wrong. Security master planning, as is suggested, considers many other implications and strives to be supportive, preventive and comprehensive in nature. Security is simply too broad-scoped for one person to know. Therefore, a team approach is necessary. Consisting of a primary, secondary and technical consultant, this team of security professionals could properly and completely analyze the different points of vulnerability and obstacles involved.

For something to be properly secured, there first must be a strong desire and willingness to protect it from any and all foreseeable risks. An old saying at nuclear power plants is—"99% security equals NO security." One must decide what level of risk he is willing to accept. Regarding the Shroud and other related relics, there is no replacement, and "zero tolerance" of risks should be the standard. This requires extreme, effective measures, yet very unobtrusively. For comparison, one might look at the protection of the Hope Diamond, the Declaration of Independence, or any other important artifact—there simply must be a fail-safe program in use to address all contingencies, *before* they are needed. Unfortunately, the Pieta in St. Peter's Basilica will never be the same after its attack several years ago—*now* it is protected.

Risk can be defined as the possibility of an undesirable event. Risk might include perils which occur naturally, such as fires, floods, earthquakes, and storms. Risk also includes hazards and threats which are man-made and most often criminal, such as arson, theft, vandalism, or terrorism. Prime examples are the recent thefts from the Louvre in Paris or the National Gallery of Modern Art in Rome. The potential for any of the above is very real. Just because the Shroud is in its new case, we must not become complacent. There are weapons and people available that could and would destroy the Shroud, if permitted access. Security should be in place at *all times*, including times of general storage, exhibitions, scientific exams, special viewings, or any time during the transition for the above.

Criminal acts occur whenever a person has the motive, capability and opportunity to do something wrong. If any one of these elements is removed by security measures—no crime will occur. The purpose of a physical security plan can best be described by the four-D's—Deter, Detect, Delay and Deny. A redundant system is the best method to protect an asset.

This "circle of defense," detects the attacker at the earliest stage and gives security a warning of his presence. Appropriate action can then be taken.

Specifically, I would recommend the following issues be addressed to begin a comprehensive master security plan. Inasmuch as there exists at least a traditional, if not yet fully scientific, association with other related Relics of the Passion, these suggestions apply to them as well, although each would have to be independently assessed. Specifically, and in addition to the Shroud, the Sudarium of Oviedo, the Tunic of Argenteuil, the Cloak of Trier, and the Crown of Thorns are included. Church authority is sought for these concerted efforts.

1. **Conduct an on-site visit by a team of security professionals.** Extensive interviews regarding policy, procedures and contingency plans shall be conducted. Discussions with Church and Security officials regarding risk management and previous security measures shall also be conducted. Physical security survey of immediate vicinity, buildings, general area and specific areas shall be conducted and analyzed for points of vulnerability, and real and potential

threats. Focused strategies may include access control, fire safety, intrusion detection alarms, CCTV applications, and other special measures. Observations and recommendations to follow survey.

2. **The appointment of a Security Coordinator to the Conservation Committee to offer vital input in every area of strategic planning.** The Conservation Committee is critical and much needed, but it is primarily made up of scientists, and to my knowledge, none with security expertise. It is my firm belief that without *first securing* the Shroud, there may be nothing left to conserve. *Security is a vital part of conservation.*

3. **Contingency plans for all foreseeable contingencies must be drafted, understood, and practiced,** within reason—just like a fire drill. All areas of risk need to be addressed including natural disasters and intentional attacks.

4. **Liaison with various Church officials and government agencies needs to be established as soon as possible, if not already done.** A coordinator at each agency, i.e., Turin Police and Fire Departments, Italian Police, Italian military, Turin Hospitals, U.S. Embassy (intelligence reporting), and others need to be apprised of necessary and coordinated plans for emergency preparedness.

5. **The security team shall oversee the implementation of recommendations to assure quality control.** Other full-time security personnel will assist and assume responsibility. Functional testing of the system will follow installation. Periodic testing to be conducted.

6. **Conduct security awareness programs for all people directly involved with the Shroud.** By making people aware of potential breaches, one actually increases security with every set of eyes and ears. People need to be cognizant of their surroundings, without becoming paranoid. If one should see a briefcase or bag innocently left near the Shroud—one should make responsible inquiry and know what to do. It might be something left behind accidentally, or it may a bomb sufficient to destroy the Shroud and anyone near it.

There are many other measures and recommendations which are too technical and/or confidential to discuss in this open forum. The above recommendations are general in nature, but require the expertise of a security professional to be properly implemented. A leftover part of my old Boy Scout days is very relevant now, and that is the Scout Motto— "Be Prepared." By taking simple actions now, one can most likely prevent a possible tragedy later. Although these measures can not fully and unequivocally guarantee the protection of the Shroud or other Relics, they will certainly enhance its security and safety, to the best that is humanly possible. **Security** is one of those things in life that "**it is better to have and not need, than to need and not have.**"

In dealing with security matters, one should look to the expertise of a security professional. If you have a broken arm, you don't go to a car mechanic for help—you go to a doctor. In April 1996, I submitted a preliminary security protocol to Cardinal Saldarini, pursuant to his worldwide request for ideas on how best to conserve the Shroud. Part of the technical aspects of this paper dealt with the specialized detection of intruders. *If,* and I emphasize *if,* the fire in April, 1997 were, in fact, the act of an arsonist as is highly suspected, I dare say that my recommendations, if implemented, would have detected him on the roof and alerted security, *possibly preventing* the outcome. If unable to prevent it, the suggested fire suppression equipment *might have reduced* the ensuing damage. I say this, not with the attitude of "I told you so," but rather, as an urgent appeal for security changes. Although the Cardinal's office, the Centro and many others have made tremendous progress in the restoration efforts and in the new Shroud vault, we still need to learn from past mistakes. The fire of April, 1997 should serve as a "wake-up call." Sir Winston Churchill once said of "Duty,"...."It's not enough that we do our best, sometimes we have to do what is required." I feel it is our *duty* to use our God-given skills, talents, technology and resources to protect these holy Relics as best as humanly possible, *before* it is too late. I hope and pray the Church agrees.

SECURITY MATTERS!

The history of the Tunic of Argenteuil, the traditional "Seamless Robe" of the Passion of our Lord Jesus Christ, is peppered with past security breaches and assaults. The threat of similar breaches or attacks is not only **real**, but **ever-increasing** as new media coverage details the Tunic's historical and possible scientific correlation with other Relics of the Passion. Risks and other areas of vulnerability should be immediately assessed and reasonable and cost-effective security measures implemented in order to remove or reduce the risks to an absolute minimum.

The risks are numerous and multi-faceted, and include both natural and man-made events. Contingency plans must be made now for the eventuality of storms, floods, hurricanes, earthquakes, fires, etc. Vandalism, theft, destruction, arson, and accidents are some of the other risks which need to be addressed. Even accidental contamination or forensic breaches can unknowingly occur during scientific examinations or special viewings if proper evidence controls are not followed. Terrorism, unfortunately, is still alive and well. Religious fundamentalism has called for the theft or destruction of Relics of opposing religions for centuries. This potential threat cannot, must not, be ignored.

Historical "close calls" regarding the Tunic include the priest who cut the Tunic into numerous pieces in order to save at least some of it from total destruction or theft during the French Revolution. Most certainly he rethought his actions during his three years of imprisonment. In December 1983, the Tunic was actually stolen and held for ransom. After some payment and the release of political prisoners, the Tunic was returned. We should do all that is humanly possible to prevent this from ever occurring again. As good stewards, we must accept this awesome responsibility and ensure its protection for future generations to venerate.

During my recent visit to the Basilica of St. Denis to view the Holy Tunic, I was amazed at the apparent lack of adequate security to protect this irreplaceable Relic of the Passion. It is sad to say, but more protection and security measures are afforded almost any museum artifact, most commercial warehouses, and even my own home and car. We must learn from other breaches and assaults on similar Relics—consider the suspected arson in 1997 involving the Shroud of Turin. We must takes steps to protect these Holy Relics and act now, **before** it is too late.

As a security professional with over fifteen years experience in security management and former US federal law enforcement, I am well qualified to discuss this topic of major importance. I firmly believe in the conservation measures which are being advocated and which are so badly needed to properly conserve these Relics for future generations. But I also firmly believe that without **first** implementing proper security measures, there may be nothing left to conserve! *These Relics must first be secured before they are conserved.*

In April, 1996, I submitted a comprehensive preliminary security protocol for the protection and security of the Shroud of Turin and related Relics. This was submitted pursuant to Cardinal Saldarini's worldwide request for information on how best to conserve the Shroud. Unfortunately, the suggestions were not openly utilized. However, it was not due to its lack of quality. This protocol was subsequently peer-reviewed, with highly favorable acceptance. Security matters, quite honestly, should be handled by security professionals, not theologians or others. If the fire in April, 1997, were indeed the work of an arsonist, as is highly suspected, then the suggestions made in my protocol would have detected him on the roof and possibly, quite probably, resulted in a different outcome. That devastating fire should serve as a "wake-up" call as to the severity of not addressing these real threats, risks and areas of vulnerability in a timely manner.

My recommendations include a comprehensive security survey to be conducted by a team of security professionals. This survey would uncover and determine all areas of vulnerability. Appropriate recommendations to reduce or remove the various threats and risks would then be submitted to officials for consideration. The protection of these Relics would be assessed from a point of risk profile, risk probability, and risk criticality. Because the Tunic has been relatively obscure and unknown outside of the local region, its profile is such that in the past the chances of breaches occurring against it were slim or remote. However, now with renewed attention and interest from the media due to its historical and possible scientific correlation to other Relics of the Passion, its religious importance is increased immensely, at least as perceived by others. Its criticality is and has always been, simply, irreplaceable. Once it is gone, it is gone forever. I truly believe that every viable and reasonable precaution must be undertaken to afford this and other similar Relics the best protection that mankind can afford, in a very unobtrusive manner. This would permit an inviting atmosphere surrounding these Relics, while at the same time removing or reducing risks to an absolute minimum.

Simply having an alarm system in place or a large contingency of police is not sufficient. The best method to protect these Relics is an Integrated Security System. This would provide for a "circle of defense," and would also utilize strict procedures and policy controls. A balance is sought between the use of hardware, procedures, personnel and electronics. By using a single team to assess all Relic sites, the same standard of professionalism and levels of discernment would be utilized, thus permitting a uniform degree of assessment. The team should consist of a primary consultant, secondary consultant, and technical consultant in order to fully assess all areas.

I would be honored to assist with the surveys and implementation of the subsequent suggested measures. As a security management consultant, my professional contacts and associations would be extremely advantageous in conducting the necessary facets of the survey and implementation of any accepted measures. My eight years former service with the US FBI, (both as a Laboratory Technician and Special Agent), coupled with years of security management experience and other professional experiences would provide the necessary managerial, investigative, laboratory, forensic controls, and security expertise for such a complex endeavor. Also, having served as the Executive Director of the Council for Study of the Shroud of Turin, CSST since 1994, I am very sensitive to the subtle intricacies and nuances of Shroud studies. All of these Relics deserve the best that we can provide, as soon as we can provide it. It is my sincere hope that Church officials agree.

(Note: The above text represents the salient points which were informally presented by Philip E. Dayvault, CPP at the "Round-Table Discussion" on the Holy Tunic of Argenteuil, France, on November 14, 1998. Other representative examples were used and are not contained herein.)

MICHAEL MINOR

CONFERENCE ORGANIZER

Michael Minor, a practicing attorney and former prosecutor, was for a number of years General Counsel for the Shroud of Turin Research Project, Inc., the American scientific group which conducted extensive tests on the Shroud in Turin in 1978. Currently he is Vice President and General Counselor of the American Shroud of Turin Association for Research (AMSTAR) and a member of the Board of Directors of the Holy Shroud Guild. Minor is also a partner in Lone Star Autrographs, a Texas rare document company, a member of the Manuscript Society, and a member of the Ediroial Advisory Board of *The Autograph Collector's Magazine*. Minor is author of a book entitled *A Lawyer Argues for the Authenticity of the Shroud of Turin*, co-author of a book on presidential autographs entitled *From the President's Pen*, as well as numerous historical articles. Minor is listed in Who's Who in the World, Who's Who in American Law and Personalities of the South.

WHERE DO WE GO FROM HERE? CONSERVATION AND COOPERATION ARE THE KEYS

BY MICHAEL MINOR

As we approach a new century and millennium two issues are of utmost importance in my estimation: conservation and cooperation--and not necessarily in that order.

During the past hundred years more discoveries have been made concerning the Turin Shroud than in the previous approximately 1900 years. Studies and testing of the Shroud have evolved from rudimentary science and equipment to space age and computer technology. We cannot now fathom what will be learned. about the Shroud in the next century.

The Shroud must be preserved for future generations. At one and the same time it is the most scientifically studied object on earth as well as the greatest relic in Christendom. In order to properly conserve this singular object cooperation among the many disciplines, groups, organizations, and church authorities is necessary. Cooperation includes sharing information.

The Shroud has .no nationality or religion. It belongs to all mankind (and "womankind" too)! The Shroud is no one's fiefdom nor does anyone have a copyright on the data gleaned from the Shroud. Shared information on the Shroud generates more discoveries which, in turn, translate into greater knowledge and understanding. As Father Peter Rinaldi was fond of saying "there is room on the Shroud for all." Cooperation is the key to conserving the Shroud and unraveling its mysteries. Great and undreamed of discoveries await the development of new technology not now known or thought of.

All of you are important parts of the large sindonological family. Like all families our love for each other at times grows quite warm. Nevertheless, we must remember that it the world of the Shroud this very precious relic is far greater than the sum of its parts and we must rise above our petty differences in the interest of future generations. We must remember the Shroud will be here after we are gone, and let it be our legacy that we leave it better than we found it.

One of the goals of this conference was to provide an informal and home like atmosphere to share ideas and knowledge. We believe this goal was achieved.

I charge you to boldly approach the new century and millennium with a spirit of cooperation and collegiality. I strongly believe great Shroud discoveries lie ahead but they will be predicated on what we do today.

As we "old timers" know—and as you welcome new arrivals will find out—once bitten, the only thing that will get the "Shroud bug" out of your veins is embalming fluid. It is much more pleasant along the way if we cooperate and get along

From the bottom of my heart I thank each of you for participating. Until we meet again in the new millennium--farewell,

This conference is closed *sine die.*

354

The American Shroud of Turin Association for Research
AM★STAR

P.O. Box 876
Kaufman, Texas 75142-0878, U.S.A

(972) 932-5141 Telephone
(972) 932-7742 Telefax

THOMAS F. D'MUHALA, President

Members of the Board:

Thomas F. D'Muhala
Dr. Alan Adler (1932-2000)
Isabel Piczek
Donald L. Lynn (1932-2000)
Dr. Robert Bucklin

MICHAEL MINOR, Vice President
& General Counsel

HISTORY OF THE 1998 DALLAS SHROUD CONFERENCE

The 1998 Dallas Shroud Conference was sponsored by the American Shroud of Turin Association for Research (AM*STAR). It evolved into an important milestone in the history of the Shroud of Turin. Like so much connected with the Shroud, the Conference, quite literally, took on a life of its own and was organized in only approximately six weeks—a miraculously brief period of time to plan and organize a conference from the beginning to the end.

Dorothy Crispino was the inspiration for this Conference. For many years Dorothy hosted an informal meeting of the "Shroud crowd" in Brown County, Indiana. She had planned such a gathering in 1998 but was unable to do so because she was involved in selling her property and preparing to move to Italy. It was decided that a similar gathering would be held elsewhere. At this point my friend, Jo Pierce, kindly offered to help find a suitable location. After many days and dozens of telephone calls she found the marvelous Catholic Conference & Formation Center, the Retreat Center of the Diocese of Dallas.

The original plan was to have an informal, invitation-only meeting of Shroud scientists and scholars at a place conducive to the sharing and exchange of ideas and information about the Shroud in a relaxed atmosphere. As the word spread people requested to present papers. Serendipitously, we had the best of both worlds—scholarly papers presented in a relaxed atmosphere where ideas and information were freely exchanged. A new spirit of collegiality was birthed at the conference. And the rest, as they say, is history.

Isabel Piczek was chiefly responsible for organizing the papers at the 1998 Shroud Conference. Without her help and guidance the conference would not have been the success it was.

Michael Minor
Vice President and
General Counsel
Conference Coordinator

III

The 1997 Fire

THE 1997 FIRE IN THE ROYAL (GUARINI) CHAPEL CATHEDRAL OF SAINT JOHN THE BAPTIST TURIN, ITALY

AN INTERVIEW WITH MARIO TREMATORE AS WELL AS HIS OWN ACCOUNT OF HIS HEROIC RESCUE OF THE SHROUD

The Fires in the History
of the Shroud

The Shroud of Turin has been in two fires during its long history. The first was on December 4, 1532 in the Sainte Chapelle, Chambery, France. There was no time to find the custodians of the keys to unlock the Shroud from its iron-grilled repository. The Shroud was rescued on that occasion through the heroic efforts of a local blacksmith but not before it sustained the most serious damage ever done to it. The Shroud was in a silver reliquary given by Margaret of Austria. The heat from the Chambery fire was so intense that molten globules of silver dropped through one corner of the mulit-folded Shroud causing burn holes along both edges. Miraculously, the Image on the Shroud was virtually unscathed. In 1534, the Poor Clare nuns expertly sewed triangular patches over the burn holes on the Shroud which are still present today.

During the evening of April 11-12, 1997 a fire broke out in the Royal Chapel, known as the Guarini Chapel, in the Cathedral of St. John the Baptist where the Shroud has been housed since 1578. The Shroud was again miraculously saved through the heroic efforts of Turin firemen and primarily through the Herculean efforts of Turin Fire Captain Mario Trematore who broke through several layers of thick, bulletproof glass with a sledgehammer, amid falling blocks of stone from the chapel ceiling, to rescue the silver reliquary containing the Shroud. The entire Chapel was an inferno.

Mario Trematore is a true hero and all Christendom as well as modern science owe him a debt of gratitude.

Mario Trematore, now a dear friend, has graciously given

permission to publish his account of "Saving the Shroud" which was written at the request of His Holiness Pope John Paul II and is in the Vatican archives. It is our honor to publish it here for the first time, as well as an interview with Mario while he was my guest in June of this yer.

We are honored to include Mario's account in the proceedings of the 1998 Dallas Shroud Symposium both because the 1997 Turin Catherdral fire occurred in close proximity to our Conference and because the fire was an important event in the history of the Shroud on several levels, including scientifically and spiritually.

Michael Minor
Kaufman, Texas
September, 2001

Courage Saving Grace:
Italian Firefighter Risks His life to
Preserve Shroud of Turin

Alison Walker
From *The Terrell Tribune*, Sunday, June 3, 2001 Dateline: Kaufman, TX

Mario Trematore will be forever credited as the firefighter who risked his life to rescue the beloved Shroud of Turin from a 1997 fire at San Giovanni Cathedral. The shroud, which many Christians believe is Christ's burial cloth, would most certainly have been destroyed had it not been for Trematore's heroic efforts.

Trematore, who was recently in Los Angeles for a shroud conference by invitation of the Italian Consulate, traveled to Kaufman (TX) this week to visit Mike Minor, vice president and general counsel for the American Shroud of Turin Association for Research.

Trematore shared his story with the help of translator Fabio Zichittella.

On April 12, 1997, Trematore was at home in Turin with his family when he looked out the balcony and saw a cloud of smoke 300 feet in the air.

"I told them, something's burning," Trematore said.

He then called the office and learned the cathedral was on fire.

Trematore had just completed an intense study of Baroque architecture at the University of Turin and had made a CD on the architecture of the building.

"I knew everything about the cathedral," he said.

Dressed in jeans, a shirt and jacket, Trematore decided to go to the fire.

"I thought we would lose one of the greatest artifacts on Earth," he said.

In his 20-year career as a firefighter, Trematore said he had never seen a fire so big.

Mario Trematore, who rescued the Shroud of Turin from a fire at San Giovanni Cathedral in 1997 (center), talks to Mike Minor, vice president of the American Shroud of Turin Association for Research (right) with the help of translator Fabio Zichittella.

"When I entered the cathedral my sensation was, 'This is what it would be like to be in Hell,'" Trematore recalled.

Trematore, who was responsible for the supervision of about 40 men, said his first thought was. "I've got to save my own skin and everyone else's."

Trematore said the real danger was not from the fire itself but from the probable collapse of the domed roof.

"Everybody working underneath it would have died and the shroud would have disappeared," he said.

Before they could get close to the shroud, Trematore and his fellow firefighters had to work at extinguishing some of the fire.

The shroud itself was protected in a silver box encased by four layers of bulletproof glass.

"My first emotion was of dying," he said.

He said it was as if a voice were saying to him, "Go over and break the glass."

Trematore, thinking of his wife and children, said he was arguing with the voice saying, "If I go over there I'm going to die."

"It's not my moment to die yet," Trematore remembers thinking.

"Don't worry about it, go over there and break the glass," the voice said to him.

"In a moment everything changed," Trematore said. "I was not afraid of dying and I knew exactly what I was supposed to do."

Trematore told his colleagues he was supposed to break the glass and save the shroud.

They followed him over and were dousing the area with water as he began beating against the glass with a sledgehammer. After a while the glass started breaking and others came and started helping him.

"When the glass had fallen down I took the box with the shroud and put it on my shoulder. At that moment I was even more afraid than I was at first," he said.

"I was shocked," Trematore said.

Trematore, who considers himself a rational thinker, said the box had no feeling of weight.

While he was walking with the box Trematore said he started feeling the loss of his own weight and had the sensation of floating across the floor.

The most extraordinary thing happened as Trematore was exiting the church. When he was on the steps he heard the cries of a newborn baby.

"I turned around and realized the cries were coming from the box," he said.

"I had the physical sensation of holding a small baby," Trematore said, adding he gave the box the same attention he would if he was holding a baby.

"It was a beautiful sensation," he said.

Trematore says he has no recollection of going down the steep steps as he exited the cathedral.

He also has no memory of the reported 2,000 people who were outside clapping as the shroud was brought out.

After Trematore handed the shroud to police, he fainted.

He was taken to the hospital where he was released after being treated for minor scrapes and cuts to his hands, neck and feet.

"It is a real miracle that no one died in the fire because in a fire like that someone always dies," Trematore said.

Trematore said his boyhood dream was to become a firefighter; something prompted in part by the death of his little sister who died in a fire when she was two years old.

In 1997, his career choice was reconfirmed when Trematore was declared a national hero in Italy for his role in saving the shroud.

Four years after the fire, Trematore is a changed man.

Trematore wasn't particularly religious before the fire. In fact, when millions came to view the shroud when it was on display in 1978, Trematore opted to go mountain climbing.

But, the events of that night obviously have caused Trematore to do a lot of soul searching.

"Whover looks at the shroud, even if they don't believe it—it will change his life," he said. "The mystery is so big."

Trematore said he believes the fire served a very important purpose.

"That fire permitted us to talk about Christ in the whole wide world," Trematore said.

"If [burning churches] is what it takes to talk about Christ, then let one burn every day," Trematore said.

*Mario Trematore with a picture of the Shroud of Turin and translator
Fabio Zichittella (above) and Mike Minor (below)*

Saving the Shroud

Mario Trematore

MARIO TREMATORE DESCRIBES HOW HE SAVED THE SHROUD FROM
TOTAL DESTRUCTION IN THE 1997 FIRE IN THE CATHEDRAL OF TURIN
—WRITTEN AT THE REQUEST OF HIS HOLINESS POPE JOHN PAUL II

...further ahead, on another table, I recognized the history professor of architecture of the University of Turin and her family who were concluding their supper before a cup of ice cream. We exchanged a glance accompanied by a simple nod of the head, which became a greeting...

Early Life

My brother, Marcello, and I, seventeen at the time, already alone, were living in Cavaglia St. in Turin. He was two years younger than I. The abode consisted of two rooms, at ground floor, between two columns of the garbage bins of a palace in a popular area of the outskirts, in 'Barriera' di Milano. The rest room in the courtyard was shared by two other families. Winter, ever so cold, was preventing us from stepping out of the house to use it because our blood would freeze. We would have liked a different location, but there was no other choice. Who would have rented a lodging to two teenagers without parents and moreover from the South, so-called *terroni*?

I have worked in various areas such as plumbing, brick laying and factory work until at twenty-three years of age, joining the Fire Department, I decided to enroll in the Technical Institute Guarino Guarini. Five years later I was already dating Rita. A diploma crowned my efforts as student worker.

That evening we feasted with Rita and Paolo, friends of yesterday and today, in keeping with the last day of July, in Piola, a little bar at the foot of the hill, eating bread and salami, and anchovy in green sauce, accompanied by a glass of red wine. The next day, with

Michael, a dear French friend who toured the world seeking employment, we left to climb the east wall of Mt. Cervino. After four hours
of sleep at the Carrel bivouac, stretched on boards along with other
climbers, we reached the peak of 4,478 meters after five hours of
climbing by the light of lamps.

Seated at the iron cross, we were enjoying the light of the sun that
was slowly dawning on that August day. That light, filled with
warmth, was blending my thoughts with the immensity of the sky
and with the vast aerial panorama visible from the peak of the
mountains, and which embraced that cross, loved by rust and time
with such sweetness as to reveal its ancient splendor.

Within a few years, in the splendor of a circular church, I was
passing between the pews filled with relatives, towards my bride, and
upon that altar, festively dressed, I promised God that I would love
Rita in good times and in bad, for better, for worse, for the rest of my
life. We became husband and wife. Two years after, Jacopo was born,
and five years later, Clare.

I was thirty-eight years old when I decided to enroll in the faculty
of the school of Architecture of Turin.

THE CITY OF TURIN

How the city of Turin became 'baroque' with a history somewhat
different from that of other Italian cities, is due to particular political
events. Between 500 and 600 A.D. the town-planning shape of the
city was formed. When, eventually, Turin became the capital of
Piedmont, the transformation began; a synthesis between religious
and lay aspects.

The major conclusions would be drawn by Guarino Guarini who
extended his own influence to a great portion of the Catholic world
and particularly to the city of Turin.

For the visitor who arrives in Turin, a short time is sufficient to
understand the orderly network of streets that moves towards the
center of the city.

As you walk under the porticos of the Po River, the most beautiful
avenue of Turin and Casa Nova, the octagonal streetlight becomes a
splendid frame to the arches that hold the pressure of the vault of
every span. The steps of the visitor are accompanied towards Castello
Square, the throbbing heart and center of the city.

A few steps from Piazza Castello stand the Ducal palace and the

Chapel of the Holy Shroud. In 1666, following the pressures of the Duke, Carlo Emauele II, the Teatine Father Guarino Guarini arrived in Turin and was charged with the completion of the chapel of the Holy Shroud. The chapel, situated in the western part of the cathedral, is not practically visible from the outside except from the cupola that emerges from the multiplicity of the roofs of the Duke's palace. The cupola is formed by a drum held by pilasters and elliptic windows which seem sucked up around a fulcrum, a rotating hinge upon which is fixed a great lantern ....

THAT NIGHT

It is late, Clare sleeps in the arms of her mother and Jacopo snoozes, wobbling from one step to the other.... Entering the apartment, Rita places Clare on the bed. The dog does not bark, and Rita, somewhat apprehensive, glances out of the balcony that overlooks the garden. Jacopo follows her. From the balcony, beyond the roofs, Jacopo and Rita see great clouds of dark smoke descend upon the city: *the Cathedral is burning!*

I decide to intervene even if I have no service obligation. I have in the house an old coat discolored by time and worn by much mountain climbing. On the sleeve, close to the shoulder, I had sewn a shield of the fire department. I put it on, slip into a pair of boots, greet Rita and Jacopo, and with their benevolent recommendation: "If you return after dawn wake us up with a good cup of coffee, warm milk, bread and marmalade," I leave.

The automobile trembles at the start. From the Martiri della Liberta Avenue to the square of 'Great Mother of God,' past the bridge of the Po River, I reach Vittorio Square which goes directly into Po Street at the end of Castello Square, between the chapel of St. Lawrence, by Guarino Guarini, and the palace of the city's Prefect. I park in the ample space before the Royal palace.

The very high flames light up the sky, and a sea of smoke and flames move into a vortex as in a confused Dante's "rampart." A strong, livid light, not like that of an ordinary fire, leaves me nailed to the stones of the square. In twenty-two years of work I thought I had seen many fires but never so terrifying as to freeze the blood in the veins. Inside the dome, the chapel was crumbling slowly under the impact of the flames, and the insistent crackling, thick and cruel, increased my will to escape. This I could have done at any moment. I had no thoughts for the masterpiece of Guarini, nor for the silent Man of the Shroud. I had in mind something else: my life and that of my colleagues.

To this day I don't know how to explain what happened; it is certain that the bulletproof glass, under the blows of the sledge hammer, was crumbling as sand falling from the palm of the hands, dispersing in the air at the first gusts of the wind. The thought transforms into action and the fear of death brings to mind, briefly, the dearest persons and the most cherished memories; the sweetness of my wife Rita, Jacopo's smile, the first birthday of daughter Clare. The sense of living in time is completely lost, and the tyrannical time deludes us as if it will never pass. Thus, from the sea of memories, the contact with reality is altered by the fear of death. The very high flames were not leaving any escape from the Guarini Chapel. Everything was burning and turning into soot and red-hot fragments on that evening between the 11th and 12th of April, Friday; thirty-two months from the end of the millennium.

The marbles and the stuccos, lapped up by the flames, crumbled as crusts of stale bread, and were falling on the great crucifix which, ignoring the danger, was turning its back to the fire on the altar of the Cathedral.

There was not much time to understand and the thoughts were falling in pieces in the acrid smell of smoke and of the worried voices of the priests and those of the firemen who were praying to that God, in whom perhaps they had never believed.

Humanity would have lost what Christ had left: a sign with its meaning kept in a church and in the hearts and faith of Christian people, for always.

St. John Square, filled with a crowd impatient to understand what was happening, was lit up by the tenuous light of the lamp posts and by that intermittent one flashed by the lamps of the fire trucks, which rhythmically lit up the stairway of the Cathedral.

Meanwhile time was passing and the red-hot night was opening on the dome that was falling into pieces before thousands of people.

It is 1:35 A.M. in this hostile night, APRIL 12. *The Shroud is saved!* The silver case is extracted from the bulletproof panels shattered by the sledgehammer, and when it appears in the ground, carried on the arms of some, as if it were a newborn baby, applause of relief takes off from the three thousand people in the square.

Some of them make the sign of the cross, some of them pray, and those, like me, thank the God Whom they know is in heaven, on earth and in every place.

The fire burned all in its path except the Linen Sheet. This has demonstrated the miraculous intervention of Providence that would not permit the Shroud to be scratched, and has left a message of hope. Thus, on this night, the trepidation of all the people for the Sacred Linen united believers and unbelievers in a unique, conscious or unconscious, act of love for Christ Our Lord.

FAITH

In the life of the Christian the family exists, the profession exists, but the primary task is to testify to the Faith. For this we have been chosen; to give testimony to the Faith, internally in our own life. Our personality, then, will no longer be that of a professional or of that of the father of the family, but that of the Christian. Whatever activity occupies us, Faith, to which I speak with spontaneity as to a loved one, is present with its content inside the materiality of one's own conscience.

Faith is to recognize that Jesus Christ is the present salvation that transformed the feeble event of human existence in history. That presence becomes revived every day by the memory whose instrumentality is the capacity to identify with the original event. That Christ, dying on the Cross, has involved all those who believe in Him, in His immortality, where everything is actively present, the smallest as well as the greatest. This image is exactly the opposite supplied by the powerful ones who carry with them unto death all that surrounds them, to the end of being able to find in the beyond, everything they were used to.

They do not know how to love while living—do not love when dead. A loveless procession accompanies them unto the beyond.

Christ, instead, dies crucified every day in the many events which weave the fabric of world history, to arise always evermore present in the mystery of Faith before human eyes.

Thus, His provident hand loaded with love, accompanies us every day. That hand gave me the strength, along with my colleagues, to take on the flames that threatened the most precious relic in the world: the Sign that brings us back to the great mystery in history, that is the Passion and Resurrection of Jesus Christ.

I must say that that night, spent in the cathedral trying to save the Holy Shroud, has marked a turning point in my life. An interior change took place in me, prompting me to be reflective, to scan with greater attention that sign of Providence in my life and in that of the persons I carry in my heart.

Since that night I have been able to notice a constellation of "signs," great and small, that in an almost daily succession helped me to understand the presence of the Lord in history and in *my* history.

That night, the force that impelled me to accomplish an action, which under normal conditions would be impossible for a man of average strength and physique to do, certainly came from above. Why the Lord had chosen me for this feat is not clear to me yet, but in that moment, on that day, I clearly sensed that, alone, I could not do what I did.

When one lives in God's grace, to speak of a heroic gesture is almost a lack of trust in our Creator. He who created us has decided everything, even if to us not everything is fully understandable. Christ would have reemerged from the rubble with us or without us. Even without the power of the hands and the hammer, wood or iron, the Holy Shroud would have been saved.

Translated on Sept. 4, 2001, by
Sr. Francis X. Neilan, C.H.F. and
Fr. Paul M. Caporali, S.D.B.
Los Angeles, CA